BIRDS

of the Eastern Province of

SAUDI ARABIA

Socotra Cormorant chicks, Kurayn island (BS)

BIRDS
of the Eastern Province of
SAUDI ARABIA

G. Bundy, R. J. Connor & C. J. O. Harrison

H. F. & G. WITHERBY LTD
in association with
ARAMCO

First published in Great Britain 1989 by
H. F. & G. WITHERBY LTD
14 Henrietta Street, London WC2E 8QJ
in association with Saudi Aramco, Dhahran, Saudi Arabia

British Library Cataloguing in Publication Data
Bundy, G.
Birds of the eastern province of
Saudi Arabia.
1. Saudi Arabia. Birds
I. Title II. Connor, R. J. III. Harrison,
C. J. O. (Colin James Oliver), *1926–*
598.2953'8

ISBN 0-85493-180-5

Designed by Cornelia Playle

Typeset in Great Britain by Rowland Phototypesetting Ltd
Bury St Edmunds, Suffolk
Printed in Hong Kong by Imago Publishing Ltd

CONTENTS

ACKNOWLEDGEMENTS

The authors wish to acknowledge the financial and logistical support provided by Aramco through its Environmental Affairs Division, in particular that of Dr J. E. Cuddeback, the Chief Environmental Affairs from 1978 to 1987 and his successor, Mr A. M. Al-Shahri, who provided the continuity necessary to bring this publication to fruition. Mr C. K. Price of Environmental Affairs also helped with coordination and logistical support as the book was developed.

Aramco's senior management provided active support and encouragement from inception through to publication. We particularly wish to thank Mr A. S. Ju'mah, Mr A. H. Saleh, Mr F. M. Saleh, Mr I. I. Nawwab, Mr M. M. Subaey, Mr D. H. Al-Douhan and Mr S. M. Redaini.

Thanks are also due to Mr C. Hudson of Aramco's Cartography Division and Mr K. Allen of Aramco's Environmental Unit for preparing the maps and tables used in the book.

Finally, we wish to acknowledge and thank Ms J. L. Horley, Mr E. Shariff, Ms E. Ross, Mr B. D. Mano and Ms B. Moloney for their secretarial and administrative support.

A NOTE ON THE PHOTOGRAPHS

The photographs which are reproduced in this book were taken by G. K. Brown, A. L. Litke and B. Stanaland. The work of each photographer is identified by his initials, which appear in conjunction with the photograph captions. With very few exceptions the photographs were taken in the Eastern Province, usually using stalking techniques. Only rarely was a hide (blind) used.

INTRODUCTION

To the casual observer the Eastern Province of Saudi Arabia appears poorly endowed with living things; vegetation is sparse and animal life even sparser. Birds are not immediately obvious.

In such circumstances a book on the birds of the region may come as a surprise; but observations in recent years, mostly by dedicated amateur ornithologists, have revealed an avifauna that is impressive in the number of different species identified, even if some have been sighted on only a few occasions.

The key section of this book is a systematic list of Eastern Province birds which provides enough information to acquaint any interested person with what he may expect to encounter; and where. The list is relatively complete. Further additions to it are likely to be species that occur infrequently, perhaps as wind-blown vagrants, or those for which man's activities have created new habitats.

Information on the landscape, climate, vegetation and geological history of the Eastern Province is scattered; and it seemed useful to summarize this fairly fully at the beginning of the book.

Prior to the early 1970s ornithological exploration in Eastern Arabia was localized and spasmodic. The collections and reports made by the few serious field naturalists who visited the area during earlier decades were valuable but limited in scope; mainly because of difficulties in transportation. The rapid expansion of the oil industry in the 1970s changed the landscape and resulted in a network of good paved roads. It was accompanied by an influx of expatriate workers, amongst whom were a handful of dedicated amateur ornithologists. While the first explorers travelled by dhow and camel, and were mainly concerned with collecting specimens, recent workers have tended to concentrate on field identification rather than museum study, and by making extensive use of four wheel drive vehicles and even helicopters have penetrated vast areas of the Eastern Province in a determined effort to establish the status of its bird life.

The earliest specimens from the western Arabian Gulf are eggs and skins, chiefly Lesser Crested Tern, which were obtained from islands off Kuwait and al-'Arabiyah during the late 1870s. Many of these are now in the British Museum (Natural History) having been collected by, or on behalf of, E. A. Butler and W. D. Cumming. Between 1902 and 1923 Col R. E. Cheesman, Sir Percy Cox and V. S. la Personne made several trips to the Gulf islands, and most of the specimens they collected were subsequently obtained by the Bombay Natural History Society and the British Museum (Natural History).

Col Cheesman visited the Saudi mainland in 1921 and explored the Eastern Province coastline between al-'Uqayr and Salwah (Cheesman 1923). In November 1923 after landing at al-'Uqayr from Bahrain, Cheesman travelled across the dunes by camel to Hofuf and spent two months there collecting specimens of birds, mammals, fish and plants in the oasis. In early February he left for Yabrin and the Rub' al-Khali, collecting specimens on the way (Cheesman 1926). With the help of Dr C. B. Ticehurst, the recognized authority of the time on the birds of the Middle and Far East, Cheesman compiled a list of 86 species which included those recorded from Bahrain. The local House Sparrow of Hofuf was described as a new pale race *'hofufae'* and a pale form of the Desert Lark (*Ammomanes deserti*), matching the pale pinkish Summan limestone, was named *'azizi'* in honour of King Abdul Aziz Ibn Saud, then Sultan of Najd and its Dependencies (Ticehurst & Cheesman 1924, 1925). H. St J. B. Philby travelled extensively in Arabia, though mostly in the west, during the 1920s and 1930s. He visited the Eastern Province in 1932 (Philby 1933,

Kinnear 1934) and again in 1938 and during the course of these travels he collected specimens of the birds that he came across. In 1938 B. Loppenthin visited the islands of Harqus, al-'Arabiyah and al-Farisiyah during fishery investigations. He saw about 2,000 Socotra Cormorants (*Phalacrocorax nigrogularis*) on al-'Arabiyah, and found about 250 of their nests; but only a few birds on Harqus (Loppenthin 1951).

Most of the specimens that had been collected by Philby were sent to London and identified by G. L. Bates who published descriptions of any apparently new forms. Bates had earlier studied the birds of West Africa and had written a book on them. In early 1934 he visited Jiddah and was encouraged by Philby to begin a book on Arabian birds. From 1935 to 1939 he published notes on Philby's birds; and drawing on early accounts, museum data and later records, completed a manuscript on the birds of Arabia, listing species and mapping distributions. The book was finished two years before his death in 1940 at the age of 77 but it was never published. Three copies of the manuscript exist, one of which is in the Aramco technical library at Dhahran.

Col R. Meinertzhagen visited southern Yemen intermittently between 1899 and 1923; in 1914 he also visited Bahrain and Muscat, while in 1948 he collected in several western regions. In late 1950 he visited Kuwait, Bahrain and the Eastern Province of Saudi Arabia spending short spells at Dhahran, Hofuf and Riyadh before travelling west to the Red Sea in March 1951. He did not publish separate notes on the visit but incorporated some comments into his later book, *Birds of Arabia* (1954). In writing the book he had access to Bates' manuscript, which he acknowledged and which appears to have formed the basis of the work. To this he added any other information that was available, and various ideas of his own. The book became the standard work on Arabian birds and the first edition is now a collector's piece and very expensive. Its use has created problems, since it includes records and contained statements which do not always agree with the observations of later field workers. If a statement about a species in Meinertzhagen's work seems questionable it is advisable to treat it as potentially erroneous unless confirmation can be obtained elsewhere. Insofar as the birds of the Eastern Province are concerned, both Bates' manuscript and Meinertzhagen's book are inadequate; simply because so little information was available to the authors.

There are two additional small contributions on the birds of the region which may be regarded as part of this earlier period of sporadic observation. S. D. Ripley made a very brief visit to Dhahran and Bahrain in July 1950, and his published list (Ripley 1951) includes 24 species seen in the Eastern Province. One of these was an immature White-tailed Eagle seen between the mainland and Bahrain on 27 July. His reference to 'Little Brown Doves' at Dhahran and Ras Tanura should probably be construed as referring to the rather brown form of the Collared Dove (*Streptopelia decaocto*), now well established in the Eastern Province, which Ripley does not otherwise mention.

The last of earlier published notes, or possibly the first of recent studies, was a list of birds seen at Dhahran and Ras Tanura by Mrs M. G. Eddy during the period 1959 to 1962. She listed 112 species, usually without any note other than species names and localities. She recorded Rose-ringed Parakeet (*Psittacula krameri*), Meadow Pipit (*Anthus pratensis*), Redstart (*Phoenicurus phoenicurus*) and Siskin (*Carduelis spinus*) for the first time in Arabia.

In the late 1960s and early 1970s an increasing number of people who had been bird watchers or amateur ornithologists in their home countries came to work in the Gulf for periods of a few years. Most observers were anxious to contribute to some permanent record and from 1969 to 1971 M. D. Gallagher produced a duplicated newsletter to record and publicize new observations and records from the Gulf area. Later Mrs F. E. Warr, then working on an occasional basis at the British Museum (Natural History), shouldered the burden of maintaining the indices concerning all aspects of the ornithology of the Gulf region.

Her first typescript devoted solely to the birds of Saudi Arabia was a 'List of Birds of Dhahran and Hasa Province' privately circulated in 1972. It brought together the historical records and laid the foundation for further research. As more information was received from pioneer field workers in the Eastern Province, prominent amongst whom was G. K. Brown (1974–1977), the typescript was expanded and eventually entitled *A List of Birds of the Eastern Province*. Updated editions have been issued periodically; the most recent in August 1988. To this day, Mrs Warr continues to correspond with individual observers, gathering information, helping with problems of identification and distribution; and steadily adding to the mass of information available to researchers. Her industry and enthusiasm have served as a catalyst and contributed in no small measure to our present knowledge.

An important outcome of the collection of this data was the publication of a checklist of the Arabian Gulf States (Bundy and Warr 1980), which included records of birds occurring in the Eastern Province of Saudi Arabia. This appeared in the first number of 'Sandgrouse' the journal of the newly formed 'Ornithological Society of the Middle East'. More recently, checklists and papers devoted exclusively to the birds of Saudi Arabia have appeared in this journal.

Although there was a dramatic increase in ornithological observations in the Eastern Province during the 1970s it seems to have been rather localized and concentrated around the Aramco compounds at Dhahran and Abqaiq. The oases at al-Hasa provided an obvious attraction, but the extensive semi desert plains of the Dibdibah, the rocky escarpments between 'Uray'irah and Nariya, and even the Qatif oasis seem never to have been visited by ornithologists before 1978. From 1977 through 1988 the whole region has been covered, at times by up to six or more observers. Remote Aramco field camps from al-Musannah in the north to Jawb on the northern fringe of the Rub' al-Khali have been the bases of two observers, R. Raby and G. Rowlands. An important contribution to the coverage of the Eastern Province during the period 1978 through 1988 were the visits to Gulf islands during the course of Aramco environmental studies by R. J. Connor; and his annual surveys of *jabal* breeding species. These studies have contributed a great deal to our knowledge of the breeding species of the region. However, there is still much to be learnt about the inter-relationship of species; and the distribution, breeding cycle and ecology of desert dwelling species, especially the larks.

Valuable information may be contributed by individuals who are located, however briefly, at any place where they can maintain observations even if few birds are present. The amateur maintaining regular observations on a patch of sparse scrub by a construction camp can contribute on equal terms with the expert at a more favourable location. An inquiring mind and the willingness to note a few facts can contribute positively to our understanding of the birds of arid regions.

The study of birds in Saudi Arabia is generally of fairly recent origin. Hardly a week passes without something of consequence being learned. It is to be expected that future observations will present a clearer picture of the status of species already recorded. Our knowledge of this area and its ecology is far from complete and some of the ideas expressed are necessarily speculative. The intention of the authors of this book is not that it should serve as the final word on the subject, but rather as a starting point for further research and discovery.

We are indebted to the many observers who have made their unpublished notes available. The principal contributors are listed below:

N. Benca
A. Bramely
D. J. Brazier
J. C. Broadley
D. J. Brooks
G. K. Brown
J. Bryan
G. Bundy
J. E. Burchard
T. Carr
P. W. G. Chilman
R. J. Connor
D. Cooke
J. C. Davies
A. Dixon
R. R. Elliot
M. A. Elwonger
S. Fawcus
K. J. Fisher
M. D. Gallagher
T. J. Hallam
R. Hedley
J. A. Heindel
T. S. Heindel
D. M. Hodges
C. S. Holland
M. S. Hooper
M. D. Hutchison
P. J. Irving
M. C. Jennings
L. Johansen
A. L. Litke
J. P. Mandaville
J. H. Morgan
W. J. F. Morzer Bruyns
J. Palfery
C. V. Peterson
W. H. Peterson
R. Raby
D. Rafferty
L. Reaney
I. Richardson
C. Robb
T. D. Rogers
W. Ross
G. J. Rowlands
C. M. Saunders
D. M. Simpson
R. A. Smith
A. J. Stagg
B. Stanaland
B. Walsh
F. E. Warr
J. A. Warren
W. Weitkowitz
R. G. Wilson

Thanks are also extended to Robert Hudson of the British Trust for Ornithology for providing information on 2 of the 4 ringing (banding) recoveries for the Province.

EASTERN PROVINCE

Landscape

AN OVERVIEW

The Eastern Province of Saudi Arabia is a geographically defined region, a low desert plain barely 80 km across at its widest, extending from the Arabian Gulf coast to the Dahna, a natural barrier of high red-brown dunes rising above the surrounding plains. From the border with Kuwait in the north the Eastern Province extends for some 1200 km into the great sand desert that dominates all of southern Arabia, the Rub' al-Khali.

Geologically, the Arabian peninsula can be roughly halved. The western half comprises a very ancient (at least 600 million years old) Precambrian complex of igneous and metamorphic rocks that were once linked to the African continent; and these rocks of great age appear again, though limited in extent, in the eastern highlands of Iran. The basin between these two Precambrian outcrops is now occupied by the Arabian Gulf, the river valleys of Iraq and the Eastern Province of Saudi Arabia. The eastern Arabian geological region is made up of sedimentary rocks, the marine deposits of which, although very old, are much more recent than the Precambrian land mass of eastern Iran and western Arabia. At first sight then, the Eastern Province appears a long, low level land. This impression is only slightly modified on closer acquaintance. It is the region where the gently tilted, eastward sloping side of Arabia is gradually immersed in the shallow Arabian Gulf. Through the later Tertiary period of the past, it was a low lying area with a history of intermittent submergence and deposition of sediments, and its present surface of eroded sedimentary formations contributes to the general low relief.

The region shows a very gentle westward rise from the shallow coast, with an average gradient of no more than 1 in 400 or 1 in 500. At about 100 km inland from the coast there is a step in the form of an escarpment bordering the Summan plateau. This creates a sudden rise, but only of about 20 to 30 m, and the plateau then continues its gentle gradient until terminated abruptly by the 'Aramah and Tuwayq escarpments of central Arabia.

Along the centre of the Summan plateau, like the plateau running roughly north to south, but with an eastward-curving arc, lies the dune belt of the Dahna sands that links the great sand desert of the Nafud in north-central Arabia with the even larger desert of the Rub' al-Khali in the south. This dune belt forms the western boundary of the Eastern Province as defined for the purpose of this book.

East of the Dahna dune belt the Summan plateau has an eastward projecting boundary and in the central part of the Eastern Province occupies nearly half the width of the region. Originally it extended further east, and beyond its present edge the relics of an eroded plateau persist in the form of occasional small tablelands and more numerous scattered rocky outcrops or *jabals*. The survival of these relics is aided by a capping of some more resistant level stratum, existent in the original plateau. As a result, all structures within an area may be at approximately the same height as though a horizontal line had been drawn along the upper edge of the landscape, tending to play down the abruptness of these features and to re-emphasize the impression of a low level region.

Rocks similar to but older than the plateau strata, associated with the presence of small *jabals*, surface again at the Dammam dome in the region of Dhahran, but in general the coastal plain is lower and more level than inland, with a large number of shallow depressions formed by salt flats or *sabkhas*. From the region of Jubail southwards a wedge of

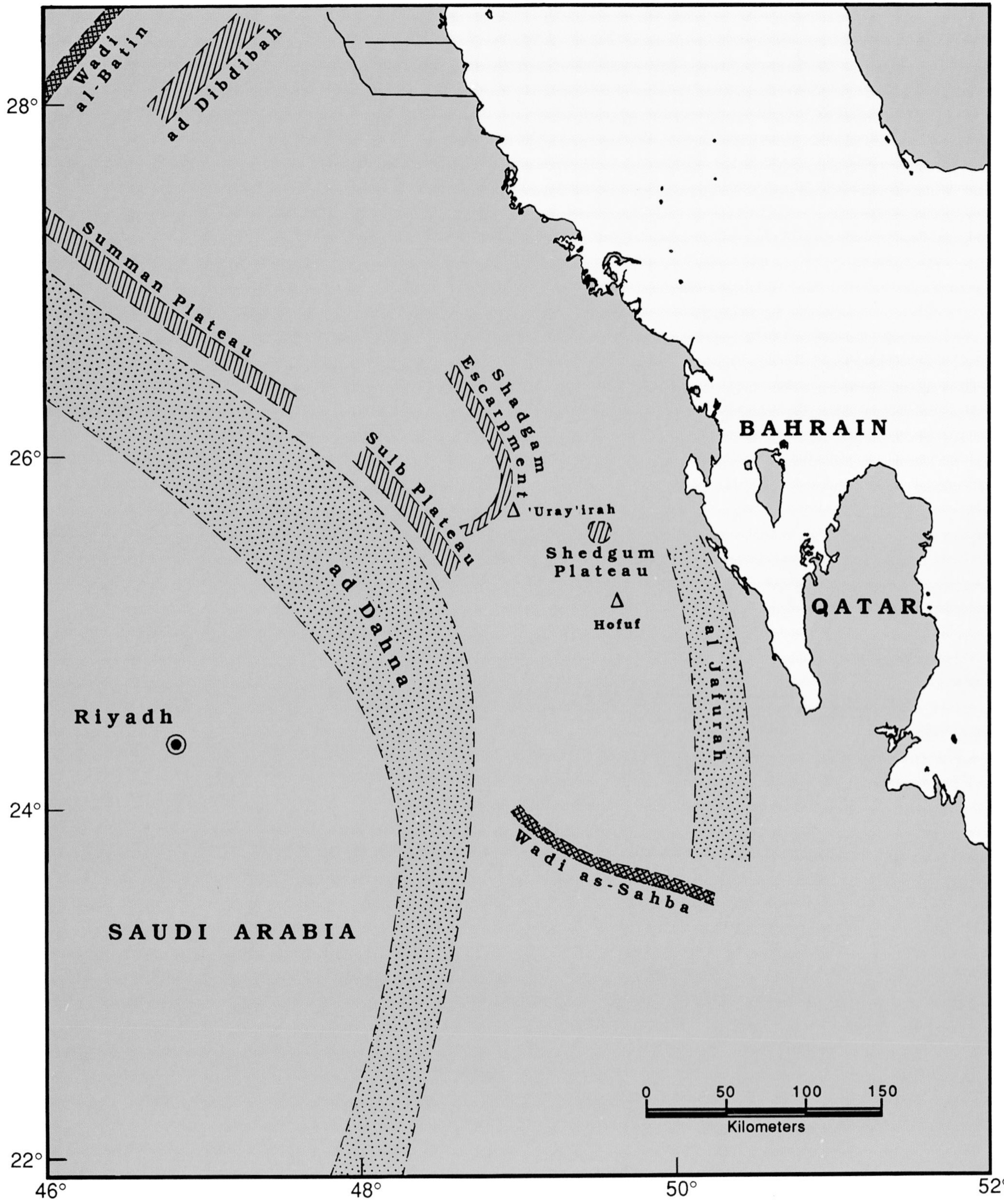

Wadi al-Batin
ad Dibdibah
Summan Plateau
Shadgam Escarpment
Sulb Plateau
'Uray'irah
Shedgum Plateau
Hofuf
ad Dahna
al Jafurah
Wadi as-Sahba
BAHRAIN
QATAR
Riyadh
SAUDI ARABIA
0
50
100
150
Kilometers
28°
26°
24°
22°
46°
48°
50°
52°

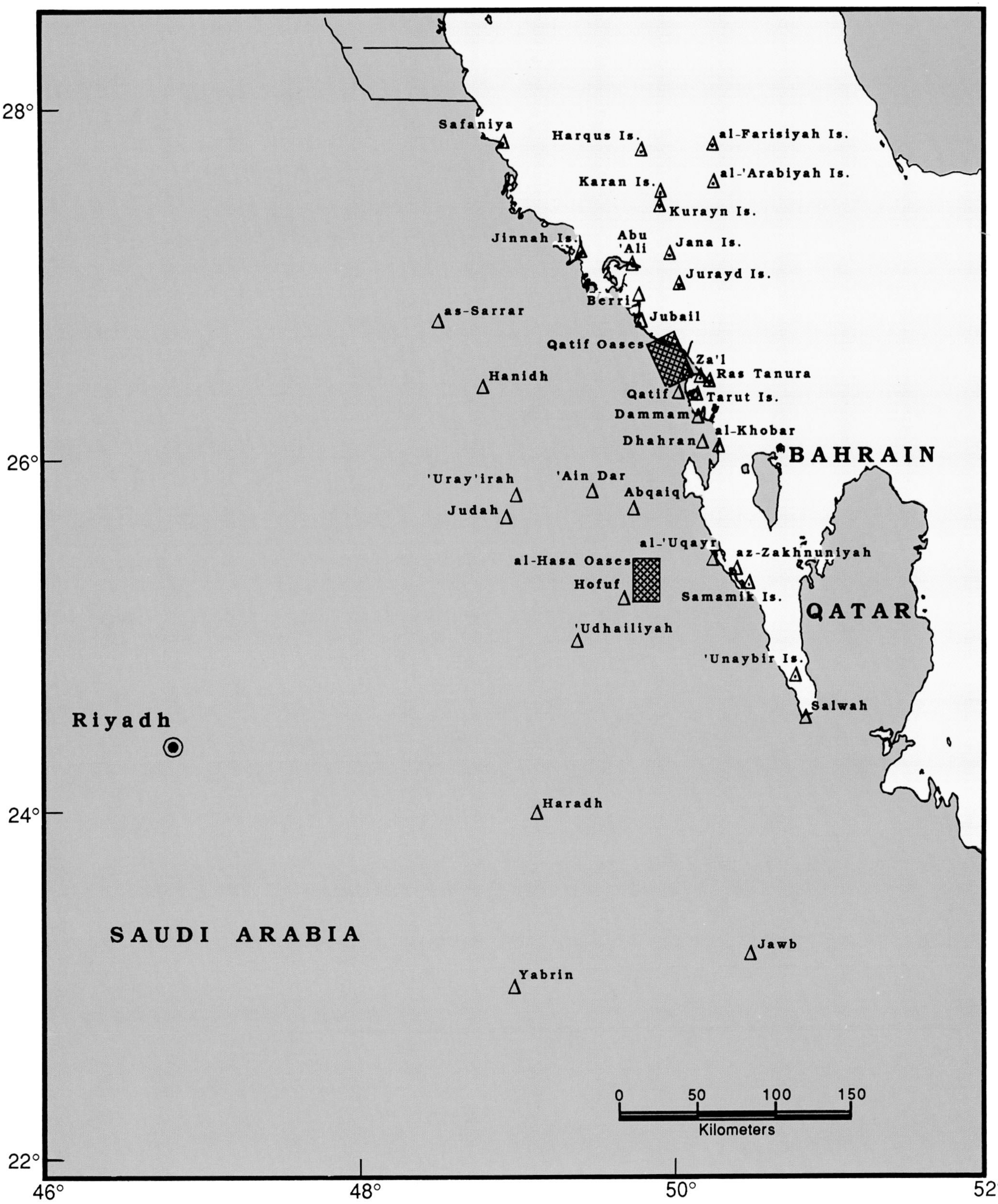

28°
26°
24°
22°
46°
48°
50°
52°
Safaniya
Harqus Is.
al-Farisiyah Is.
Karan Is.
al-'Arabiyah Is.
Kurayn Is.
Jinnah Is.
Abu 'Ali
Jana Is.
Jurayd Is.
Berri
as-Sarrar
Jubail
Qatif Oases
Za'l
Ras Tanura
Hanidh
Qatif
Tarut Is.
Dammam
al-Khobar
Dhahran
BAHRAIN
'Uray'irah
'Ain Dar
Abqaiq
Judah
al-'Uqayr
az-Zakhnuniyah
al-Hasa Oases
Hofuf
Samamik Is.
QATAR
'Udhailiyah
'Unaybir Is.
Salwah
Riyadh
Haradh
SAUDI ARABIA
Jawb
Yabrin
0 50 100 150
Kilometers

sand dunes occurs a little inland from the coast, widening further in the south in the dune region known as the Jafurah which in turn merges into the dunes of the northern Rub' al-Khali. These sands are superimposed on the coastal plains.

The north-western edge of the Eastern Province is formed by the long broad Wadi al-Batin, which forms a shallow valley running north-eastwards from the Dahna sands towards Kuwait. Associated with this and lying to the east of it is a large, level gravel plain, the Dibdibah, which occupies the north-western part of the Province south to about Wari'ah.

In the southern part of the Province, south of Haradh and around Yabrin, the Wadi as-Sahba and more southerly relics of a wadi system are directed eastwards towards Sabkhat Matti. Associated with these are other level gravel plains, the *hadabahs*, which are extensively concealed towards their eastern sides by the dunes of the Jafurah. These wadis and gravel plains are the relics of an early and extensive Arabian river drainage system, pre-Pleistocene in origin.

Although the Province is generally arid, a few natural artesian springs occur, fed by underground water. They arise on the plains east of the edge of the Summan to create the large al-Hasa oasis and are also present to a lesser extent at Qatif on the coast where another oasis exists. The much smaller oasis at Yabrin is centered around some sub-surface water sources.

At the edge of the Gulf the land terminates in a uniformly low coastline bordering a shallow sea. The coast is fairly well defined where sand or rock occurs, but in places forms large shallow muddy bays. Currents produce a general southward shift of coastal material along the shore, resulting in sandy southward curving promontories bordering the bays, or in some instances elongated inshore islands.

Further out in the gulf, coral reefs occur in a few of the more shallow areas; and at the highest point of the reef an accumulation of coral sand may form a small low lying island.

DAHNA SANDS AND RUB' AL-KHALI

The Dahna forms a long arc, about 2,000 km long and up to about 80 km in width. It is a zone of loose sands, tinted a deeper reddish-orange by iron oxides, unlike the whiter sands of the Jafurah region. The dunes tend to form massive long parallel ridges running roughly north-west to south-east, aligned with the prevailing winds. These formations are known as *'uruq*. The high ridges are separated by broad valleys which often have smaller sheets, transverse arcs and ridges of sand. In places the sands are stripped away by wind on the valley floors to leave level and more consolidated gravels.

Towards the western side of the Dahna the sands build up into more complex dunes at times over 35 m high, and include the large crescent shaped *barchan* dunes. These lie across the direction of the prevailing winds, with the horns of the crescent pointing downwind. The long and less steep windward slope rises to an abrupt curved crest and steep leeward scarp face. Loose sand blows up the slope to build the ridge; and spills down the steep face. On the eastern edge of the Dahna the sands are lower and overlie the limestone pavement of the Summan plateau, which is deeply eroded and potholed in places. Some shrubby vegetation is present, supporting grazing animals and some birds when conditions are right; but in general the Dahna is a barrier limiting the east–west spread of various small creatures. In recent times it has been breached by surfaced roads, a railway and by pipelines, all of which may provide avenues for future dispersal.

At its southern end the Dahna merges with the sands of the western side of the Rub' al-Khali, the Empty Quarter, sometimes referred to simply as *al-Rimal*, 'the sands'. This is the largest continuous area of sand in the world, some 1,200 km from east to west and up to 640 km wide. Its sands vary from the mobile to the more stable, and it differs in surface features from one part to another.

There are extensive *sabkha* salt flats with superimposed crescent dunes on its northern edge. Viewed from the air, much of it shows a variable crescent dune pattern, massive on the ground but from high above appearing like a mass of fine interlocking ripples. In other areas it begins to show an *'uruq* pattern like that of the Dahna with huge shallow and elongated valley hollows, the narrow longitudinal parallel crests well spaced and broken at intervals into shorter ranges. The hollows between are filled with a secondary crescent dune pattern of complex transverse ripples. In other areas again, the ridges build up into a series of sand mountains rising to heights of 160 to 250 m and bearing complex ridge patterns.

In some south-eastern parts the scene is increasingly dominated by numerous scattered salt

Barchan *dune, near Hofuf (GKB)*

Shadgam escarpment (ALL)

flats among the dunes; in its most extreme form producing a landscape resembling a grotesquely magnified part of a coastal sand flat where the receding tide has left a close pattern of sand ripples with little elongated residual pools between them. In this instance however the pools are great greenish-white dry sand flats with a pale salt crust on the surface. At a distance they appear to be like drying water, while the sand ripples between them are huge steep-sided red sand ridges that become chains of hills when viewed at ground level.

The area is largely devoid of life. A few widely scattered shrubs and small trees survive, usually in raised dune hollows; and rare rain showers, possibly years apart, may produce a brief growth of herbs and grasses. There is a chain of wells extending southwards from the southern end of Qatar and others are scattered elsewhere. Those of the north-east are rather saline, but they serve for watering camels and allow a limited Bedouin exploitation of these parts.

SUMMAN PLATEAU

The plateau surface on which the Dahna sands rest is a relatively level region extending the length of the Eastern Province from the northern gravels to the Rub' al-Khali. It increases slowly in height, from about 250 m above sea level in the east, to around 400 m where it meets the Dahna. The underlying structure consists of thin strata, layer on layer, of limestone, sandstone, silts and shales. The softer of these strata are vulnerable to erosion, resulting in a surface that is predominantly limestone in character.

Over much of the area the Summan forms a limestone pavement, cracked and broken in places and in some areas carrying small ridges of wind-blown sand. It supports a sparse shrubby growth but towards its eastern edge is very thinly vegetated, in places almost bare, with just thin lines of plant growth in small shallow run-off channels and hollows. Its eastern border is cut away by erosion, terminating in an abrupt and irregularly meandering escarpment about 20 to 30 m high.

The escarpment is maintained by the more resistant strata which prevent it collapsing completely; but it erodes into deep vertical clefts, horizontal grooves and ledges; and disintegrates in places into huge loose blocks. Over much of the region the result is a rambling escarpment, breaking down into a complex mass of tablelands and smaller outcrops; dissected by dry watercourses, deep clefts and wide wadis. This gradually gives way on the eastern side to a low undulating landscape in which the plateau relics stand up as small isolated tablelands and outcrops, here grouped under the general term of *jabal*.

The softer rocks of the escarpment weather in a way that suggests a landscape almost melting into a soggy collapse and then hardening again. The upper edges curve smoothly down to form overhanging 'curtains' and the sloping talus debris at the base extends well up the cliff face and collects on ledges which in turn tend to slope downwards, the whole showing deep vertical clefts and run-off grooves in its face. It gives the impression of a soft formation wasting away rapidly under winter rains.

JABAL REGION

The surface of the plain immediately to the east of the Summan escarpment is mainly composed of material eroded from the plateau. It tends to be uneven and undulating and scattered over it are the *jabals*, singly and in small groups or rows.

These are small relic formations of more resistant rock. The upper stratum which has prevented total erosion is present as a near horizontal capping layer; often projecting, though smoothed down and rounded at the edges. *Jabals* formed from softer rocks tend to break down more completely, collapsing into a conical heap of debris with just a slightly projecting lip around the flattened top to indicate the presence of a capping layer. Even where *jabals* are subject to greater erosion the process may be interrupted by a more resistant layer. An area of slightly elevated land may show a partly projecting harder edge, indicating the presence of the stratum that formed it, with an upper pavement surface more devoid of vegetation than the surrounding lower land. The final erosion may leave no more than a small prominent mound or ridge; its nature only indicated by an even greater absence of sparse vegetation than on the surrounding area.

Sometimes the strata persist as a slight stepping of the landscape, barely apparent from the higher side, but in places producing a sudden low escarpment with small rocky outcrops; or there may be merely a small ridge remaining, marked only by a pavement at ground level.

Some sandstone layers present in the plateau

formation are more resistant and have produced a series of sandstone *jabals* extending northwards from about the region of Hofuf. They are often fairly small but prominent and steep sided, the more resistant rock resulting in vertical surfaces with well defined horizontal ledges. The capping shows the same tendency to become rounded away at its edges but retains more of its shape, and erodes to produce irregular rounded hollows which eventually deepen into 'bowls' towards its lower edges. There is a smaller basal talus slope. It is formations of this type which provide the majority of suitable nest sites for cliff nesting birds of this region.

COASTAL PLAIN

Towards the coast the landscape is more level. In the north of the Province it tends to have a slightly irregular undulating appearance and to carry a more stabilized vegetation, an even stippling of shrubs or grass tufts, but with some sand present. Further south it is flatter. The whole area, south to the Rub' al-Khali, is characterized by the presence of salt flats or *sabkhas*. When rain falls the ground may be temporarily covered by a thin sheet of water, but the salt renders it sterile and typically forms a white crust on the surface when the area dries. In hot periods the surface may be hard and dry, but for much of the year only a hardening crust covers the saline mud or sand, and may give way if too much weight is placed upon it.

These *sabkhas* are irregular in shape and variable in size, but often very extensive. They are frequently partly concealed by wind-blown sand or silt which may support plant growth above the salt layer. *Sabkhas* very close to the coast may be intermittently flooded at periods of very high tides or strong onshore winds.

GRAVEL PLAINS

Under the superficial accretion of desert sands and dunes the surface of Arabia shows a system of valleys and watercourses that would drain northeastwards towards the Iraq marshes and the Arabian Gulf. It is now a system of often discontinuous wadis visible in areas between the sands, but it is still possible to trace evidence of the original pattern. This indicates that in historic times surface water was present for long enough to create a network of watercourses to drain it away. The main visible branching system of wadis is in western and central Arabia. Those now present in the Eastern Province are the larger fragments of a lost system, few in number, usually wide and shallow, flat bottomed and without an obvious channel.

The past function of these channels is obvious, but the extent to which this previously wetter climate would have affected other landscape features is less apparent. The rush of water that carved these channels must also have eroded and carried away a great deal of material, sand, earth and stones, and deposited this at lower levels. In subsequent arid conditions sand and silt could be blown away, but stones and shingle would remain, and the extensive areas of gravels associated with the wadis appear to be relics of just such action. Large quantities of small stones, smoothed and rounded by the action of water (possibly enhanced by the later action of wind and sand), are spread in great level stretches across the lower parts of eastern Arabia in the region of the larger wadis. In some places in the centre of the Province bordering the Summan, ridges of gravel indicate the routes of past watercourses. The material is derived from the breakdown of resistant rocks that are found outside the Eastern Province. The stones, large and small, form the main part of the substrate and offer a poor foundation for plant growth, but silt and sand are present between them. In dry seasons the gravel areas appear as featureless plains of small stones and little else, but after rains they support an extensive and uniform growth of grasses and annual plants.

The Rub' al-Khali is in reality a vast defunct alluvial plain of pre-Pleistocene age, reworked by arid winds during Pleistocene and Holocene times into the present aeolian dune topography.

The Dibdibah of the north-western part of the Eastern Province is an old alluvial fan. It is a raised but flat and far-reaching plain of small stones, often black, sometimes white; but differing from the local rocks, and set in a sandy substrate. It is an area in which it would seem difficult for anything, even a bird, to hide; but given good winter rains it changes its character from a rather barren waste to a sea of thin grasses that supports a breeding population of larks and other ground nesting birds. The plain was formed by the outwash of the alluvial fan of the Wadi Ar Rimah drainage system which extends far back into central Saudi Arabia. It is triangular in shape with its apex near Qaisumah, spreading

Sandstone jabal *cliff face, near Hofuf (GKB)*

Coastal salt marsh near Safwa (BS)

north-eastwards almost to the Tigris and Euphrates valley. The Wadi al-Batin is a later secondary channel eroded into its surface and is probably Pliocene in age.

In the south of the Province, between the sands of the Jafurah and the southern part of the Summan plateau there are the *hadabah* gravel plains. They are similar to those of the north but in some areas composed of larger irregular stones, though still smooth and waterworn. Rainfall is less than on the Dibdibah and vegetation generally less in evidence, occurring, when it does, more often in the form of small well spaced shrubs. These southern gravels are derived from another big alluvial fan, that from the eastward flowing Wadi as-Sahba. The fan is a half cone with an apex near Haradh and a radius of about 150–200 km. It extends from Hofuf in the north, to the south-western part of Qatar, and in the south disappears under the dunes of the Rub' al-Khali. The present channel of the Wadi as-Sahba in this area, like its northern counterpart, is a smaller wadi eroded into the alluvial fan and disappearing into the sands as it extends somewhere towards the southern end of the Qatar peninsula. The dunes of the Jafurah lie upon the eastern parts of this gravel plain, and some of the Rub' al-Khali dunes conceal its southern and south-eastern edge. Some of the gravels reappear along the coast of the Gulf of Salwah.

COASTAL SANDS AND THE JAFURAH

In a long, northward tapering zone, between the Summan plateau and *jabals* and the coastal zone, and between the northern and southern gravel plains, much of the land surface is affected or dominated by wind-blown sands. If reasonable rains occur there may be some degree of stabilization while moisture persists, but as summer progresses, with increasing aridity and persistent strong northerly wind, some movement of sand across the surface of the ground becomes increasingly apparent. It may vary from a few grains rustling past dry plant stems to dust storms raised by strong and prolonged winds. The prevailing wind is north-north-westerly and the main movement of sand is therefore south to south-eastwards, influencing the shape of sand formations and their distribution.

In the northern part of the Province the low landscape consists of stabilized soil with spaced small shrubs and grass tufts. However, even in this area some evidence of the admixture and presence of sand is apparent in dry windy periods. Further south, where sand is still not wholly dominant it may occur in thin layers overlying firmer surfaces. Sand sheets cover the ground irregularly, tending to be a little thicker towards their southern edges, and they may carry a reasonable, if thin and discontinuous, vegetation.

Where more sand is present it tends at first to build up as low ridges, aligned with the prevailing wind. Over the region generally, widely spaced grass tussocks and low twiggy shrubs are characteristic vegetation where conditions allow. Sands tend to build up around such growth to form small sandy mounds. The plants tend to respond by more rapid vertical growth and the twin processes produce a mass of small elongated sand hummocks each consolidated around a shrubby growth. This type of terrain is known as *dikakah* and it dominates stretches of various inland areas of the Eastern Province.

The coastal sands are mainly derived from limestone and sandstone formations, varying in tint but usually very pale, due to the presence of microscopic fragments of re-worked shell material; and so are sometimes referred to as the 'white' sands in contrast to the 'red' sands of the Dahna and parts of the Rub' al-Khali.

Throughout the white sand zone from west of Jubail south to the Rub' al-Khali the sands show frequent variation in formation and thickness, in many places overlying the other landforms; salt flats, plains, low rocky formations, etc, and these show through between the dunes or where sand has blown away. In general the sands increase in thickness to the south where the larger and more continuous dunes form the Jafurah region.

COAST AND ISLANDS

The Arabian Gulf is, geologically, of late Quaternary origin and its present level was only attained about 10,000 years ago. Today it is a very shallow sea with an average depth of only 35 m. Its salinity is higher than comparable areas due to the region's hot climate and low rainfall both over the Gulf and over the land on either side; consequently, evaporation is much greater than the input of water from rivers. This high salinity is one of the key environmental factors controlling the distribution of marine life in the Gulf (Basson *et al* 1977).

From the Kuwait border south to Ras Tanura the coast has a north-west to south-east trend and is exposed to the prevailing northerly winds. From the wide, shallow Tarut Bay to Salwah, on the border with Qatar, the coast lies more nearly north/south and is protected from wind and waves by several factors. Like the land the coast is rather flat, at times complex in its detail, but topographically unexciting. Its importance lies in the zone exposed by the twice daily tides. The slope of the underwater substrate reflects the gradual and gentle slope of the land surface, and consequently an average tidal rise and fall of a little under 1·5 m may produce an inter-tidal zone approaching 1 km in width at low tide. Beyond this again, there will be an extensive zone of shallow water. High temperatures during periods of exposure prevent a heavy growth of seaweeds, but the inter-tidal zone is very rich in small animals, crabs, worms, molluscs and crustaceans, and is an important source of food for birds.

The more prominent sectors of the coastline, and the southern part within the Gulf of Salwah, are sandy with a typical sand beach thrown up along the upper limit of the tides. A dune belt may form along the upper beach which may carry its own distinctive flora and fauna. The beach itself is a shifting substrate, liable to become lethally hot at the surface, and offering a long term habitat only to small mobile burrowing creatures such as crabs and sandhoppers.

At lower levels, below the inter-tidal zone, the sands have a richer flora and fauna and in depths of less than 18 m may support extensive sea grass beds which, in addition to feeding large vertebrates such as dugongs and turtles, also support small shrimps and fish which constitute an important food source for many species of birds.

About half the coastline consists of five large irregular bays, extending only some 15 km inland on average, but very wide and tending to subdivide into smaller subsidiary bays. Unlike coastal bays of non-arid regions they are not fed by freshwater streams. This fact, combined with weak tides and currents, produces water vulnerable to changes or extremes in air temperature or solar radiation, and with a high salinity increased still further by evaporation. Northwards from a little south of al-Khobar the bays and some more prominent stretches of coast consist mainly of mud or mixtures of mud and sand rich in both animal and plant life. In the bays the material tends to accumulate, forming flat muddy areas drained slowly by complex networks of meandering channels. Where mud predominates, the higher levels exposed for most of the time carry a low, sometimes continuous, growth of halophytic (salt tolerant) vegetation that stabilizes the mud as level salt marsh. In the shallow channels of fine silt exposed for long periods the Black Mangrove occurs in some areas to form low thickets half submerged at high tide. Tarut Bay has a higher than average productivity on its tidal flats (Basson *et al* 1977) and this is reflected in the large numbers of waders wintering there. It has been suggested that the high biological productivity is partially the result of human activities in the area. Fresh water from irrigated cultivation in the adjoining Qatif oasis empties into the bay at several points. It flows through reed fringed channels and past flats green with mangroves; a unique habitat zone in eastern Saudi Arabia.

In places the low eroded strata of rock that lie under the inland sands are exposed along limited areas of coast. For the most part they form flat rock platforms, often in the inter-tidal zone, and only in a few places are they high enough to rise as ridges or low outcrops. Some rock platforms have been formed *in situ* by cementation of materials present. Heat and wave scouring combine to render these rocky areas poor habitats for shore creatures.

Offshore, in shallow waters of less than 10 to 15 m, corals may grow on firmer areas of the sea bottom. In the Gulf these form small, flat topped platform reefs up to several hundred metres across. Several hundred such reefs occur offshore between Safaniya in the north and the tip of Abu 'Ali island. South of this they are much scarcer, but several large reef systems are present in the shallow sea between Jubail and Dammam.

In very shallow water a large rising reef tends to accumulate sandbanks on its flattened top and these may be exposed at high tide. At a further stage the banks may build up to form an elongated island surmounting the middle of the reef, and six such islands occur offshore in the northern part of the Eastern Province. Five, Harqus, Karan, Kurayn, Jana and Jurayd, are aligned near the edge of the Gulf's increase in depth to 35 m, while the sixth, al-'Arabiyah, is isolated well out in deeper waters. They vary from 35 to 90 km in distance from the nearest shoreline. In structure they are similar: oval, flat topped and raised only a little above sea level. They are bordered by a beach, sometimes with areas of beach rock platform, and the level top of the island is usually covered by low scrubby plant growth.

The small, flattish, wave washed, rocky island of 'Unaybir towards the head of the Gulf of Salwah appears to have originated as a reef in the past. Other islands close along the coast, such as Abu 'Ali, Az Zakhnuniyah and Samamik, appear not to be structures of marine origin but rather to be slightly elevated portions of the mainland cut off from it by the Gulf's present water level. They have a flat, sandy edged appearance similar to the coral islands of the Gulf but are more extensive, and in places a little muddier, with a more varied range of low growing shrubby plants.

INLAND WATERS

In the past, fresh surface water of a supply constant enough to sustain plant growth was an exceptional occurrence in the Eastern Province. The most striking example of a supply of this kind, rising from artesian springs, is that which has given rise to the al-Hasa oasis with its major town, Hofuf. Two major springs produce a flow of warm and relatively fresh water which has been estimated to average about 30,000 gallons per minute. This is supplemented by some 50 additional smaller springs and several hundred wells within the same area. It was a very obvious site to establish a settlement and has been occupied from the earliest times.

The water was used mainly for groves of date palms and other crops that could be grown in conjunction with these, around or under them. It has recently been estimated that as many as three million date palms may be present in the whole oasis, together with other trees, shrubs and humbler plants. The cultivated area spreads north and east from Hofuf over some 600 km^2.

Canalization and utilization of water for irrigation and cultivation on this scale uses a great deal of what is available, but the outflow of excess water creates more natural areas as it drains away northeastwards. It formed at least one extensive lagoon and several smaller pools when described by Cheesman in 1926, and although the flow may have been reduced in recent times a vast area of reed beds and lagoons still exists to the north of the al-'Uqayr road. The pools contain water plants, fish, Marsh Frogs *Rana ridibunda* and Caspian Pond Turtles *Clemmys caspica*. The run-off percolates away towards the coast, travelling beneath the dunes and from time to time reappearing in the hollows of the dune as an erratic chain of small pools partly fringed with reeds, which decreases in frequency away from the source.

Another oasis based on artesian springs occurs by the coast at Qatif. Here again there are miles of palm groves, and associated trees and bushes. On the inland side some water is used for irrigating fields. Unlike the al-Hasa oasis there is little evidence of open water apart from some intermittent flooding in the groves and a channel that carries surplus water to the sea at Tarut Bay.

The palms occupy some 20 to 30 km^2 and the total area under cultivation is about 75 km^2. The wells were originally hand dug, but are now drilled to greater depths. A recent survey showed some 372 wells of which 121 were ruined or without discharge. The discharge over the total area of cultivation is estimated to be about 1,250 cubic metres per minute. There are also submarine springs in Tarut Bay itself.

The water for both these major oases originates from several different aquifers, the most productive of which is the Umm er Radhuma formation which surfaces on the western edge of the Summan plateau west of Riyadh; and also in the as-Sulb region of the plateau in the north of the Eastern Province. The stratum dips down under the Gulf. It stores rainwater from these higher levels, but the water which rises from it in the oases appears to be derived from periods of higher rainfall in the past.

The little oasis in the south at Yabrin is on the edge of the limestone outcropping of the edge of the Summan plateau. It is not based on springs but on pools, with wells down to a watertable at about 12 to 14 m. It supports a small growth of palms, but its former importance is now completely overshadowed by extensive agricultural cultivation near Haradh in the Wadi as-Sahba area which is sustained by artesian flow from recently bored wells.

The verdant nature of these oases demonstrates that to a large degree the absence of a vigorous growth of vegetation over much of the Eastern Province is due not to any inherent infertility in the soil but to the lack of water. This is also evident elsewhere in places where recent human activity has made a source of water available. Most such supplies are of relatively short duration but the rapid response of both plants and animals to the new conditions enables them to exploit these resources as they occur.

Waters of this type are usually effluent outfalls

Marsh Harrier flying over reeds at Abqaiq sewerage effluent ponds. (GKB)

Imhoff Gardens, Dhahran, before the water supply was cut off. (GKB)

from sewage works near settlements. There are two such at Abqaiq; the older one has been modified and the excess water used to irrigate a swath of trees planted to reduce soil erosion. Overflow and seepage from the newer site meanders erratically in the hollows between dunes to form a long series of pools and lagoons bordered and invaded by dunes. As at Hofuf a heavy growth of reeds has formed around the edges in most places, and shrubby tamarisk is present.

Another site formerly existed to the north of the USA Consular Compound at Dhahran. This site held a number of sewerage lagoons and was known as Imhoff Gardens, perpetuating the name of Karl Imhoff, inventor of the Imhoff tank sewerage treatment system. Up until 1981 there were as many as four lagoons and about four hectares of well maintained grassland with a surround of tall trees, mostly tamarisk and some mesquite. The major water supply has since been cut off, allowing the lagoons to dry out, but some vegetation still survives and supports a reduced breeding population of Collared Doves, Olivaceous Warblers, Rufous Bush Chats and House Sparrows. It formerly produced some unexpected rarities among the many migrants that occurred there. There is a newer sewage treatment plant to the west which has some open water within concrete tanks but this does not support the abundance of plant or animal life which was such a feature of the original Imhoff ponds.

Within the Aramco compound at Dhahran treated sewerage effluent is disposed of by a system of automatically controlled sprays which spread the water over many hectares. This has promoted an exceptional plant growth dominated by phragmites and various species of tamarisk but the constant spraying makes most of the area unsuitable as nesting habitat.

Associated with this system is a shallow lake into which excess water is pumped. The bottom is covered with a thick layer of rich sediment which promotes a vigorous growth of aquatic plants and marginal reed beds. Its attraction as a feeding place and refuge for birds is enhanced by low trees and shrubs which border the lake to the north; and this has resulted in numerous sightings of rare and interesting species.

There are some quite extensive areas of reeds in

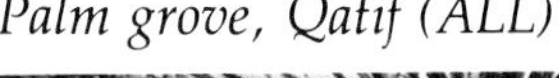

Palm grove, Qatif (ALL)

the Qatif oasis and along the shore to the north of al-Khobar but wetland sites in this area are diminishing with the rapid program of urbanization. The new sewage plant on the western outskirts of Dammam eliminated the need for the run-off lakes nearby when it was completed in 1980. These lakes with their surrounding tamarisk scrub were very attractive to wintering ducks, waders and other migrants. Similarly, the reed fringed ponds near Dhahran airport and the great Dammam marsh to the north of town have gone. The latter area was almost certainly the most important wetland site in the Eastern Province. A wetland habitat of major importance has since been established to the west of the Second Dammam Industrial City on the Dhahran–Abqaiq road. It is fed by effluent from industrial processes and provides a year round feeding ground for flamingos and supports large numbers of migratory and wintering ducks and waders. Various species of herons, white storks, spoonbills and geese occur from time to time, although in much smaller numbers.

Intensive cultivation of alfalfa and winter wheat, nurtured by artesian water sprayed from huge motor propelled arms rotating about a central pivot, is a relatively recent development. Such cultivations range from the very extensive to isolated circles of green in otherwise quite barren areas. The 12,000 hectares of cultivated land at Haradh produces a considerable harvest of alfalfa and winter wheat; and even supports a small herd of dairy cattle. Since it is surrounded by pure desert it is especially interesting to ornithologists because of the trans-desert migrants that are attracted to its greenery. It is also the only known breeding place in the Eastern Province of the Quail, Spotted Sandgrouse and, irregularly, the Great Grey Shrike.

In addition to the irrigation-based cultivation of crops at the oases of Qatif, Al Hasa and Yabrin, smaller scale farming utilizing well-drawn water takes place on the outskirts of many towns and villages.

Climate

The Eastern Province lies within a belt of arid regions which have a climate liable to extremes in everything except excessive rainfall; and are climatologically unpredictable. However, the Province itself has a more modified climatic pattern that is consistent enough to maintain a predictable cycle of plant and animal activity.

The most constant climatic feature of the Eastern Province is a long, hot, rainless summer with northerly winds, often accompanied by dust storms. This situation is created by a long term region of low pressure that develops over the Asian continent as the land mass heats up in early summer, and there is a counter clockwise circulation of wind around this area which becomes a permanent summer feature. The eastern coast of Arabia lies on the south-western edge of this anticyclonic low pressure system and the winds are thus persistent north-westerlies, referred to locally as the *shamal*. The system develops in late May and June; the winds are dry, producing a clear sky and allowing the sun's full heat to reach the ground.

The Eastern Province has, on average, hardly any rain in May, none from June to October, and a small amount in November (Appendix IV). Temperatures at this period are constantly very high but relative humidity tends to be low, increasing markedly towards the coast, and evaporation rates are high (Appendix IV). By mid-July the Asian and Arabian air pressures begin to equalize and the north-west winds weaken. Along the coasts, onshore and offshore breezes modify the wind, but temperatures continue to rise and August is usually both the hottest and calmest month (Appendix IV). In early autumn, temperatures become lower and relative humidity rises; and as the Asian anticyclone weakens it yields to the eastward-moving succession of cyclonic depressions that move in from the Atlantic across the Mediterranean and Middle East. Winds circulate around these, and as an anticyclone passes across any given area the winds there may change round from south or south-east to north-west. Rain may fall during the latter part of the passage. The succession of weather cycles accompanying these systems creates varied conditions through the winter months; mild weather perhaps alternating with strong winds and blowing sand, thunderstorms or occasional rain. Temperatures, although lower than in summer, vary and may drop to freezing on some occasions at inland localities during the many cloudless nights. In late winter the storms tend to be weaker and less frequent and overall temperatures begin to rise again, but localized strong thunderstorms may still occur at this time. In winter and spring, low temperatures inland combined with high humidity may result in early morning dew forming; and during calm weather in winter the warmer Gulf waters produce coastal fogs, though these are infrequent. The presence of moisture in the form of this dew may be of considerable importance in sustaining plants and animals in places where conditions might otherwise appear too arid.

Diurnal variations in temperature in the Eastern Province can be considerable with winter variations of 11°C and summer variations of 18°C at inland localities. For coastal areas, such as Ras Tanura, the variation is far less, i.e. approximately 7°C in winter and 9°C summer.

For the plants and animals of the Eastern Province, the rainfall is probably the most important climatic factor. Though decidedly sparse everywhere, it is highest in the north, on the coast and on the plains of the Dibdibah, decreasing southwards towards Ras Tanura, as this region lies in the path of the eastward-moving low pressure areas from the Mediterranean. Amounts decrease inland and further towards the south. In the Rub' al-Khali there have been periods of over ten years without rainfall. Throughout most of the Eastern Province the highest average rainfalls are in December and January; although the figures for inland localities in the south, admittedly averaged over shorter periods, suggest that there may be a tendency for the highest falls there to be later, about March. The problem of interpretation is that these are average figures calculated from very variable data. Rain occurs sporadically, and may be local and heavy, or non-existent. The average regional rainfall is about 75 mm, but typical annual values vary from about 15 mm to 150 mm and the figures for Abqaiq include annual totals of 7 mm in 1965 and 194 mm in 1982. This variability is illustrated by the average monthly rainfalls listed in Appendix IV; also by the fact that the October average shown for Ras Tanura is derived from rain falling in this month in only five of the 49 years covered by the records. In most localities there are frequently months, other than the normally dry summer months, without any rain; and when rain does occur it may well fall as brief, heavy and local storms, rapidly percolating into the sands, or producing local torrents and flash floods in rocky gullies.

The growth of vegetation, which in turn may affect the presence and breeding of various creatures, including birds, depends not only on the amount of rain that fell in the previous winter, but also on the extent of the land mass on which it fell or to which it subsequently flowed or drained; and the extent to which it was retained by surface or subsurface ground conditions. The apparently nomadic tendencies of some inland nesting birds are an adaptive response to such conditions.

Vegetation

Except in the limited areas of oases, palm groves and a few similar sites, vegetation is not a dominant feature of the landscape in the Eastern Province. Sand, rock and *sabkha* are the main structural components, and the vegetation is scattered over it as a thin sprinkling of small shrubs, grass tussocks and occasionally some large shrubby growth such as tamarisk. The rapid vigorous growth of plants in some areas where permanent water becomes available indicates that lack of water is the primary factor limiting vegetation.

The plants of arid and semi-arid regions are adapted to survive in areas of scanty rainfall. Short lived annual plants rely on the water available after rain in surface layers of sand or soil. They have limited growth and root systems and survive by a rapid response to the short term availability of water. During their period of growth and flowering they may make a thin carpet over the surface of the ground, with an often spectacular, if brief, display of flowers. Perennial plants survive through deeper and more extensive root systems. They must compete for available water and tend to be evenly and widely spaced on the surface of the ground, the visible growth being less than the spreading roots. This spacing produces the sparsely speckled appearance so characteristic of arid-country vegetation when viewed from a little distance.

The perennials may be grasses in the form of thick tussocks with a wide and relatively deep network of roots. Sedges and some grasses have rhizomes; root like modified stems that extend through the ground a little below the surface and send out roots and aerial shoots. The small woody shrubs tend to be the deepest rooted of all. They often have a stout tap root that extends vertically, deep into the ground, before sending out a network of lateral roots to draw water that is present at a greater depth and not available to surface rooted plants. This gives them an extra chance of survival when rainfall is scanty or sinks rapidly into the ground.

The major problem facing living creatures, both plant and animal, in hot arid regions, is survival through the long hot and dry period of the summer months when the absence of rain and lack of water are exacerbated by constant high temperatures and rapid evaporation. During the ordinary processes of transpiration a green plant loses a great deal of water, particularly through the leaves. In general the plants of dry regions have evolved small leaves or else entirely dispensed with them in favour of green stems that can carry out their function with less loss of water. In arid areas, water loss becomes a threat of rapid desiccation and death that must be overcome by various strategies.

Annual plants survive by having the whole life cycle occur within the more favourable part of the year. When rain falls seeds germinate and there is a rapid cycle of growth, flowering and seeding while water is still present. A prolonged period of wetter weather may allow more than a single cycle in one season; but in response to summer drought the whole plant shrivels and dies, leaving a crop of dispersed seeds to germinate with the next rains. In perennial grass clumps too, the surface vegetation may die back in the summer; but shoots persist within the shelter of the dead material at ground level to sprout in the next winter rains. Shrubs cannot dispense with all of their upper branches and twigs, though they do shed branchlets and leaves as water becomes scarce and temperatures rise. The stems that remain may have thick skins with few pores through which water can be lost, or a waxy coating that reduces water loss.

The result of these water conserving strategies is an overall vegetation which for a major part of the year appears dry and dead. A typical scene consists of withered annuals thinly coating the ground between dry brown grass tussocks or small shrubs which show as thickets of apparently lifeless stems. However, if a lower twig is snapped it shows green and fresh inside, revealing a structure not dead but dormant. In this respect the summer vegetation of the region is the equivalent of the winter vegetation of more temperate zones. The need to withstand adverse climatic conditions and to await an improvement in a dormant state produces the same dead looking landscape: a winter hibernation in one instance, a summer aestivation in the other.

The exception to this general appearance of aridity is furnished by the salt tolerant plants, the halophytes. These come from groups of species which evolved in areas where the available water was in fact almost too saline for the plants to use. The plants were therefore living in a kind of desert and have structurally adapted to store water and to reduce its loss. If leaves are present they tend to be rather thick and fleshy, sometimes with a very hairy or felted surface, though more often the leaves are lost and the stems become adapted for leaf-like functions. Stems tend to be swollen and often jointed in a manner suggesting a series of swollen units joined end to end. They have water storage cells inside them (filled on the occasions when fresher water is available), their outer walls are thick and fleshy or silicaceous with few pores, and since they have taken over the leaves' functions they are usually bright green or grey-green, sometimes reddish. Being already adapted for arid conditions they may not show much seasonal change, and low lying saline areas, shores and islands may carry some vegetation appearing green even in the dry summer period.

SOME DOMINANT PLANTS

The plants of the Eastern Province are part of a more widespread arid-country flora, sometimes referred to as the Saharo-Sindian or Saharo-Arabian flora, which occupies this broad desert region. It is not as highly specialized as the flora of some other climatically similar regions of the world, suggesting that it may have evolved in a more recent period, with less time and perhaps less adaptive pressures to develop many peculiar endemic forms. Variety is limited and the number of plant species is small compared with that of many other areas. A handful of species dominates the scene and provides the major, conspicuous part of the vegetation. Although there is uniformity of landscape, in some areas there may be numerous subtle variations within the vegetation and in the association of species. However, it is possible to see some obvious broad divisions within the vegetation as a whole, and while their boundaries may not be clear cut and unambiguous, a recognition of them can be helpful to anyone trying to comprehend the general divisions and variation within the Province.

The most widespread plants in the region are probably three shrubs, two grasses and a sedge; with a number of annuals that may appear widespread at times but are more dependent on the previous rain. On stonier and drier areas a typical shrub is 'arfaj *Rhanterium epapposum*. It is low growing, often no more than half a metre high, forming a thick clump of spindly twigs and generally appearing as a small rounded bush. The twigs have a smooth white surface and for much of the year appear lifeless. With autumn rains the bush becomes greener; the small oblong leaves grow slowly and it becomes fully leafed in March, usually producing its thistle-like yellow flowers, about 10 mm across, in April.

Another dominant species is the rimth salt bush *Hammada elegans* (previously recorded as *Haloxylon salicornicum*). This is a bushy shrub usually up to about a metre high with rather loose growth and a straggly top. It is a halophyte with leaves absent or reduced to minute scales; the stems are long, thin and slightly swollen structures showing a series of joints. The whole bush has a grey-green colour which it retains at drier times of the year. The flowers are relatively tiny and inconspicuous.

The third important shrub is 'abal *Calligonum comosum*, which has a woody trunk, usually buried in sand, and thin branches ending in upright bunches of thin dark green twigs. These persist through summer, with leaves and pale pink flowers in mid-winter, followed by scarlet or yellowish fruits. In the Rub' al-Khali it is replaced by a similar species, *C. crinitum*.

Stipa capensis is an annual grass growing in small tufts. It sprouts rapidly and flowers in the early winter rains, producing feathery headed clumps that in places form a silvery grey carpet, drying to yellowish-brown. *Panicum turgidum* is another grass but perennial and forming more solid clumps. It branches at the stem joints in a cluster of dry leaf sheaths and can lean over in the wind or rise to form a branching, metre-high bush. It can also continue to grow when partly submerged in sand. The sedge *Cyperus conglomeratus*, with a creeping buried rhizome and spiky-tufted head, is another plant that can cope with loose sand, spreading on the lower, stabilized slopes of dunes.

The other characteristic and obvious element in the vegetation is the mass of superficially similar salt tolerant plants with swollen leaves and jointed swollen stems. They include species of nine different genera, four of them with stems taking over the leaf function, and all but one belonging to the goosefoot family, the *Chenopodiaceae*.

VEGETATION ZONES

Vesey Fitzgerald (1957) separated the region into several basic plant communities, each dominated by one or two key species, although those species and others are not necessarily limited to that particular community but present to some degree in several of them. Zones dominated by *Rhanterium* or *Stipa* are recognized, and *Hammada* and *Panicum* dominate the coastal salt bush associations.

CENTRAL RED SANDS ASSOCIATIONS

These are represented in the Eastern Province by the Dahna and Rub' al-Khali regions. If rain does fall it soaks rapidly into the sands and is held there, though the outer 10 cm of sand tends to dry out and water is lost from it. Any plant utilizing this surface level must absorb any water in it rapidly, and perhaps rely on some dew to prolong its existence. Once the outer sand layer has dried it helps to seal in, and hold, the remaining water, some of which is held by the sand, some seeping to lower levels. In the looser sands it is the lower parts of deep hollows in the sides of dunes, and the depressions between, that carry the limited vegetation. It tends to be absent from surfaces, however low lying, where sand is constantly moved by wind.

Calligonum is a frequent shrub, able to grow in loose sand. Its woody stems make good firewood and it tends to suffer where Bedouins camp. A shrubby *Artemisia* is also present in the Dahna. After rain in winter, annuals appear as a thin coating in some hollows, around depressions and at the base of dunes; and are followed later, in spring, by short lived grasses. Even well out in the Rub' al-Khali some shrubby plant growth is present on the larger dunes, usually a few larger shrubs (such as *Calligonum*) with deeper and wider root systems able to utilize any available water. Small single shrubs or trees of *Acacia* may be found outside the fringing sands.

RHANTERIUM STEPPE

Towards the eastern side of the Dahna, where shallow layers of sand are present over more solid strata or gravels, *Rhanterium* begins to be present as abundant, well spaced bushes; with plantains and a well developed carpet of other annuals after rain. It is also present in sand patches and sandy gullies of the Summan plateau, and along the runnels in the drier parts. It forms a fairly continuous zone through the region.

STIPA STEPPE

Where the soil is more stable and finer textured, on the Summan and more particularly through the plains zone to the east, *Stipa* grass takes over on the lower lying ground and in hollows. It responds quickly to rain, flowers early and later may be mixed with annual herbage. Its distribution is often patchy and mixed in places with scattered shrubby growth of *Rhanterium* and *Artemisia*; and where looser sandy patches occur *Hammada* or shrubby tamarisk *Tamarix* may be present. *Stipa* grass is a dominant plant of the shrubless plains of the north where after good rains it may produce extensive and fairly continuous stands that persist as a dry herbage well into summer. In contrast, the gravel plains of the south, around Yabrin, tend not to have a rich grassy cover. However, they carry in places large stretches of *Rhanterium* shrubs, and *Calligonum* is present where the dunes and sand ridges begin to cover the gravels on the eastern side. The northern Wadi al-Batin has *Stipa* as a dominant species but *Hammada* and *Artemisia* bushes are also present and *Ephedra alata* grows locally in loose sand bordering the wadi banks. In places the wadi floor has small areas of cultivation bordered with shrubby bushes. In the south the Wadi as-Sahba has *Hammada* and other shrubs, and in places small *Acacia* bushes; the latter present as thorn scrub in the wadi and around the irrigated area of Haradh.

To the east of the *Stipa* zone, where the *jabal* area merges with the coastal zone and the northern white sands of the Jafurah, the grass *Panicum turgidum* is more dominant. In more northerly areas it is present extensively as a stippling of evenly spaced tussocks, tending to be replaced by low *Hammada* salt bush association, and increasingly giving way to *Rhanterium* steppe inland.

West of Abu Hadriyah there is an extensive area of low *Rhanterium* mixed with other small shrubs such as spiny *Cornulaca*; there is *Stipa* in some favourable spots, with salt bush and other halophytes.

COASTAL WHITE SAND ASSOCIATIONS

Further south the white sands begin to occur in *dikakah* formation (see p. 21), building up in heaps around plants. To survive, the plants need to be able to grow through the accumulating sand; and also to possess long root systems to reach down to the water. *Panicum turgidum*, with its ability to sprout from the stem nodes, is well adapted for this type of growth; *Calligonum* reappears, but *Rhanterium* is less able to cope. Two other shrubs, the leafless, slender stemmed, broom-like *Leptadenia pyrotechnica* and the spiny, berberis-like *Lycium shawii* tend to occur in this habitat. Small tufty growth on top of the sand hummocks may be the visible ends of tall and complex plant growth concealed in the drifted sand.

These sand adapted species tend to recur through the coastal white sand zone, but become increasingly sparse as the dunes build up. In addition to scattered grasses such as *Panicum turgidum* and some annuals, the sedge *Cyperus conglomeratus* is a typical plant, colonizing the lower windward slopes and hollows of the dunes. Areas of water seepage below the dunes are marked by increasing growth of shrubby tamarisk and small scrubby date palms *Phoenix dactylifera*, at times partly overwhelmed by moving sand.

One improbable looking plant for a desert area, rare and scattered in the Jafurah dunes but increasingly common near settlements, is *Calotropis procera*. It tends to have a cluster of thick vertical stems about 3–4 m high bearing a heavy growth of fleshy, grey-green, cabbage-like leaves and bearing heads of small, swollen, purplish flowers followed by large, pale green, spongy seedpods.

These coastal sands often overlie *sabkha*, and although these flats have no vegetation themselves, their sandy borders are colonized by low growing halophytes with fleshy leaves, such as *Seidlitzia rosmarinus* (also capable of growing up through loose sand) and *Zygophyllum qatarense*, which form low green mats around the *sabkha*'s edge.

COASTAL SALT BUSH ASSOCIATIONS

Hammada is the main shrub here, sharing the ground with other fleshy leaved or swollen stemmed halophytes; and in drier coastal places with the more typically leaved sea-lavender *Limonium*. On the shore itself the tall beach grass *Halopyrum mucronatum* occurs in some southern areas where it may help to stabilize the sands at the upper edge of the beach, and the long sprawling and scrambling *Aeluropus* grass and other grasses may be present. In marshy areas with fresher water the thick spiky rush *Juncus rigidus* occurs.

SEA SHORES AND ISLANDS

The thin layer of vegetation that covers the muddy coastal salt marshes consists mainly of two low and spreading shrubby halophytes with leafless fleshy stems: the spiky stemmed *Arthrocnemum glaucum*, and at levels of longer submergence by sea water the similar *Halocnemum strobilaceum*. In places, the rich muddy channels are occupied by a shrubby growth of black mangrove *Avicennia marina* surrounded by masses of finger-like woody pneumatophores projecting from mud that is covered by each tide.

The islands' flora tend to be low sparse halophytes more adapted to a drier sandier existence. Small shrubby *Suaeda* bushes tend to dominate them, with *Salsola* and *Arthrocnemum*, and other fleshy stemmed species such as *Halopeplis perfoliata* which has stems like tight rows of badly strung rounded green or reddish beads.

INLAND WATERS AND CULTIVATION

In startling contrast with most of the region's sparse, dry vegetative cover is the relatively lush growth in areas where there is adequate water. The principal species found in oasis areas is the date palm, and fruit trees such as loquats or citruses are sometimes present. On irrigated land, around and under the trees where regular cultivation is not occurring, a heavy growth of reed *Phragmites*, reed mace *Typha* and tall grasses often occurs. Reeds also extend along the edges of any open waters, with rushes and grasses on drier edges. Shrubby tamarisk tends to grow on the sandy borders of such areas, but around some of the groves and cultivated areas a tall upright species, the athel tamarisk *Tamarix aphylla*, is increasingly planted. In favourable conditions this can become a substantial tree. The plantings around the Imhoff sewerage evaporation ponds at Dhahran consisted mainly of this tamarisk and the mesquite *Prosopis juliflora*.

Recent exotic plantings, such as those in the Aramco compounds at Ras Tanura, Dhahran and Abqaiq, have included pinnate leaved trees such as mesquite, siris and acacias, and more typical broad leaved trees such as banyan, fig and *Eucalyptus* species. There is a well established shrubby growth, hedges of hibiscus and the false jasmine *Clerodendron inerme*; and creepers and climbers such as kudzu and bougainvillea. These cultivated and residential areas offer a vegetation somewhat similar to that of the temperate regions from which many of the passage migrant and winter visiting birds have come, and they are likely to halt for a while. The Aramco compounds, with their green shrubberies, well tended gardens and shaded lawns, are especially suburban in character and attract breeding species that will tolerate the presence of man.

THE ORIGINS OF EASTERN PROVINCE BIRDS

Pre-history: Miocene to Pleistocene

MIOCENE–PLIOCENE

Geographically speaking, the Arabian peninsula came into existence when the northward-drifting continent of Africa encountered that of Eurasia, becoming recognizable in its present position in the Miocene period. In the previous geological period, the Oligocene, the region had been covered by sea. One expanse of sea, extending north to south from what is now the Arctic Ocean to the present Indian Ocean, divided Eurasia into western and eastern land masses; and the African continent was separated from these by a western arm of the Tethys Sea. During the Oligocene the northern gap closed to produce a single Eurasian continent, and about 18 million years ago, in mid-Miocene, Africa and Eurasia were joined.

It was during the Miocene also that the land mass of Arabia broke away from Africa, producing the gap that is now the Red Sea and shifting eastwards towards Asia. Where the two plates of the drifting land masses met, there was an upheaval which produced the high mountain masses of eastern Turkey, Iran and Afghanistan, while the Arabian sector dipped slightly to produce a lower and more level region, sloping gently downwards towards the north-east. To the west of it was the Mediterranean Sea, its eastern outlet closed and the western one increasingly constricted by the northward movement of Africa. The growth of a large Antarctic ice sheet in the late Miocene then brought about a general lowering of sea levels and, as a result, the Mediterranean became cut off altogether from the larger ocean. It formed a land-locked sea, becoming increasingly saline, and for a period of over a million years at the end of the Miocene it became a series of deep isolated basins in which repeated evaporation produced deposits of salt and other evaporites.

When the gap finally closed in the Miocene, African elephant species, pigs and bovids entered Eurasia, while the Ostrich may have gone in the opposite direction. Later, when the Mediterranean appears to have presented a barrier to extensions of range, Arabia could at times have provided a bridge between the two continents, but there is reason to suggest that this may have been limited by the type of vegetation that was present.

There is some lateral evidence from fossil birds, in particular from those of certain families which at present occur only in Africa and are regarded as characteristic of the Afrotropical region. These include the ostrich (Struthionidae), touracos (Musophagidae), wood-hoopoes (Phoeniculidae) and mousebirds (Coliidae). However, together with other families now typical of the tropics both in Africa and elsewhere, such as trogons (Trogonidae) and parrots (Psittacidae), these occur as fossils in Europe at an earlier period. Trogons, parrots and ostriches are known from the Eocene onwards, and the other three in the Oligocene and early Miocene. There is at present no evidence of these families as fossils in Africa prior to this. In the Miocene, possibly when conditions deteriorated in the Mediterranean region, there appears to have been a southward shift of both fauna and flora into Africa. It seems possible that it was not until the Miocene that Africa gained these bird families, which did not subsequently re-establish themselves in Europe. What may be significant is that these three families of arboreal birds, now endemic to Africa, do not appear to have been able to enter and establish themselves in Asia via an Arabian route. This is an additional indication that Arabia once had a savanna type vegetation which did not provide adequate niches for a spread of birds requiring forest or tall scrub; and that any changes were towards less vegetation rather than more.

The incursion of water across the lower north-east side of the Arabian land mass to produce in its present form the large but shallow inlet of the Arabian Gulf occurred in the latter part of the subsequent Pliocene period, about three to four million years ago. At the beginning of this period the opening of the Straits of Gibraltar had already restored the Mediterranean as a sea. Prior to this, however, the Eastern Province had been subjected to a succession of inundations and exposures which laid down the succession of late Tertiary strata that form its surface rocks. These were intermittently eroded by the rising seas of the inundations and by run-off from further west in the more rainy periods.

There is some evidence of conditions from Lower Miocene fossils at as-Sarrar on the edge of the Summan plateau. The area was covered by sea for parts of this period, and the fossil fragments of vertebrate animals indicate a near shore environment with tidal flats and a large estuarine system with a subtropical to tropical climate. The larger mammals are those of fairly open country: mastodons, rhinoceros, cattle and giraffoids, of extinct species. The smaller mammals found suggest even more open country. At least four species of birds have been found, the earliest from Saudi Arabia. They include storks *Mycteria* and ibises, but have not been fully identified. The larger waterbirds such as these are less affected by ecological barriers and tend to move for long distances. Evidence from elsewhere suggests that in the Miocene a waterbird fauna, that possibly involved the same species throughout, extended from north-west Africa, across north and east Africa and Arabia, into Pakistan.

Later Miocene rocks at Jabal Dawmat al-'Awdah, 100 km inland in the northern part of the Eastern Province, have produced evidence of more mastodons, and of mangrove roots. Interpretation of conditions in this region about the Middle Miocene period by Whybrow and McClure (1981), based on fossils and pollen, suggest that inland there were open savanna type grasslands, with areas of freshwater accumulation fed by shallow, vegetation fringed rivers and streams flowing at least seasonally; and with a generally dry but not arid climate. The coast had tidal flats with mangroves, backed by broad alluvial floodplains with local swamps and marshes fed by palm fringed streams. The coastal climate was tropical to subtropical and rainfall was seasonal, possibly monsoonal. These conditions should have supported a large and varied population of grassland and waterside birds, but as yet we have no evidence of them.

In the Middle to Upper Pliocene the incursion of the Gulf waters on to the land mass of what is now the Eastern Province cut the line of the Summan escarpment as its coast before retreating; and in the last two million years of the Pliocene the rainfall was sufficient to create massive wadis that cut eastwards through the Tuwayq escarpment and deposited their gravels across the northern and southern ends of the Eastern Province (see p. 19). Towards the end of this period, however, the climate became drier, and with the formation of the north polar ice cap the Pleistocene ice ages began.

THE PLEISTOCENE PERIOD

For a period of some two million years the greater part of the northern hemisphere was dominated by a series of ice ages: major glaciations of large continental areas alternating with warmer inter-glacials when the ice retreated and the climate ameliorated. The effects of these in terms of wetter or drier, and cooler or warmer periods, extended into regions of the earth beyond the immediate reach of the ice caps and their peripheral influence.

From observations based on the European alpine region it was originally thought that there were four glacial periods, with intervening inter-glacials, during the Pleistocene. Later this was increased to six periods. More recently, studies of long term peat accumulations and the deposits of ocean floors have indicated that, for western Europe at least and probably elsewhere, there were between 14 and 20 alternating periods of significantly cold and temperate climate. For the most part we can only study what remains of the final stage, and in many instances cannot be certain in our attempts to correlate the effects of glaciation with any particular climatic fluctuation.

The results of the spread and shrinkage of ice caps are complex. In general the effect on both plants and animals in regions such as Eurasia was to cause a gradual southward shift each time the climate became colder, with a northerly re-invasion when conditions improved. The periods involved were long in human terms and the changes at any given time might have been barely perceptible; they might be comparable with the small changes in climate and vegetation that we are conscious of at the

GEOLOGICAL TIMESCALE OF THE CENOZOIC ERA

PERIOD OR EPOCH	YEARS AGO
Quaternary period	
Holocene epoch	10,000 – present
Humans hunted and tamed animals, developed agriculture and began to use metals, minerals and other resources.	
Pleistocene epoch	10,000 – 2 million
Modern humans developed. Mammoths, woolly rhinos and other mammals flourished.	
Tertiary period	
Pliocene epoch	2 million – 5 million
Sea life became much as today's. Birds and many mammals became like modern forms and spread throughout the world. Humans appeared.	
Miocene epoch	5 million – 24 million
Apes appeared in Asia and Africa. Other animals included bats, monkeys, whales and primitive bears. Flowering plants and trees resembled modern types.	
Oligocene epoch	24 million – 37 million
Primitive apes appeared. Camels, cats, dogs, rhinos, elephants and rodents developed.	
Eocene epoch	37 million – 58 million
Birds, amphibians, small reptiles and fish abundant. Primitive bats, camels, horses, rhinos and whales appeared.	
Paleocene epoch	58 million – 66 million
Flowering plants abundant. Invertebrates, fish, reptiles, amphibians and small mammals common.	

present time. Indeed it has been suggested that we are living in an inter-glacial period which began about ten thousand years ago, was at its warmest about five thousand years ago, and may be slowly cooling again, its pattern of change partly obscured by short term fluctuations within it.

The spread of birds and mammals is easy to understand. For plants it may be a little harder to visualize; but a proportion of wind-blown seeds establish themselves each year. The droppings of some animals contain undigested seeds and birds such as jays and nutcrackers will fly several kilometres carrying acorns, nuts or pine seeds to bury them out in open ground where many might grow.

In this context, plant communities and their associated animals can thus be regarded as mobile units of living things; and in visualizing the changes that occur over the tens of thousands of years involved in many of these glacial fluctuations the general distribution of the whole range of living organisms can therefore be envisaged as a constant dynamic sequence of ebb and flow.

In colder periods the spread of glacial conditions from the north was accompanied by a southward shift in the distributions of living things. It was not necessarily wholly disadvantageous. For cold adapted species it may have offered a much wider range to exploit. However, in the more extreme conditions the temperate and boreal species, particularly those of forest and scrub, were forced down to the southern edges of Eurasia. This meant that there was not always a continuous zone of suitable habitat available for them. The presence of seas, the division of land into promontories and the presence of mountain ranges combined to fragment these more temperate zones into a series of separate areas offering refuges to a wide range of species.

Such refuges varied in size and conditions: some species might become extinct in certain of them but survive in others. A further effect arose from the isolation of these fragmented populations. Natural selection could modify the genetic inheritance of such sub-populations to suit local conditions, producing differences that would affect relationships between them when the climate improved and they spread back out of their former refuges and re-encountered each other.

Some populations might have evolved differences in characters, such as colour, pattern or voice, which made them recognizable but did not prevent them integrating and breeding with other populations of the same species when they encountered them. Such recognizable populations are subspecies, and their presence in present day species is often useful in providing some evidence of the past history of their changes in distribution. More prolonged isolation in refuges, or repeated periods of isolation, gave rise at times to evolutionary changes in populations which, when they came together again, were sufficient to inhibit or prevent interbreeding and re-integration. In this way new species could evolve, either relatively similar and closely competing species or those which differed significantly in their behaviour and requirements.

By studying the distribution of bird species at the present time it is possible to identify the approximate position of some of these refuges. There appears to have been a chain of Pleistocene refuges, allowing some degree of differentiation in population, extending from the Canary Islands through the Mediterranean region, the Middle East, India and Malaysia, as far as Japan. It is not always easy to identify such areas, and different species, forest birds, waterbirds, grassland birds, have differing requirements. In addition, a single refuge may provide a variety of habitats. As well as the main identifiable zone, the peripheral fringes of it might offer suitable conditions for the survival of a species with less exacting requirements, the subsequent spread of which might not be obviously referable to the refuge.

The low lying upper part of the Arabian Gulf depression, with its rivers and swamps, would have been an obvious refuge area for birds and its importance was almost certainly enhanced by another result of glaciation. In each ice age, as the polar cap and its subsidiary ice masses grew, it represented an accumulation of water, piling up in a solid state in a limited area. Water which might have spread around the earth was increasingly confined in this way and one result was a general fall in sea level.

The Arabian Gulf is a very shallow sea, averaging only 35 m deep and with a maximum depth of 100 m, so the drop in sea level of about 120 m which occurred at the height of some glaciations emptied the Gulf basin entirely. Even under less extreme conditions a partial change of this type must have occurred. At such periods the Gulf would have been a wide shallow valley: a long depression of lowland or swamp vegetation traversed by the fresh waters of the proto-Tigris and Euphrates; probably fed by additional meltwaters of snow and ice on the higher ground to the north. Temperatures would have been cooler, the climate moister, and the surrounding land that is now arid or semi-arid probably carried more extensive vegetation. It can be argued that the Gulf region must have offered an extensive refuge for birds during the glacial phases of the Pleistocene. Evidence to support this must be sought in the current distribution of bird species within this and the surrounding regions.

There is evidence of a past movement of more northerly birds into this region, followed by an isolation of some populations south of the Gulf which were subsequently cut off still further, possibly by increasing aridity. These populations tended to take refuge in the higher, more mountainous regions of southern Arabia and were isolated long enough to differentiate to species level, their closest affinities subsequently lying with species to the north of them. Examples of these are the two *Alectoris* partridges, Philby's Partridge (*A. philbyi*) and the Arabian Redleg (*A. melanocephala*), the Arabian Woodpecker (*Dendrocopos dorae*), an isolate dunnock (*Prunella fagani*), sometimes treated as a race of Radde's Dunnock (*P. ocularis*) and Yemen Linnet (*Carduelis yemenensis*). Hume's Tawny Owl (*Strix butleri*) may also belong to this group. Two species are still endemic to the Gulf area itself: the Grey Hypocolius (*Hypocolius ampelinus*), a highly distinct and discrete relative of the boreal forest waxwings, and the Iraq Babbler (*Turdoides altirostris*), which has evolved some differentiation in bill shape and is limited to the wetter area at the head of the Gulf.

These species can be linked with the past history of the Gulf on the basis of their present distribution. It is less easy to identify those species or subspecies which may have differentiated in the Gulf region in the past, but with the advent of a warmer climate have moved back into other, perhaps more extensive areas of suitable habitat, and have severed all connection with the Gulf; or those which may only use it for overwintering or during migration.

If one examines the general distribution of Eurasian birds and attempts to correlate this with their probable Pleistocene history there are several species which, from their present ranges (including those of their subspecies), are likely to have originated in the general region of the Middle East. Some may have had their primary refuges nearer the Mediterranean, but many of them probably utilized the glacial refuges offered by the Gulf region. The possible members of this group are the Pygmy Cormorant (*Phalacrocorax pygmeus*), Levant Sparrowhawk (*Accipiter brevipes*), White-tailed Plover (*Chettusia leucura*), Long-billed Pipit (*Anthus similis*), the black-headed form of the Yellow Wagtail (*Motacilla flava*), Radde's Dunnock (*Prunella ocularis*), Upcher's Warbler (*Hippolais languida*), Menetries' Warbler (*Sylvia mystacea*), Green Warbler (*Phylloscopus nitidus*), Finsch's Wheatear (*Oenanthe finschii*), White-throated Robin (*Irania gutturalis*), Cinereous Bunting (*Emberiza cineracea*), Grey-necked Bunting (*Emberiza buchanani*), Black-headed Bunting (*Emberiza melanocephala*), Pale Rock Sparrow (*Petronia brachydactyla*), Dead Sea Sparrow (*Passer moabiticus*), Pleske's Ground Chough (*Podoces pleskei*) and the dark-crowned form of the Jay (*Garrulus glandarius*). Other species that may have had similar origins but for which the evidence is less obvious are the Masked Shrike (*Lanius nubicus*), Plain Willow Warbler (*Phylloscopus neglectus*), Hume's Wheatear (*Oenanthe alboniger*) and Rock Nuthatch (*Sitta neumayer*).

This list necessarily results from a simplified general approach. It is obvious that over the period of time involved and with constant climatic fluctuations, the changes must have been complex, and there is a hint of this in the presence of the two partridges, two babblers, and the two dunnock populations. Nevertheless, from the zoogeographical evidence available there is good reason to believe that the Gulf region was an important Pleistocene refuge area.

The condition of the main Arabian area away from the Gulf at this period and its variations in aridity are uncertain. From the affinities of the present bird faunas of the Afrotropical and Oriental regions, and from evidence of bird distribution on a smaller scale in Oman and the Yemen, it is obvious that as well as past periods when these shared a common and presumably continuously distributed fauna, there have been other periods during which populations were divided, presumably due to arid conditions. As a result there are genera of birds with some species in Africa and others in the Indian region; some showing evidence of fairly close affinity. The Collared Dove (*Streptopelia decaocto*) has an African counterpart, the African Collared Dove (*Streptopelia roseogrisea*), and the Indian Silverbill (*Euodice malabarica*), is replaced in south-west Arabia and Africa by the African Silverbill (*Lonchura cantans*). In both instances the differences are relatively small ones of plumage colour and voice. In addition there are a number of species with subspecific populations in India and in Africa separated by the Arabian gap.

In general there is evidence of marked changes in aridity over the main part of Arabia, possibly correlated to some extent with glacial fluctuations. One might expect periods of high rainfall during northern glaciations, and drier periods in the interglacials. The increasing aridity which has continued through historic times to the present may be the latest of these. Some information on the latter part of this period has become available from studies of past conditions in the desert of the Rub' al-Khali. These dune sands accumulated through the drier, windy periods of the Pleistocene, but during the last major glacial period freshwater lakes, fed by monsoon type rains, were present in the hollows between the dune ridges. The surrounding conditions varied from semi-arid with wild cattle and buffaloes present, to savanna grassland with hippopotami in the lakes. The lakes contained molluscs and ostracod crustaceans but, it seems, no fish.

Post-Pleistocene Changes

Between the last period when the Gulf constituted a refuge area and the present, the changes in the local environment have been dramatic. With the increase in aridity there appears to have been considerable loss of plant and animal diversity, though the process may have been relatively slow and has certainly not been continuous.

In the Rub' al-Khali the period of hyper-aridity which ushered in present desert conditions began at the end of the last glaciation, about 17,000 years before the present (BP). It was broken again for a while by a northerly displacement of the south-west monsoon between 9,000 and 6,000 years BP. This brought periodic heavy rains, and freshwater lakes were re-established for significantly long periods. These, however, were lost again when the weather systems reverted to their present positions.

In both the wetter Late Pleistocene and post-Pleistocene periods more extensive areas of open water existed at the al-Hasa oasis and possibly elsewhere. Although not a scrap of solid evidence exists it is reasonably certain that lakes there must have been important to many birds, particularly those types frequenting fresh water and the waterside; and they must also have influenced bird migration across the region.

Some further evidence is available for a slightly later period, about 5,000 years BP, from excavations on the small island of Umm an-Nar in the coastal lagoon by Abu Dhabi. Here relics of an early settlement were found with bone of animals used for food. These included some bird bones studied by Hoch (1979). She identified remains of the Greater Flamingo (*Phoenicopterus ruber*), the Socotra Cormorant (*Phalacrocorax nigrogularis*), and a small duck, not identifiable to species but about the size of a Garganey (*Anas querquedula*). There were also a number of bones of the Darter (*Anhinga melanogaster*). Today this species occurs in the marshes of Iraq but is not known along the Gulf shores. It requires fresh or brackish waters bordered by taller vegetation including trees in which it can perch and nest. It may utilize lagoons or estuaries, but not salt water. Its presence at this earlier period, when from other evidence it is known that the sea level in the Gulf was a little higher, indicates the presence of a more vegetated shore and some less saline water.

If the Darter was more widespread around the Gulf at this period, then similar birds still present in the marshy areas at the head of the Gulf may have had a more extensive and possibly resident distribution around the shores. These include the Dalmatian Pelican (*Pelecanus crispus*), Pygmy Cormorant (*Phalacrocorax pygmeus*), Purple Heron (*Ardea purpurea*), Grey Heron (*Ardea cinerea*), Goliath Heron (*Ardea goliath*), Night Heron (*Nycticorax nycticorax*), Sacred Ibis (*Threskiornis aethiopicus*) and Spoonbill (*Platalea leucorodia*). Small birds of similar habitats, such as the Fantailed Warbler (*Cisticola juncidis*) would also have had a wider range.

The unexpected find at Umm an-Nar was some bone fragments of a giant heron, larger than the Goliath Heron (*Ardea goliath*), by the same extent that it in turn overtops the Grey Heron (*Ardea cinerea*). Another incomplete bone apparently referable to the same species was found on the island of Faylakah, near Kuwait, and is dated about 3,800 years BP. Ella Hoch named this new species *Ardea bennuides*, tentatively identifying it with the Bennu bird depicted in Egyptian paintings from the time of the Pharaohs. The existence of such a bird in this area is perhaps not so surprising in view of the extent of the freshwater lakes in the Rub' al-Khali a little earlier, but it does suggest that there may be the remains of other extinct birds from the Pleistocene and post-Pleistocene periods still to be discovered around the Gulf.

In general, though, the period since the Pleistocene ice ages seems to have been one of slowly increasing aridity, the tendency to create desert conditions being accelerated to some extent by human activity and overgrazing by domesticated animals.

FAUNAL SUBDIVISIONS

In general distribution birds cover the world, and although species differ in their requirements the pattern of overlapping ranges is continuous from one region to another. In studying the plants and animals of the world it is possible to recognize major biotopes, ecological subdivisions each inhabited by groups of species which in aggregate are characteristic of it and in which it differs from others. Because of their mobility birds often have rather hazily defined limits of distribution, but it is nevertheless possible to recognize groups of species within the major biotopes that constitute characteristic bird faunas. Major biotopes can be separated into smaller subsidiary ones, and the birdlife of the Eastern Province of Saudi Arabia can be seen to contain a number of these faunal divisions which together contribute to its complexity.

The Province is situated in part of an arid zone, the Afro-Sindian or Afro-Arabian Desert Zone, that extends from the west coast of North Africa to southern Pakistan. In such a region one would expect a limited and sparsely distributed range of bird species, but local interactions with other factors enrich its avifauna.

In the area of the Arabian Gulf for example, the Gulf itself, cutting across this desert zone, brings its own birds and introduces intrusions from other faunas lying to the north and east. In addition, the whole area lies below a part of what is probably the most heavily used migratory flyway in the Old World. And finally, man has modified some areas by his activities, creating new habitats favourable to some additional species. It is this combination of desert, Gulf, migrants and man-modified habitat that gives the Eastern Province an enlarged avifauna within which these separate influences can be recognized.

Arid-country Faunas

Arabia lies roughly at the meeting point of three of the major faunal regions of the world: the Palearctic (Eurasia from Atlantic to Pacific), the Afrotropical (Africa south of the Sahara) and the Oriental. The long Afro-Sindian Desert Zone is usually treated as the southern edge of the Palearctic. However, this is the viewpoint of those living in the Palearctic zone who see the desert as a convenient faunally impoverished boundary to a cooler and richer region. If one is examining it as a desert it is less obviously a Palearctic border zone. The desert as a whole takes its species from both Palearctic and Afrotropical sources; it is thus a separate but transitional zone between the two, bordering the southern edge of the western Palearctic. *For the purposes of this section the Afro-Sindian Desert Zone is being treated as a separate entity, and is excluded from the term Palearctic as used here.*

The desert has a number of forms, both subspecies and species, which show varying degrees of differentiation from closely allied northern counterparts and appear to have evolved as distinct arid-country forms during some period, or periods, of separation. They tend to show browner and paler plumages, sometimes much paler, than northern birds and they are mostly distinctly smaller. Examples are the Barbary Falcon (*Falco pelegrinoides*) and Peregrine (*Falco peregrinus*), desert and northern forms of the Eagle Owl (*Bubo bubo*), and Little Owl (*Athene noctua*), (probably) Hume's Tawny Owl (*Strix butleri*) and Tawny Owl (*Strix aluco*), Temminck's Horned Lark (*Eremophila bilopha*) and Shore Lark (*Eremophila alpestris*), Desert Sparrow (*Passer simplex*) and House Sparrow (*Passer domesticus*), and Brown-necked Raven (*Corvus ruficollis*) and Raven (*Corvus corax*). The African and European forms of the Chaffinch (*Fringilla coelebs*) and Great Grey Shrike (*Lanius excubitor*) show similar trends.

Birds do not generally live in pure desert, but they are variably adapted to arid conditions and some can live in slightly modified desert areas. Others inhabit the semi-arid areas that border the desert. A theoretical simplified pattern of distribution for birds in such a region might show a few species in the central arid area, with others occurring in continuous zones in the semi-arid borders around it. In the present instance, the arid zone extends as a belt across the whole width of the region from the Atlantic to the Indian Ocean and does not allow a continuous peripheral ring of less arid country. The semi-arid zone is therefore divided into two separate bordering strips, to north and south of the arid central zone, each deriving some species independently from adjacent faunal regions. There are thus three parallel zones from east to west: the central one inhabited by species that can tolerate hot, arid conditions, and two lateral zones with separate semi-arid faunas present along, and at times intruding into, the northern and southern edges of the central zone; the whole is traversed by narrow bands of water and waterside fauna formed by the Nile valley, Red Sea, Arabian Gulf, and Indus valley.

The birds of the inland arid habitats of the Eastern Province can be assigned to these three subdivisions which have been identified within the desert zone as a whole.

Northern Fauna

Long-legged Buzzard (*Buteo rufinus*), Kestrel (*Falco tinnunculus*), Barbary Falcon (*Falco pelegrinoides*), Houbara Bustard (*Chlamydotis undulata*), Collared Dove (*Streptopelia decaocto*), Pallid Swift (*Apus pallidus*), Thick-billed Lark (*Ramphocoris clotbey*) (winter visitor), Temminck's Horned Lark (*Eremophila bilopha*), Lesser Short-toed Lark (*Calandrella rufescens*), Olivaceous Warbler (*Hippolais pallida*).

Central Fauna

Cream-coloured Courser (*Cursorius cursor*), Spotted Sandgrouse (*Pterocles senegallus*), Bar-tailed Desert Lark (*Ammomanes cincturus*), Desert Lark (*Ammomanes deserti*), Hoopoe Lark (*Alaemon alaudipes*), Pale Rock Martin (*Ptyonoprogne fuligula*), White-crowned Black Wheatear (*Oenanthe leucopyga*), Brown-necked Raven (*Corvus ruficollis*).

Southern Fauna

Namaqua Dove (*Oena capensis*), Black-crowned Finch Lark (*Eremopterix nigriceps*), Dunn's Lark (*Eremalauda dunni*).

Species with widespread scattered distributions not fitting into these divisions include Crested Lark (*Galerida cristata*), Rufous Bush Chat (*Cercotrichas galactotes*), and Trumpeter Finch (*Bucanetes githagineus*). The Mourning Wheatear (*Oenanthe lugens*), a winter visitor, appears to be an African species preferring montane habitats and colonizing these within both northern and southern semi-arid desert border zones.

Of the three southern species the Namaqua Dove (*Oena capensis*) owes its spread in recent years to an extension of cultivated and irrigated areas in otherwise arid country. Dunn's Lark (*Eremalauda dunni*) occurs mainly in central Arabia and enters the Eastern Province from the south-west. The Black-crowned Finch Lark (*Eremopterix nigriceps*), although a southern bird elsewhere, is able to extend northwards in the Arabian region, possibly in slightly more tolerable areas modified by the central highlands and coasts.

The arid-country avifauna of the Eastern Province therefore fits into the typical pattern as a basically central to northern Afro-Sindian Desert Zone fauna, in an area that allows a limited incursion from the southern fauna of the zone.

For these desert species as a whole there is little evidence of past local speciation in isolation. The Pleistocene changes discussed in the previous section resulted in the production of subspecies and species following prolonged fragmentation of forest and scrub biotopes; and the Afrotropical region provides many examples of a similar type of differentiation during periods when there were changes in the relative distribution of forest and savanna. Fragmentation, producing islands of savanna in forest, or forest in savanna, helped to create the large number of bird species found there. Theoretically the same could occur in arid regions and the relative paucity of species suggests that these deserts may be of relatively recent origin, or that there has been little fragmentation of them in the past, or that some new species created have subsequently become extinct due to the narrow range of niches available.

In the general area of eastern Arabia there are a few pairs of similar species with extensively overlapping ranges, but preferring slightly different habitats within them. These must have originated from isolation of a divided population, followed by differentiation and the opportunity to recolonize a shared area. This suggests that the second of the three options listed above is the likeliest.

The minimum requirements for the differentiation that is now present would have been the division of an arid area to which a species was adapted, producing populations in two refuges. From present evidence one refuge is likely to have been rockier than the other. The fairly similar Crowned Sandgrouse (*Pterocles coronatus*) and Spotted Sandgrouse (*P. senegallus*) form one pair, the former tending to prefer stonier localities than the other. The Desert Lark (*Ammomanes deserti*) and Bar-tailed Desert Lark (*A. cincturus*) are likewise similar, the former associated with rockier habitats. The Short-toed Lark (*Calandrella brachydactyla*) and Lesser Short-toed Lark (*C. rufescens*) are another pair, although the former prefers stonier and more vegetated ground.

Some distinctions which have led to the recognition of named subspecies are based upon minor variations of colour, of a type which tends to be of only local significance in arid regions where body coloration may match the habitat background. The only two which seem important are in the bulbuls and babblers, neither of which are truly desert species. The Black-capped Bulbul (*Pycnonotus barbatus*) has red under tail coverts in Afrotropical Africa, whitish in North Africa and yellow in Arabia. The latter is sometimes separated as a species, the Yellow-vented Bulbul (*P. xanthopygos*), an unfortunate name since the White-cheeked Bulbul (*P. leucogenys*) is also yellow vented.

The second example is in the *Turdoides* babblers. The Fulvous Babbler (*T. fulvus*) is present in North Africa; the Arabian Babbler (*T. squamiceps*) replaces it in Arabia but is more confined to upland areas. The Iraq Babbler (*T. altirostris*) is an endemic of marshy areas at the head of the Arabian Gulf, and the Common Babbler (*T. caudatus*) extends from the Indian region, through Pakistan and southern Iran, to overlap with the Iraq Babbler in southern Iraq.

The Arabian Gulf

MARINE BIRDS

The birds grouped here are those for which the waters of the Gulf appear to have a major influence on distribution. Colonization of the Gulf appears to have occurred from the northern Indian Ocean, an area not particularly rich in seabirds, though some other species that are more widely distributed in warm seas are also now present and breeding in the Gulf. The latter include Red-billed Tropicbird (*Phaethon aethereus*), Swift Tern (*Sterna bergii*), Lesser Crested Tern (*S. bengalensis*), and Bridled Tern (*S. anaethetus*).

In addition there is a group of species sharing a common type of distribution confined to the inshore waters of the north-western corner of the Indian Ocean and tending to extend to both the Arabian Gulf and the Red Sea. It seems possible that they had their origin in this general area, though in view of the considerable fluctuations in size of the Gulf prior to and during the Pleistocene era and its intermittent availability as a marine refuge, it seems more likely that the exact centre of origin was the Red Sea. The group includes the Socotra Cormorant (*Phalacrocorax nigrogularis*), Sooty Gull (*Larus hemprichii*), White-cheeked Tern (*Sterna repressa*), Saunders' Little Tern (*S. saundersi*), and Crab Plover (*Dromas ardeola*) (which has extended its range further south and east in the Indian Ocean); the White-eyed Gull (*L. leucophthalmus*), resident in the Red Sea, also belongs to the group.

Truly marine species such as the Procellariiformes do not appear to have colonized the Gulf for breeding, but offshore movements of Audubon's Shearwater (*Puffinus lherminieri*) have been observed in the Gulf, and Wilson's Petrel (*Oceanites oceanicus*) seems to be regular between July and September. Other birds with mainly marine interests which use the Gulf at times are Red-necked and Grey Phalaropes (*Phalaropus lobatus* and *P. fulicarus*) and Pomarine and Arctic Skuas (*Stercorarius pomarinus* and *S. parasiticus*); these breed in subarctic and arctic regions and winter at sea off Arabia in the Indian Ocean.

In addition to the species that use the Gulf waters and offshore coral islands, Western Reef Heron (*Egretta gularis*), Osprey (*Pandion haliaetus*) and Kentish Plover (*Charadrius alexandrinus*) use the coastline and islands close inshore for feeding and breeding.

GULF LAND BIRDS

In the earlier discussion of the Pleistocene history of the Gulf several passerine birds were identified as having apparently evolved in the Gulf region and now occurring around it. They are the Grey Hypocolius (*Hypocolius ampelinus*), White-cheeked Bulbul (*Pycnonotus leucogenys*) and White-throated Robin (*Irania gutturalis*). All three occur in the Eastern Province but only the second breeds there, the others moving in for the winter.

PALEARCTIC BIRDS

The Palearctic is the name given to the faunal region that encompasses most of the land mass of Eurasia, but as explained earlier (p. 38) we are defining it here to exclude the Afro-Sindian Desert Zone. It is the source of most Arabian migrant birds: those which only pass through, to and from southern wintering grounds, and those which remain essentially within the Palearctic but make variable north–south movements between seasons. The semi-arid desert edge would be the normal limiting boundary for these birds but the Gulf region offers tolerable habitats extending into an otherwise arid zone, although conditions gradually diminish in suitability towards the south. These movements result in a considerable annual incursion into the Gulf region as a whole during the cooler parts of the year. In the Eastern Province, such regularly occurring non-breeding species number about 190, and many others turn up on a more casual basis (this compares with a total of 60 species known or presumed to breed in the area). A broad spectrum of species is involved, including grebes, herons, ducks, raptors, rails, waders, gulls, terns, owls, bee-eaters, larks, pipits, chats, thrushes, warblers, starlings and buntings; the only major groups not represented are those which are either too northerly, pelagic, or resident in woodland.

ORIENTAL BIRDS

Another potential incursion of species into Arabia which is aided by the presence of the Gulf is that of birds from the Oriental region or, more precisely, birds originating in Pakistan and India and extending their ranges westwards. These may extend into southern Iran, or into Oman and the United Arab Emirates, but few have reached the Eastern Province of Saudi Arabia. Of the 18 species that show this pattern of westward extension only three, Red-wattled Plover (*Hoplopterus indicus*), Rose-ringed Parakeet (*Psittacula krameri*) and Indian Silverbill (*Euodice malabarica*), have been recorded in the Province with any frequency. The Plover is basically a vagrant and the other two probably both have origins as escaped cage birds, though the Parakeet seems to be established. Others occurring rarely are the Indian Roller (*Coracias benghalensis*) and Yellow-throated Sparrow (*Petronia xanthocollis*). The Black Francolin (*Francolinus francolinus*) may belong in this group: it is present in northern India but extends westwards as far as Turkey and occurred in historic times in some north Mediterranean countries from which it seems to have disappeared through over-hunting. The Graceful Warbler (*Prinia gracilis*) is similar in distribution but more southerly, breeding from northern India to Egypt.

GENERALLY DISTRIBUTED BIRDS

Apart from these various groups of species which can be rather tentatively assigned to discrete faunal groupings there is a small number which have very extensive general distributions, usually linked with a tolerance of habitat variation, and their occurrence in the Eastern Province appears to be merely a part of this. Others are present mainly in the southern Palearctic but have populations in the Afrotropics and sometimes elsewhere, indicating a wider distribution in the past. This group includes the Cormorant (*Phalacrocorax carbo*), Cattle Egret (*Bubulcus ibis*), Greater Flamingo (*Phoenicopterus ruber*), Griffon Vulture (*Gyps fulvus*), Bonelli's Eagle (*Hieraaetus fasciatus*), Osprey (*Pandion haliaetus*), Barn Owl (*Tyto alba*), Eagle Owl (*Bubo bubo*), Great Grey Shrike (*Lanius excubitor*) and House Sparrow (*Passer domesticus*).

Man-modified Habitats

Human activity modifies the landscape in various ways, but the two most significant in Arabia are the creation of sources of fresh water, and the spread of herbaceous plants and woody vegetation associated with crops and gardens. These have distorted natural patterns of bird distribution.

FRESHWATER BIRDS

Of the species breeding or probably breeding in the Province's areas of water and waterside vegetation only two, the Graceful Warbler (*Prinia gracilis*) and the Clamorous Reed Warbler (*Acrocephalus stentoreus*), are typical of swamp areas in semi-arid regions. The others are mostly opportunistic Eurasian species taking advantage of local habitat changes on the southern edge of their range; these include Little Grebe (*Tachybaptus ruficollis*), Little Bittern (*Ixobrychus minutus*), Ruddy Shelduck (*Tadorna ferruginea*), Ferruginous Duck (*Aythya nyroca*), Water Rail (*Rallus aquaticus*), Moorhen (*Gallinula chloropus*), Coot (*Fulica atra*), Black-winged Stilt (*Himantopus himantopus*), Avocet (*Recurvirostra avosetta*) and Moustached Warbler (*Acrocephalus melanopogon*).

CULTIVATION AND GARDEN BIRDS

A number of species rely on the presence of vegetation which is often largely provided through cultivation, the planting of shade trees, and the creation of gardens. Species of such places are the Collared Dove (*Streptopelia decaocto*), Turtle Dove (*S. turtur*), Namaqua Dove (*Oena capensis*), Rose-ringed Parakeet (*Psittacula krameri*), White-cheeked Bulbul (*Pycnonotus leucogenys*), Rufous Bush Chat (*Cercotrichas galactotes*), Olivaceous Warbler (*Hippolais pallida*) and House Sparrow (*Passer domesticus*).

BIRDS AND BIOTOPES

Adaptations to Aridity

Most birds of the Eastern Province are faced with the fundamental problems that affect desert species anywhere: high temperatures and water shortage. To overcome these, birds may use the simple reaction of avoiding extreme conditions by searching out more favourable localities for feeding and nesting. They may also use various methods of temperature and water loss control, aided to some extent by adaptive characters of plumage and structure.

NOMADISM

For a creature as mobile as a bird the obvious reaction to adverse climatic conditions is to move away to a less inclement area; but to retain the option of returning when, and if, conditions again become favourable. Obvious examples are the winter visitors to the Eastern Province and the migrants passing through. They take advantage of the conditions in the cooler part of the year, at the same time avoiding the more extreme winter conditions of their own breeding areas. This is strikingly illustrated by the fact that the majority of Eastern Province species fall into this category and only about a sixth of them are resident.

Some of the resident species show a similar avoidance reaction of a more limited kind in the form of nomadism. In some desert regions of the world this may involve conspicuous long distance movements, but the evidence available from Arabia suggests that equally satisfactory alternative areas may be found after more limited shifts.

Birds requiring specific nest sites that are limited within an arid area, such as the *jabal* nesting species, have little choice. It is ground nesting species such as the larks, Cream-coloured Courser (*Cursorius cursor*) and Houbara Bustard (*Chlamydotis undulata*) that may search out suitable areas where spring vegetation has responded to more adequate rains before they nest. As a result, within a particular general habitat these birds may be found nesting, perhaps in some numbers, in a given area in one breeding season; and may be scarce or wholly absent in another when they have found the conditions they need elsewhere. The Bedouin statement, that the Houbara will breed only after it has filled its stomach with flowers, is an early observation of this nomadism in search of suitable breeding conditions. In addition, birds which have bred and reared their young may then move away to a better area when the breeding site becomes drier and vegetation shrivels as summer advances. This is particularly apparent in larks, and to a lesser extent in the Cream-coloured Courser.

Another group which has a tendency to nomadism is the waterbirds. This is to be expected since they are particularly vulnerable and may suffer a total loss of habitat if a pool or marsh dries out. Their normal behaviour appears to include random dispersive wandering of a type which enables them to discover and exploit remote and widely scattered waters. The colonization of the small and recently formed effluent pools in desert areas of the Eastern Province is an example of this. In waterbirds this nomadic tendency is not confined to individuals in arid areas. It is a much more general and widespread behavioural pattern which has been observed in most parts of the world. Even where it does not lead to actual colonization of new sites it may result in sporadic visits from numerous different species.

TEMPERATURE CONTROL

Birds are to some extent pre-adapted to higher temperatures in their surroundings than are mammals. Their normal body temperature is about 40°C and they are capable of coping with rapid rises of body temperature of about 3°C. However, the upper, lethal level is about 45°–46°C, and to keep their bodies below this limit various strategies are needed.

The most obvious reaction is an avoidance of direct exposure to heat by seeking shade. This is more difficult in arid environments since the plants, which elsewhere might provide shade, react to desert conditions with a reduction in leaf size and growth, and a loss of leaves in summer. Shade is likely to occur in the shelter of rocks and broken ground, and in the shadow of shrubs and dried tussocks of grass. In conditions of extreme heat birds seek out the more complete shade provided by deep hollows, ledges, cavities and caves, or they may use the entrances of burrows made by reptiles or small mammals.

Lack of activity also helps. This involves rest during the hottest part of the day, with activity greatest at dawn and dusk, or during the hours of darkness. Since a similar strategy is used by other living creatures in desert environments, both vertebrate and invertebrate, it is likely that the periods of greatest activity for insectivorous and raptorial birds will coincide with that of their prey.

Use of a raised perch may also help lower body temperature, even if it only involves perching on a rock. The temperature of the surface of the ground is usually considerably higher than the air temperature, and there is a significant decrease at only short distances above the ground. It has been suggested that large birds soaring high above the ground may enjoy a reduction in the temperature of the surrounding air. However, they would still suffer the effects of direct solar radiation and the theoretical cooling does not seem to have been substantiated either by experiment or behavioural observation. Soaring desert birds such as the Long-legged Buzzard prefer to rest in the shade rather than to soar high at the hottest times of day.

The body plumage of birds forms an insulating layer. The immediate reaction of birds to heat is to sleek down the plumage to reduce this effect, and birds of warmer climates often appear slimmer and neater than their counterparts elsewhere. However, with more intense heat parts of the plumage may be ruffled. Feathers are not a continuous body cover. They achieve their effect by overlapping and at the skin's surface they are separate structures arising at intervals from the feather follicles. By raising them the bird is able to lose some heat from the skin between the feathers, while the deeper layer of feathers produced may help to prevent the full effects of external heat from reaching the body surface.

Since excess heat is dissipated from the body through surfaces which are not covered by feathers, birds of warmer regions usually have a sparser feather structure; and bare areas of skin through which some loss of heat can occur are more frequently present. The undersides of the wings and the inner flanks are usually sparsely feathered or partly bare. Heat loss through these surfaces is aided by holding the wings a little away from the body, drooping them or raising and slightly spreading them. Such postures are particularly apparent in birds suffering from overheating.

To maintain a streamlined shape, most birds normally carry the legs and feet tucked up in the feathers of the underside when in flight, but in very hot conditions they may allow them to hang down. Terns cool their legs and feet by dipping them into water while in flight.

Temperature of the body can be effectively reduced by evaporation occurring at its surface. Birds lack sweat glands and only a limited amount of evaporation occurs at the skin surface. A more rapid loss of heat is achieved through evaporation where air passes over moist and highly vascularized parts of the body surface. In the bird these are found within the mouth and respiratory system. Panting is a primary response, and in the Eastern Province most land birds from ravens to sparrows will be seen panting with open bills during extremes of summer heat. Bulbuls have been observed opening the bill to pant even in the short pauses in singing. This behaviour can be intermittent or of low intensity, but at high temperatures becomes a vigorous action involving not only throat and trachea but the lungs and body air sacs as well. Although it involves use of energy and the production of some heat as side effects of the action, it is effective in lowering the temperature of the bird by several degrees. It appears to be more highly evolved in desert species, enabling them to maintain their body temperatures below the critical fatal level.

Some birds, including species of pelicans, boobies, cormorants, herons, doves, owls, cuckoos and the nightjars and their relatives, achieve heat loss through a similar but more specialized throat movement known as gular flutter. This involves a very rapid vibration of the floor of the mouth, the throat and chin. It appears to be operated by the hyoid apparatus in the throat at the base of the tongue, and is used for increasing periods as the temperature rises above 40°C. Extreme panting has been calculated at about 300 movements a minute, but the gular flutter may rise to about 690 movements a minute in some nightjars.

WATER LOSS CONTROL

Ability to cope with extreme heat will not enable a bird to survive desert conditions unless it is able to obtain sufficient water to maintain itself. Where water is available, either in the form of surface water or as dew, most birds (including those that can in theory do without it) will drink regularly.

Birds such as sandgrouse, doves and finches eat mainly dry seeds and appear to need a daily drink at a water source, consequently their distribution is limited to areas within reach of it. Doves, and to a much greater degree sandgrouse, will feed in arid areas and fly a considerable distance each day to drink at an often limited source of permanent water, such as a pool or well. Although young birds will obtain most of the water they need in the food given to them by their parents, some transportation of moisture to the nest may be necessary. When the opportunity presents itself birds may wet the feathers of the underside by dousing them in water before flying back to the nest to incubate eggs or brood small young. In the sandgrouse this behaviour has been evolved to a more elaborate extent. The feathers on the underside of the male are modified in structure so that when saturated they can hold more water than those of a normal bird, and it has been calculated that up to 18 g of water can be carried for about 35 km. The water thus transported to the nest is taken directly from the feathers by the young. Other birds use other methods. Species such as cormorants and storks carry water to the young in the gullet.

A major source of water for arid-country birds is that present in their food. Birds feeding on insects and invertebrates, or on reptiles, other birds and small mammals, or on fleshy plants or fruits all take in water in this form when they feed. This would seem to account for the large number of birds such as larks, wheatears, shrikes and birds of prey which appear able to survive, in some cases indefinitely, without drinking. There seems to be some degree of adaptation here, since in groups of species only some of which occupy arid habitats there are observable differences in their dependence on sources of water.

Another source of water for survival is the metabolic water produced in the body during the internal digestion and utilization of food. This seems to explain the ability of some species to live on apparently dry food and to survive for periods when very little water, or none, is available. Birds also have a pre-adaptation to conserving water in the body in that they excrete nitrogen in the form of semi-solid uric acid, re-absorbing most of the water. In arid-country birds, the water loss may be reduced still further and drier droppings produced.

The problem that faces desert birds (and seabirds) is that most of the available water is likely to be saline. An intake of too much salt may seriously affect the water balance in the body and threaten the bird's existence. Most birds on, or at the edge of, salt water take an occasional sip of it; but in some instances this may be no more than a bird deliberately taking a small amount of salt in solution to maintain its bodily salt balance, in the same way that grazing mammals may take salt or minerals at a salt lick.

In theory the kidneys of birds are poorly adapted to cope with salt excretion. In experiments, admittedly with finite limits, it has been found that a number of different songbirds including some desert species, quails and small desert doves can utilize water with a salinity of about 12–18 g/litre (roughly 37.5% to 50% of the concentration of sea water), which would appear to be a relatively high tolerance.

Birds such as penguins, shearwaters and petrels, divers, pelicans, gannets and cormorants, as well as waterfowl, flamingos, waders, gulls and terns, possess salt excreting glands. These are modified nasal glands, usually on the surface of the skull within or above the orbit of the eye. In many of these species they are apparent as paired longitudinal structures in deep grooves bordering the orbits or recessed into the top of the skull above them. The salt is excreted in solution via the nostrils or along the palate to the tip of the bill. Although these glands may aid utilization of salt, waterbirds such as flamingos and marine gulls will deliberately travel daily to small sources of fresh water such as the outflows of streams on coasts or lake shores in order to drink and bathe in fresh water.

In theory the combined action of the salt glands and kidneys might be expected to confer a high degree of salt tolerance on the birds concerned. However, it would appear to differ in various groups of birds. It has been found that Kentish Plovers and Semipalmated Sandpipers had a tolerance of only about 12–15 g/litre in the long term, not much better than the songbirds studied. These waders appeared to rely on insects and similar animal food to help them maintain their water intake, and this may be true of other species.

On present evidence it would appear that while birds in general may have a higher salt tolerance than some other animal groups, desert birds are not specially adapted to cope with the problem of saline water.

PLUMAGE COLOUR AND PATTERN

In plumage colour and pattern, desert birds can be roughly divided into two groups. A larger one has restrained pale buff, brown, rufous and grey plumages, with or without subdued streaking, barring or vermiculated patterns. The other group has plumages wholly or partly with striking patterns or patches of black and white.

In the first group the most obvious character is the overall pale tint of the plumage pigmentation. This should confer an advantage by reducing heat absorption and therefore be an aid to temperature control. It may be another pre-adaptation, the result of a general trend in those birds whose plumage colour is produced mainly by brown and black melanin pigments. Species with these pigments generally have paler plumages in warm dry areas and darker ones in cool wet areas. Species with a wide range in Europe, for example, can be seen to have darker individuals in the north-west compared with those of the south-east. This is one of the basic ecogeographical tendencies in living creatures, known as Gloger's Rule after its first expounder.

In theory this trend might result in the production of almost white plumage in desert animals, but selection for crypsis, concealment against a natural background, appears to have played an important part in determining the final appearance of arid-country birds. A character of most desert regions is a relative lack of cover compared with moister and more heavily vegetated areas, and with this difficulty in concealment there is a greater need for birds to be camouflaged so that they merge with their background and are less readily seen by predators. Indeed, the various browns, buffs, greys and rufous colours of these plumages are often finely matched to a particular local environment.

Larks in particular may show adaptation to the soil or rock colour of various localities; in some arid regions of the world this produces complicated mosaics of populations with colours linked to their immediate backgrounds, tending to upset the usual concept of subspecies. In some respects such adaptations may run counter to the idea of possessing pale plumage for less heat absorption, for larks on blackish volcanic terrain may evolve a dark plumage to match it.

This type of dull uniform plumage for concealment against a terrestrial background may be combined with striking but hidden patterns, often black and white, on wings and/or tail, which become suddenly visible when the bird flies and disappear again when it settles. They may be useful as distant signals to other birds, conveying a warning of danger and the need to fly or crouch, or of the presence of a bird in its breeding territory. They also have a value as an anti-predator device; the sudden appearance and disappearance of the pattern producing an unpredictability which helps to baffle potential or pursuing predators. This is sometimes called Protean behaviour, after the shape-changing deity of Greek mythology. Patterns of this type are well developed on the wings of the Hoopoe Lark (*Alaemon alaudipes*), Thick-billed Lark (*Ramphocoris clotbey*), Cream-coloured Courser (*Cursorius cursor*), Stone Curlew (*Burhinus oedicnemus*) and Houbara Bustard (*Chlamydotis undulata*), and contrasting patterns also occur on the tails of some other lark species.

Conspicuous patterns involving black and white colouring, such as those of the wheatears, have been the subject of some debate in the past, but appear to be merely adaptations to concealment in rocky environments. The contrast between pale sunlit surfaces and almost black shadows of rocks and stones in strong light produces a background against which a bird with a disruptive black and white plumage may be very difficult to see. The need for the plumage to assist in reducing heat absorption is less acute in such an environment where more shade is likely to be available.

There are some plumage patterns intermediate between these types. Black and white or mainly black patterns may occur on face, breast or underside of birds with more uniformly brownish backs. Examples are the Black-crowned Finch Lark (*Eremopterix nigriceps*), Thick-billed Lark (*Ramphocoris clotbey*), Temminck's Horned Lark (*Eremophila bilopha*), some sandgrouse and smaller plovers. These patterns tend to break up the outline and convert the birds, particularly if they crouch, into a semblance of one or two rounded stones complete with dark shadows. Colouring of this type as a dual purpose pattern is very effective. To an avian predator, viewing a close crouching bird from above, the bold markings of underside or flanks may be almost completely concealed; but an upright bird seen by others at eye level, or the same bird flying overhead, vividly advertises its specific identity and its presence.

In general, arid-country birds have plumages which aid concealment and in most instances may also help to reduce heat absorption. Often this is combined with signal patterns which enable them to convey information over a distance to others of their own species. Some dull-coloured species such as larks may have conspicuous display flights and songs which help to compensate for a lack of bolder signal patterns on the plumage.

GENERAL STRUCTURAL ADAPTATIONS

Arid areas are mainly open places with few perches for birds and food items are often widely scattered. Arid-country birds tend to be designed to cover open areas fairly rapidly. They mostly keep to the ground itself when not flying, and are often long legged. In birds with running habits the long legs may also have feet with toes reduced in length. The Ostrich is an extreme example, in which the number of toes is also reduced to two, but some evidence of this trend can be seen in the shortened toes of the Cream-coloured Courser (*Cursorius cursor*). In a hot environment long leggedness will also confer some advantage in helping to cool the body by raising it further above the ground.

Sandgrouse have adapted in a different manner. Their legs are relatively short, possibly because there is little need for running when feeding on seeds, and they have long wings and a swift strong flight to carry them rapidly from one place to another. They may of course have evolved primarily for cold montane desert where this character might have been of some advantage.

In general, narrow tapering bills are typical of birds that feed on insects, and stouter shorter ones of those that feed on seeds. Slender and slightly decurved bills are characteristic of some desert species. In ground feeding birds this type of structure reaches its zenith in the long curved bill of the Hoopoe (*Upupa epops*), which is principally used for probing for insects such as crickets. The slender, slightly curved bills of the Hoopoe Lark (*Alaemon alaudipes*) and Cream-coloured Courser (*Cursorius cursor*) are obviously useful in digging for buried insects in this way. The former can use its bill as a very effective small pick-axe, rapidly excavating quite large cavities. However, in desert areas where the sand and soil offer a loose substrate there may be an additional advantage in such a bill. Insects and small creatures such as lizards can bury themselves easily, and seeds become covered by windblown sands. A slender curved bill is ideal for rapidly and systematically raking through loose material to pick out the hidden food, as effective for seeds as for insects.

Short stout bills are usually thought of as seed crushers, and the occurrence of them in a number of arid-country species might be linked with this mode of feeding. However, they occur in several species of larks, a group of birds which is mainly insectivorous. This might imply a greater proportion of seeds in the diet of such birds in arid areas, or perhaps a need to deal with more specialized insects such as the hard bodied beetles which are present in these areas. Another possible explanation is suggested by observations on the behaviour of Trumpeter Finches (*Bucanetes githagineus*). Typical cardueline finches when offered clumps of seeding grasses will immediately feed on the seed heads and probably ignore the rest. The Trumpeter Finch is a more terrestrial species of arid regions, with a very stout bill, and if offered similar grasses (under aviary conditions) it will first attack the fleshy bases of the grass stems instead.

It seems possible, then, that in desert areas such bills are useful for macerating rough plant material to extract water and any nutriment that is present. The stout bills of such birds as the Black-crowned Finch Lark (*Eremopterix nigriceps*), Desert Lark (*Ammomanes deserti*), Dunn's Lark (*Eremalauda dunni*), and more particularly the massive bill of the Thick-billed Lark (*Ramphocoris clotbey*), might be adapted as much for this purpose as for the more conventional seed cracking. More observation on the subject is required.

Extremes of heat and aridity present problems when birds are nesting. Some species avoid the worst by nesting early in the year when temperatures are lower and any rain will have fallen. Nests are often built to take advantage of whatever shade or shelter is available, for full exposure to strong sunlight would soon kill an embryo or a very young bird. Birds that nest in exposed sites usually attend the nest constantly and are extremely reluctant to leave it; adults scared from a nest will return to it as soon as possible. In the hottest part of the day birds may simply stand over eggs and young and shade them rather than incubate them, and older chicks of birds such as terns or plovers may be shaded by a parent standing with slightly spread wings.

Migration

Although migration over Arabia involves enormous numbers of birds only a tiny fraction of them are ever seen here. The majority pass over on movements about which we still know very little.

We have no certain information of the past history and origin of this bird migration although remains from fossil sites with unlikely combinations of species seem to indicate that it may have occurred at least as far back as the early Pleistocene; and that its subsequent history may have been one of gradual modifications to an already existing pattern of migration. For most land birds and some waterbirds the major Old World system may have originated when birds moved north to take advantage of temporarily suitable breeding grounds, but it is now seen as a massive southerly movement in the autumn of a vast bird population that cannot be sustained through the winter on its nesting area.

The southerly winter refuges are more limited in size than the land mass from which these birds came. The majority move into Africa, the Indian sub-continent and Indo-Malaysian region; some of the more mobile shorebirds continue through Indonesia and into Australasia.

Prior to migration birds accumulate fat, mostly within the body cavity. Moreau, in his study of migrants wintering in Africa, concluded that the Greenland form of the Northern Wheatear (*Oenanthe oenanthe*), must make a flight of 2,000–3,000 km without stopping during its migration. The evidence indicates that in the autumn birds normally cross the Mediterranean Sea and the Sahara Desert in a single flight, possibly commencing it further north; and it seems certain that further east birds may cross the Arabian Gulf, Arabia and the Red Sea in similar single flight. Hypotheses about such migratory movements in this area are made more complicated by the relatively inhospitable terrain of much of the Transcaspian and Iranian areas over which they would have to fly before reaching the Gulf; and it seems possible that flights might be much longer than originally imagined.

In general birds tend to fly high, being likely to find favourable winds that will aid their passage, and air that is cooler and free from desert sand and dust at heights of over 1,500 m. Some species fly at night although they are diurnal in their normal activities. There is continuing research into the factors that aid bird navigation during migration, but there appears to be good evidence that at night they can use the patterns of the stars, even if only a small part of the night sky is visible.

Most birds pass unseen, although low flying birds can often be heard calling. Some individuals with inadequate resources for the flight may be stimulated to take part when they see other birds leave, and these may fall out when they become tired. If the sky becomes obscured and the wind and weather become unfavourable during the night, large numbers of birds may be delayed or blown off route. At daybreak these will land at the nearest place offering something resembling suitable conditions and continue their flight the following night. Such conditions produce the so called 'falls' of migrants, which suddenly appear during migratory seasons. These falls, often in very large numbers and involving only a few species, frequently occur in areas unsuitable for the birds, which are then at risk unless they can quickly resume their journey.

The majority of species migrate by day, only a few

A Lesser Crested Tern shields its chick from the heat of the sun. (BS)

utilizing most of the full twenty-four hours. In the early 1950s considerable attention was paid to the visible migration of birds in seemingly favoured places, usually coastal promontories or hill ridges. Later, using radar studies, it was discovered that the majority of birds involved migrated in a manner similar to night migrants, flying high and direct and mostly undetected at ground level.

The smaller number which flew at lower altitudes tended to be strongly influenced by the topography of the land over which they passed. They tended to follow obvious linear features such as coastlines and ranges of mountains and hills. These might cause them to diverge temporarily from their original path. Large raptors and birds such as storks, that rely heavily on rising currents of warm air to gain height before setting off in a gliding flight, frequently take advantage of ridges of high ground or isolated mountains when migrating.

Recently less attention has been paid to visible migration; but the species involved are a part of the main movement and provide information about it, even if it is not possible to determine what relationship they bear to the total migration. These diurnal migrants settle and roost at night and, as with nocturnal migrants, individuals with insufficient energy may remain in one place to recuperate for a time before moving on.

The long flights of autumn migrants over these desert regions may be assisted by mainly northerly winds prevailing at levels where the main movement takes place. At this period the arid areas are at their driest and it is dangerous to stop. In spring the winds are less likely to be constantly favourable, but winter rains may have improved conditions in the arid and semi-arid areas. Migrants are more likely to settle; and the evidence from bird banding in North Africa indicates that some at least continue safely to their breeding grounds.

Tiring birds tend to search out the safest place to pause on the journey and this is likely to be some conspicuous or cultivated site. Desert camps and rigs as well as new areas of cultivation are likely to attract migrants, especially in the spring, and to provide evidence of more extensive passage than was previously suspected. This is nowhere more dramatically demonstrated than at Haradh where surprisingly large numbers of herons and egrets, rails and other unexpected species have recently been encountered in the well watered crops during the autumn. Appendix II indicates the differences between autumn and spring passage for the species occurring most regularly.

Although the number of migrant species regularly encountered in the Eastern Province may at first seem impressive, in fact very few are ever seen in large numbers. Many of the places where migrants have recently been sought after in spring and autumn, the vegetated surrounds of sewerage evaporation ponds, the scrubby environs of the Abqaiq lagoons, and the cultivated areas at Haradh and Hanidh, are all relatively new products of man's exploitation and development of those areas.

Often there seem to be as many species at a favoured place as there are individual migrants. Exceptions to this general scarcity are those species which could conceivably have been numerous in the arid conditions before these small and scattered green areas which now attract migrants were created. Some examples are the Isabelline Wheatear (*Oenanthe isabellina*), Northern (*O. oenanthe*) and Pied Wheatears (*O. pleschanka*); the Tawny Pipit (*Anthus campestris*) and Red-throated Pipit (*A. cervinus*), and the Isabelline Shrike (*Lanius isabellinus*), and Red-backed Shrike (*L. collurio*). The aerial feeding Swallows and perhaps the Yellow Wagtail (*Motacilla flava*) might also be considered natural original migrants. Some species more dependent on cover such as trees and shrubs are annually quite numerous, though this abundance may be only a recent phenomenon. Chiffchaffs (*Phylloscopus collybita*) and Willow Warblers (*P. trochilus*) are often locally abundant in spring although at different times. To a less obvious extent Lesser Whitethroats (*Sylvia curruca*), Common Whitethroats (*S. communis*), and Barred Warblers (*S. nisoria*), are locally quite numerous at favourable times in spring. All these migrants, except the warblers, are about as common in autumn as they are in spring.

Visible migration in the Eastern Province is negligible. There is no conspicuous raptor passage and very obvious diurnal movements seem to have been noted only for Hoopoes, Bee-eaters and Swallows. The continuous fine and clear weather in this region probably assists migrants but very occasionally a sudden storm, a dramatic change of wind direction, an unexpected dust haze, or just low cloud and overcast conditions, may bring a 'fall' of migrants.

One such occasion was on 1 May 1981. There had been heavy rainstorms over the desert to the south-east; some coastal towns in the Emirates were flooded, and in the north there were further rainstorms spreading from Jordan and Iraq, south into Kuwait and northern Saudi Arabia. These unusual conditions brought one of the most spectacular falls of migrants seen in the Eastern Province and illustrated for a few days the volume of migrants passing overhead. Hundreds of thousands of Willow Warblers, Whitethroats and especially Red-backed Shrikes were in evidence as well as smaller numbers of many other species. The shrikes were noticed throughout the Province from Haradh in the south to the small islands far out in the Gulf; and from the plateau of the Summan to the Dibdibah where there are few bushy perches and birds were sallying after prey from mounds of earth and stones.

Birds passing over the Eastern Province may be subdivided into African and Indian migrants.

AFRICAN MIGRANTS

The tendency for prolonged high flights may explain why so much of this migration passes unnoticed in spite of the vast number of individuals involved. This is particularly striking in the case of Africa, for Moreau estimated that the autumn passage of birds into Africa involved some 5,000,000,000 passerine and raptorial birds in addition to an incalculable number of waterbirds. He also estimated that in the period between leaving their breeding grounds and returning to them in the spring about 50% would probably die.

These birds are drawn not only from Europe but also from further east in Eurasia. In some species which have an extensive Palearctic range the eastern part of the population migrates to India or further east, possibly reflecting a split in the population during the Pleistocene ice ages. In others, again possibly because of the past distributional history of the species, the whole population moves into Africa. This group includes very widespread species such as the Willow Warbler (*Phylloscopus trochilus*), and the Northern Wheatear (*Oenanthe oenanthe*). The latter has a breeding range extending from south-east Greenland and Iceland across Eurasia to the Bering Straits and into western Alaska, but still heads for Africa in winter.

Much of the eastern part of this huge migrant population will tend to pass south-south-west, between the Caspian Sea and the mountain borders of Mongolia and Tibet, and is likely to cross Arabia. Birds moving south from Russia are also likely to cross Arabia; and banding of migrants at Azraq in eastern Jordan, near the northern borders of Saudi Arabia, has revealed that birds from as far west as Poland pass on migration. The banding of migrants in Africa has also revealed that these migratory movements are less haphazard than was previously believed, since individuals may temporarily pause or overwinter at the same place year after year.

The relatively small numbers of migrants noted in the Eastern Province are obviously only a tiny sample of the whole annual migrations, but a surprisingly complete one. Moreau recognized 187 migrant species entering Africa annually; 74 of them songbirds, 22 perching or aerial non-passerines, 25 raptors and 66 waterbirds. Of the 187, 170 have been recorded as migrants in the Eastern Province and another 7 have occurred as vagrants (Appendix II). Of the remaining 10, 6 have more westerly migration routes so are unlikely to cross Arabia.

Within this large range of migrants a few of the species involved have the southern limit of their breeding range in the Eastern Province; and a large number of the others, mostly shorebirds and ducks, are winter visitors to the Province as well as passing migrants. The last list includes Steppe Eagle (*Aquila nipalensis*), White Wagtail (*Motacilla alba*), Bluethroat (*Luscinia svecica*), Black Redstart (*Phoenicurus ochruros*), Desert Wheatear (*Oenanthe deserti*), Red-tailed Wheatear (*O. xanthoprymna*), Desert Warbler (*Sylvia nana*), Lesser Whitethroat (*S. curruca*), and Great Grey Shrike (*Lanius excubitor*).

There is one species which migrates from the Indian region to Africa but has not been recorded from the Arabian region and is assumed to make a direct sea crossing of the Indian Ocean south-east of Arabia. This is the Little Cuckoo (*Cuculus poliocephalus*). The Manchurian Red-footed Falcon (*Falco amurensis*) which breeds in east Asia and winters in south-east Africa may also follow a similar route, since its recorded status in the Arabian peninsula is little more than that of a vagrant.

INDIAN MIGRANTS

Most of the south and south-easterly migration into the Indian and Far Eastern regions occurs too far to the east to affect Arabia; but a few species breeding to the north of it have south-easterly migrations, and the south-western edge of these movements may bring stray birds into the Eastern Province. The species involved are the Citrine Wagtail (*Motacilla citreola*), Clamorous Reed Warbler (*Acrocephalus stentoreus*), Booted Warbler (*Hippolais caligata*), Red-breasted Flycatcher (*Ficedula parva*), Rose-coloured Starling (*Sturnus roseus*), Common Rosefinch (*Carpodacus erythrinus*), and the Buntings: Pine (*Emberiza leucocephalos*), Rustic (*E. rustica*), Little (*E. pusilla*), Yellow-breasted (*E. aureola*), and Black-headed (*E. melanocephala*).

ACCIDENTALS

Migrants follow a predictable pattern but occasionally individuals stray from their normal routes and territories and turn up outside their normal areas. These may occur in wholly unlikely places, as additions to the expected range of species. The longer and more systematically the birdlife of any particular locality is studied, the greater grows the list of accidentals. In some instances the individuals will be from species whose normal range is nearby, and that have only strayed a little beyond their usual boundaries. In other cases birds may have travelled much further or become caught up in weather systems that have taken them further and further off their usual course.

The list of Eastern Province birds includes the Grey-headed Gull (*Larus cirrocephalus*) from Afrotropical regions; Long-toed Stint (*Calidris subminuta*), Pectoral Sandpiper (*C. melanotos*), Eversmann's Redstart (*Phoenicurus erythronotus*), Arctic and Yellow-browed Warblers (*Phylloscopus borealis* and *P. inornatus*) from the eastern Palearctic; and the Buff-breasted Sandpiper (*Tryngites subruficollis*) from North America.

Ringed (banded) birds recovered in the Eastern Province of Saudi Arabia

SPECIES	RINGED		RECOVERED	
	PLACE	DATE	PLACE	DATE
Egretta garzetta Little Egret (juvenile)	Azerbaijan, USSR	15 June 1960	Rub' al-Khali	October 1960
Sterna caspia Caspian Tern (chick)	Volga delta, USSR 46°N 49°E	15 June 1975	Abu'Ali	1 March 1976
Hirundo rustica Swallow (nestling)	Czechoslovakia 50°N 18°E	11 June 1976	Dammam	16 April 1977
Lanius collurio Red-backed Shrike	South Czechoslovakia 48°N 17°E	18 June 1966	Qatif	6 May 1967

Above: *Buff-breasted Sandpiper (GKB)*
A very rare visitor from the Arctic regions of North America photographed at Abqaiq.

Left: *Pectoral Sandpiper (GKB)*
A rare visitor from the Arctic regions of North America and Siberia photographed at Abqaiq.

Habitats and Birds

The regions and zones identified within the Eastern Province, each with its characteristic landform and vegetation, offer a suitable habitat for occupation by particular species of birds. Those that visit the Province in winter or on passage have more scope in their use of the various areas. It is the resident breeding birds that are tied to more specific habitats and which are most likely to demonstrate the characters and adaptations necessary for indefinite survival in a particular area. Within the Eastern Province as a whole these birds divide themselves fairly evenly into five groups utilizing the broad divisions of the region; similar in species totals, but differing widely in the range of families and species represented in each.

In the following sections the birds are briefly discussed in relation to their habitats. Information available to us is very incomplete; yet more may be contained in the notebooks of field observers who do not appreciate its significance or who have not had the opportunity to make it more generally available. There is much scope for further study and we hope that what is offered here will serve as a stimulus to others who find themselves in the area. For much of the time the climate of the Eastern Province is not ideal for prolonged field work, but a gradual assembling of small fragments of information will help to build a more complete picture; not just of what birds are to be found in the Eastern Province, but of how they interact and their role within the biotopes of the region.

ARID REGIONS

There are few birds in true desert. A sand desert such as the Rub' al-Khali can support little bird life. Some sparse perennial plant growth is present in places, but surface water is absent and rainfall virtually non-existent. Some seasonal dew is the most that can be hoped for.

The absence of water and shade makes survival difficult for creatures of all kinds. Most birds that have been observed occur as passing migrants, probably not there from choice. The Hoopoe Lark (*Alaemon alaudipes*) appears to be adapted to life in loose sands and to be independent of the need for a water supply, presumably relying on insects and lizards to provide the moisture necessary for sustenance. It is the only species that travellers have noted as singing (presumably in nesting territory) in such areas.

The other species of the true desert is the Brown-necked Raven. It is a predator of small creatures such as lizards, mammals and birds. It is also a scavenger, and soon takes an interest in any human activity. It is adaptable, and as well as nesting on *jabals* will also nest on man-made structures such as pylons, power cable poles and oil well markers. In dune country it has been found nesting no more than two metres above the ground on low shrubs such as *Calligonum*, presumably relying on isolation and concealment among dunes for successful nesting. It breeds early in the year, taking advantage of cooler conditions and avoiding some of the temperature problems of an open nest site. The first eggs are laid towards the end of January but more generally in February and early March (RJC). Some juveniles are out of nests, though still attended by adults, in early April.

Towards the desert edge isolated *Acacia* trees and thorny shrubs provide potential nest sites for larger raptors which are able to fly vast distances to hunt. For them undisturbed isolation when nesting is the most important factor.

Most of the arid-country birds occur in areas of more stabilized sand or soil, with some vegetation and a more adequate food supply. With the demise of the Ostrich (*Struthio camelus*), the Houbara Bustard (*Chlamydotis undulata*), now rare itself, is the largest nesting bird of the open arid regions. Some 64 cm in overall length, it is typically adapted for open country, being long necked, and long legged with short toes. It runs quickly and tends to crouch when alarmed, but has a strong fast flight. Its sandy plumage is marked with a series of broad dark bars which on larger feathers are reduced to fine broken vermiculations, graduated across the bars; while on smaller feathers the markings become irregular chevrons. The colours and pattern are remarkably effective camouflage on a background of sand and fine gravels. It has another plumage character that frequently occurs in these open country birds: the body plumage is cryptically coloured, but the wings are conspicuously patterned black and white. The details of its nesting in Saudi Arabia are poorly known, but it appears to prefer irregular ground or areas with some sparse scrubby growth. Its traditional breeding grounds in the Eastern Province seem to have been on the eastern borders of the Dahna sands and Summan plateau; through the *Rhanterium* steppe areas; and on the borders of the Rub' al-Khali. It feeds mainly on various parts of plants; from shoots and leaves to flowers and berries, but will also take insects and occasional small lizards.

The next largest bird is the Stone Curlew (*Burhinus oedicnemus*). Originally thought to nest, it is now believed to be a migrant, though it does breed as close as Iran and southern Iraq. It shows interesting parallels with the Houbara, being another running and skulking bird of these dry sparsely vegetated regions. It too has a long neck and long legs with short toes; it is also cryptically coloured with largely black and white wings, though the wing pattern is different from the Houbara's. For food it mainly takes small live prey, insects and similar creatures. It is crepuscular and nocturnal in its activities, with big golden irised eyes that may be closed almost to slits when it rests during the day.

A third cursorial desert bird is the Cream-coloured Courser (*Cursorius cursor*). It is a slender bird, about 23 cm long; barely a third the size of the Houbara. It also has long legs with short toes, and if alarmed will often run for considerable distances though its long slender wings make it capable of rapid flight. It has the same elements of crypsis and advertisement in its plumage. It is sandy coloured, and has a black eye stripe which sweeps down towards the nape concealing rather than enhancing its dark eye. The wing pattern is simple and conspicuous: the end half of the wing is black on the upper surface, and the whole underwing black. Like the Houbara it tends to be nomadic in its nesting, choosing open sites with very little vegetation.

The remaining species typical of open arid areas, other than songbirds, are the sandgrouse. Unlike the previous three species these are almost wholly seed eaters, and they need to be within flying distance of a daily source of fresh water. Possibly because of these two facts they are relatively short legged, but with strong, swift flight. The Spotted Sandgrouse (*Pterocles senegallus*), which breeds around Haradh, is the only species definitely known to breed in the Eastern Province. It is a bird of open level areas and seems well established on the southern gravel plains. It has a pale sandy coloured plumage, heavily spotted in the female. It does not have a conspicuous wing pattern, but there is a black belly-patch visible in flight. Like the previous species it uses a bare scrape on the ground as a nest. These larger terrestrial desert species usually lay clutches of no more than 2 or 3 eggs. This is possibly an adaptation to the harsh conditions, but if, as in the case of the Houbara, there is exceptionally heavy mortality, the rebuilding of a population may be a very slow process.

The superficial similarity of these four birds masks the fact that they represent four families of three different avian orders. They are species of widely different origin, similar in their adaptations. The characters they have in common are those that fit them for existence in open arid country, and their general similarity suggests that there is limited scope for variation in this type of habitat. In contrast to this diversity of origin, eight of the ten songbird species of these open arid areas are from a single family, the larks. The remaining two are the Brown-necked Raven (*Corvus ruficollis*), already briefly discussed, and the Great Grey Shrike (*Lanius excubitor*), a species widespread through the northern hemisphere. The latter is a small, weak footed passerine predator of insects, small lizards, rodents and birds. Its prey presumably provides the moisture it needs for desert life. It will hunt from low scrubby bushes, but for nesting requires a taller shrub or small tree in which to build its typically cup shaped nest. These nest site requirements perhaps limit its distribution, for in the Eastern Province it has been recorded as resident only near Haradh. Jennings (1981) commented that over Arabia as a whole its distribution is linked with that of acacias, which usually produce well spaced small trees. Other species of bird uncommon or absent in the Eastern Province which he listed as showing the same affinity are the Little Green Bee-eater (*Merops orientalis*), Blackstart (*Cercomela melanura*), Scrub Warbler (*Scotocerca inquieta*) and Arabian Babbler (*Turdoides squamiceps*). If the provision of trees is the critical factor, rather than the species of tree involved or the conditions associated with it, then such species may expand their future range with the increasing planting of trees around settlements and cultivation.

The larks have a basic advantage in that they are terrestrial feeding, ground nesting birds of open country, though one is so closely linked with rocks that it has been listed with the *jabal* species. Ironically it is the one called the Desert Lark (*Ammomanes deserti*). The arid-country larks have longish legs, and although only one is called a short-toed lark (*Calandrella brachydactyla*), most of them have relatively short toes for the length of the leg. Those of the very long legged Hoopoe Lark (*Alaemon alaudipes*), are noticeably short for its size. In general appearance these birds vary from rather squat, thick-billed, short-tailed forms looking like finches, through more typical larks, to the thrush-like Desert Lark, and the remarkable Hoopoe Lark a slender, upright, long-billed, and long-tailed bird which looks surprisingly like a small courser.

The species of more temperate origin extending into arid regions, the Crested Lark (*Galerida cristata*), Lesser Short-toed Lark (*Calandrella rufescens*), and the winter visiting Bimaculated Lark (*Melanocorypha bimaculata*), have brown backs with darker streaking. The others have paler and more uniformly coloured upper parts: grey, buff or sandy. Conspicuous flight patterns are less in evidence than in the larger, non-passerine desert birds; though the Hoopoe Lark is an exception. North African birds of this species have an inner wing marked by two bold white bars; in the Arabian birds these white areas are more extensive and form a large white patch which contrasts with a large black one on the wing tip and is particularly conspicuous in flight.

The winter visiting Thick-billed Lark (*Ramphocoris clotbey*) is also obvious in flight, the wing having black flight feathers with a broad white band on the hinder edge, and the white tail a blackish terminal bar and mid-streak.

A blackish tail with brown central feathers and sometimes white on the outer edge is common to most species; an exception being the Bar-tailed Desert Lark (*Ammomanes cincturus*), which has a sandy coloured tail with a black terminal band. Bold patterns on face and breast are typical of some species. Crested (*Galerida cristata*) and Lesser Short-toed Larks (*Calandrella rufescens*) are merely streaked on the upper breast, but the Bimaculated Lark (*Melanocorypha bimaculata*) has a pale throat with two bold black patches on its lower border. Temminck's Horned Lark (*Eremophila bilopha*) has a black breast-shield and white face with a black bar across forehead and cheeks, and small black 'horns'. The Arabian Hoopoe Lark (*Alaemon alaudipes*), has two small black face streaks and a lightly spotted breast; the Thick-billed Lark (*Ramphocoris clotbey*) has a more extensive black face pattern and heavily spotted underside; while the male Black-crowned Finch Lark (*Eremopterix nigriceps*) is wholly black below and on the head, with white on its forehead, cheeks and nape. In contrast Dunn's Lark (*Eremalauda dunni*), Desert Lark (*Ammomanes deserti*), and Bar-tailed Desert Lark (*A. cincturus*), like the female Black-crowned Finch Lark (*Eremopterix nigriceps*), lack any obvious markings.

Conspicuous song flights in the breeding season occur in most species. That of the Hoopoe Lark is particularly striking, a steep climb ending in a slow descent, accompanied by song ending in a series of clear, far carrying whistles. However, the song flight of the Desert Lark is very subdued and amounts to no more than a series of thin, piping calls while the bird is performing a circuitous flight at no great height above the ground.

The presence of eight breeding species of larks in the Province is interesting because of the general ecological principle that two species occupying the same niche cannot coexist indefinitely in the same area if the food supply is a factor limiting their numbers. A major aspect of the niche which a bird occupies is its food supply, and for these larks, whose diet is mostly very little known, we can only assess feeding habits by size and shape of bill. These exhibit a range of variations that might in theory be indicative of a partitioning of food resources between the species, thereby reducing competition. Several of the Eastern Province lark species do not in any case occupy exactly the same habitat as one another and so would avoid competition by that means. Dunn's Lark (*Eremalauda dunni*) has a stout, blunt bill like that of the Bar-tailed Desert Lark (*Ammomanes cincturus*) but larger, while Temminck's Horned Lark (*Eremophila bilopha*) has a more slender, tapering bill like that of a Crested Lark (*Galerida cristata*), but shorter. These variations in feeding apparatus, together with the differences in preferred habitat, result in a greater segregation of species within the environment than is at first apparent.

The slender-billed Crested Lark is generally a bird of more cultivated areas, extending into the borders of the arid regions in places where a reasonable, if sparse, growth of vegetation occurs. It is likely to be within reach of better watered areas. The Lesser Short-toed Lark, with its small stubby bill, is also basically a bird of moister areas but it will extend into drier and more open habitats. The Black-crowned Finch Lark, with a stout and stubby bill, is tolerant of hotter, drier and more open sites than either of the other two, although many move to open ground near water after breeding. The slender-billed Temminck's Horned Lark has been found nesting on the level gravel plains at the northern end of the Eastern Province, and it is suspected that it has also nested in similar habitat much to the south.

The next three species, larks of the true desert, are relatively stout billed. Dunn's Lark has the largest and heaviest bill, and that of the Desert Lark is finer. In the Eastern Province Dunn's Lark occurs in inland areas of more stabilized sandy country with widely scattered shrubs, such as thinly vegetated *Rhanterium* steppe. The Bar-tailed Desert Lark goes for more extensive sandy areas, and the Desert Lark favours rocky places, although it often feeds on more open ground nearby.

Finally the desert specialist, the Hoopoe Lark, occurs in areas of looser sand and dunes. In the Eastern Province it has been found nesting on the ground (JP); but in such instances it has to contend with constantly blowing sand, and consequently more frequently places its nest not on the ground but in the low shrubs that come up through the sands. By so doing it raises its nest above the shifting sand hazard, and provides an increased circulation of air around it that will help to keep it a little cooler in summer. It is the only species that can really make good use of dikakah and dune areas.

Lark nests are generally cups fitted into small hollows in the ground, and sheltered by grass tufts, small shrubby growth or stones which provide some shade. Many larks, particularly those of arid areas, add to the nest a 'rampart' of small stones laid along the edge by which the bird normally approaches. There have been various speculations on its function. In the situations where this occurs it does not appear to help drainage or ventilation but has an obvious advantage in strengthening and shoring up the side of the nest. In arid areas the soil or sand on the more exposed edge of the nest, consistently used by the adults in their comings and goings, is liable to become loose and break or blow away. The instinctive habit of placing small stones along the edge of the nest would strengthen the most used side and ensure that the nest was likely to remain intact during its occupation, especially at a later stage when it contains a brood of young, thereby enhancing their prospects of survival.

Although used by many vagrant or migrant individuals pausing on passage, the open inland areas of the Eastern Province attract only a small range of habitual winter visitors. A startling addition to the avifauna of the Eastern Province is the Dotterel (*Charadrius morinellus*), a near arctic species which since 1986–87 has been recorded wintering in flocks of up to 1,000 on the Dibdibah. Birds from steppe areas of Eurasia might be expected to use it, but apart from the Caspian Plover (*Charadrius asiaticus*) most of them occur only in areas where there are other factors such as surface water to explain their presence. A few of the more terrestrial songbirds are scattered over it in winter: Isabelline (*Oenanthe isabellina*), Desert (*O. deserti*), and Mourning Wheatears (*O. lugens*) are of widespread occurrence; with Finsch's Wheatear (*O. finschii*) more often in the north. The Desert Warbler (*Sylvia nana*) is widespread in areas of low scrub, to a point where earlier observers suspected it of being resident.

Birds of prey are another group frequenting open inland areas in winter, and the more vegetated northern plains support numbers of wintering Steppe Eagles (*Aquila nipalensis*), as well as Imperial Eagles (*A. heliaca*) and an occasional Short-toed Eagle (*Circaetus gallicus*).

SETTLEMENTS AND CULTIVATION

The vegetation around settlements, compounds, villages, oases and cultivated areas constitutes a series of islands in the more uniformly arid landscape. These are the only sites where trees are present in any numbers and are therefore an obvious attraction for many species of birds. They show some of the typical aspects of islands; some birds using them to roost and nest, and dispersing more widely around them in order to feed. This can be seen in a localized form in the behaviour of the Collared and Turtle Doves of some areas. Although generally territorial in their nesting they tend to occur at exceptionally high density in some palm plantations and areas of tamarisk and mesquite from which they fly out to feed in the immediate surroundings. A more striking example still is the small area of trees near Nariya which is used as a roost by large birds of prey wintering on the northern plain. In the recent past, trees lining the banks of the Imhoff sewerage effluent evaporation ponds at Dhahran were used as a roost by Cormorants which flew in from the coast; the numbers building up at one time to over a thousand.

Such concentrations apart, the point that strikes visitors from other countries to these well vegetated areas of the Eastern Province is the small number of species that appear to have colonized them as breeding birds. It is normal for small isolated areas to support only a low number of breeding species, since the total resources are insufficient to support a viable population of a greater number of species. In theory, local extinctions of such species are thus more likely; while the rate at which fresh species are liable to colonize the area remains much less affected by its size. There is, however, little evidence that this has happened in the Eastern Province.

Buildings seem to offer little. The early ones were too small and inadequate, the newer ones too smooth and well finished. The only birds interested in them are likely to be the Rock Dove (*Columba livia*), House Sparrow (*Passer domesticus*) and, in the case of older ruins, the Barn Owl (*Tyto alba*); but it is interesting to note that one of the Ospreys (*Pandion haliaetus*) nesting in the Eastern Province, on Jinnah island, built its nest on a ruined house.

Within areas of gardens and trees around permanent settlements, as at Ras Tanura, Dhahran, Abqaiq and Hofuf, the Collared Dove (*Streptopelia decaocto*) is commonly present and nesting, and the Turtle Dove (*S. turtur*) to a lesser degree. The resident songbirds of these localities are the White-cheeked Bulbul (*Pycnonotus leucogenys*) and the House Sparrow, the former feeding mainly on insects and fruit, the latter on seeds and some insects. Their interests sometimes overlap. At Dhahran in summer both species will compete and squabble over the little greenish figs of a cultivated *Ficus* which offers both flesh and seeds, although apparently uninterested in the similar but larger fruits of the banyan (*F. benghalensis*). These two trees have been planted for shade since they are large leaved and tolerate the climate. They produce hanging secondary roots in clusters from the undersides of branches and if these reach the ground they form additional supports. In their early stages or when cut back these tangled clusters on the branches offer useful sheltered supports for the nests of both Sparrows and Bulbuls.

As well as tucking them in cavities or crevices, House Sparrows build domed grass nests in the thinner outer twigs of trees and shrubs, sometimes over water, occasionally even in abandoned vehicles. Building starts in January, egg laying possibly as early as February (as young have been seen from mid-March), and many partially fledged birds are out of nests by mid-April. Juveniles from presumed second and third layings appear from June through August. House Sparrows, being sociable, form small colonies where circumstances permit, and increasingly take over their surroundings.

White-cheeked Bulbuls occur as pairs maintaining territories, although they may be accompanied by their grown young for part of the year. A combination of circumscribed habitat and space requirements of each pair limit their population. Males have a fruity, musical four-note song phrase, frequently repeated, which suggests a speeded up Golden Oriole. There seems to be considerable subtle variation between birds and the call may identify the individual to its neighbours. The species also has a repertoire of conspicuous postures and the behaviour would merit more detailed study. The nest is a standard cup affair, built usually into a lateral fork in a shrub or low tree. There are two broods, sometimes three, with the majority of first clutches laid in the latter half of March and layings continuing until June or July (RJC); recently fledged juveniles have been seen in late March and August.

Where a more lush habitat of broad leaf trees and well watered shrubs gives way to drought adapted species such as athel tamarisk with similar scrub, the birds tend to change. Doves and Sparrows still persist, the White-cheeked Bulbul is present in smaller numbers and the Rufous Bush Chat (*Cercotrichas galactotes*) is more likely to occur.

The Olivaceous Warbler (*Hippolais pallida*) is a small drab bird, inconspicuous until it sings. Its favoured habitat is tamarisk and mesquite scrub near water, and although territorial it may breed in some numbers where conditions are favourable. The nest is a small, deep, thick walled cup bound to slender vertical twigs, or suspended between the extremities of a lateral. Singing starts in April, becoming spasmodic after June. The first eggs are laid in late April, and fledglings start to emerge from nests about 20 May (RJC), with second clutches laid soon afterwards. Some late broods are still being attended by adults in September. The average of 52 clutches found at Imhoff in 1980 was 3.5 eggs (RJC). Although most migrate to Africa, Olivaceous Warblers appear to be partially resident in the Gulf area, Lower Egypt being the only other part of their breeding range where overwintering occurs.

The Rufous Bush Chat is likewise territorial and migratory, but adapted to drier scrub conditions and so tends to occur towards the outskirts of settlement and cultivation. Also, unlike the Olivaceous Warbler, it gets much of its food, insects and similar creatures, from the ground. The nest is an untidy cup, usually low in shrubby growth at a height of one or two metres, often against a tree trunk. Birds are conspicuous in their posturing and song, most evident in early May. Juveniles have been seen with attendant adults from June through August.

The Palm Dove (*Streptopelia senegalensis*) has spread gradually in some of the settled areas of the Gulf outside Saudi Arabia, though as yet it has rarely been seen in the Eastern Province. The smallest dove is the Namaqua Dove; tiny and long tailed, with a chestnut underwing, and given to mouse-like creeping about on the ground. It is adapted to nomadic and opportunistic breeding and has colonized new areas of cultivation, moving across Arabia from the south. In the Eastern Province nesting has been confirmed only at Haradh, though numbers are now present in the Dammam area and breeding has probably taken place there. It breeds in the same general habitat as Collared Doves and Turtle Doves, though later: eggs are laid in May and June and have been seen in early August.

The extensive areas of palms and other trees and bushes appear under-occupied by resident birds, but do offer food and shelter to a large range of visiting and vagrant species. In winter there are flocks of Starlings (*Sturnus vulgaris*); and small numbers of the Grey Hypocolius (*Hypocolius ampelinus*), which breeds in Iran and Iraq, occur regularly but unobtrusively in certain areas of palms. The trees are also attractive to passing Scops Owls (*Otus scops*), Wrynecks (*Jynx torquilla*), Rollers (*Coracias garrulus*), Bee-eaters (*Merops apiaster*), and Golden Orioles (*Oriolus oriolus*) as well as less obvious species. Occasional Hoopoes (*Upupa epops*) overwinter in these areas in addition to those that pass through.

Elsewhere, settlements offer watered lawns and gardens, and there are cultivated areas with large stretches of irrigated crops such as grain and alfalfa, as well as grasses. The Quail (*Coturnix coturnix*) is a summer visitor to cultivated areas, nesting on the ground in a hidden hollow in or on the borders of growing crops. Crested Larks (*Galerida cristata*) also occur and nest among shorter and more open ground vegetation. Other species such as White Wagtails (*Motacilla alba*) and Spanish Sparrows (*Passer hispaniolensis*) occur as winter flocks in these areas, and desert birds such as larks and sandgrouse move into crops such as those at Haradh where the desert is close by.

With an increasing area of cultivation and settlement in the Eastern Province and on the southern coasts of the Arabian Gulf there is greater opportunity for species which can thrive in association with human activity to spread and to colonize new areas. It can be difficult to separate those species which are self aided in this respect from those which may have escaped from an existence as cage birds.

The Indian House Crow (*Corvus splendens*), a slender-bodied grey and black bird of the Oriental region, owes its success to its ability to tolerate the close proximity of humans without abandoning the basic wariness that ensures its survival. It occurs near ports and has perhaps reached new countries by the simple process of hitch-hiking on the superstructure of ships, abandoning them when it reaches a new port. This may have aided its spread in the Gulf where it appears to have moved erratically west from Oman. It breeds regularly and successfully in the Aramco compound at Ras Tanura. Over 30 were seen in one tree on 22 July 1986 (BW, RJC). Single birds have also been seen in the Aramco compound at Dhahran.

The Rose-ringed Parakeet (*Psittacula krameri*) is another oriental species and one which has certainly been helped to spread by the import and escape of cage birds in the Gulf area. The suspicion that individuals might have captive origin has probably inhibited a study of its occurrence, though it appears now to be present along the western Gulf coast from Oman to Iraq. Its survival through the winter may be aided by the current tendency of an affluent society rather to neglect the date crop, more of the ripe fruit being allowed to remain on the trees or to fall. From the regular presence of family parties with newly fledged young, it is safe to conclude that it breeds in the Aramco compound at Dhahran, but no occupied nest has been examined.

The Indian Silverbill (*Euodice malabarica*) is also presumably of cage bird origin. It is a small seed eater, brown and buff with a white rump, which feeds mainly on the ground and makes a domed nest in tall grasses or low shrubs. It has occurred intermittently at Dammam, and regularly in the Aramco compound at Dhahran.

INLAND WATERS

In many respects this is the most artificial, vulnerable and variable habitat of all. The only open inland water that might be regarded as natural has its sources in the springs of the oases at Qatif and al-Hasa. At Qatif the flow is diverted into canals and irrigation channels and soon finds its way to the sea. At al-Hasa there is likewise an extensive network of canals and irrigation channels but a substantial volume of water flows north, and emerges amongst the dunes to form a network of reed fringed pools and lagoons east-north-east of al Marah. The only bird for which there is evidence of a long term residence, long enough for it to have differentiated in small details of plumage pattern from species elsewhere, is the Graceful Warbler (*Prinia gracilis*).

The others are opportunists, associated with water, and capable of rapidly exploiting a new source; obviously a necessary trait since open water habitats can disappear more rapidly than most. This is particularly apparent in the Eastern Province where within the last decade large areas of surface water, some of which had not long been in existence, have already been drained and dried out; though some new ones have come into being.

The Little Grebe (*Tachybaptus ruficollis*) looks an improbable traveller, but in fact wanders far, and will establish itself on very small areas of open water so long as there is an adequate food supply of small fish or small aquatic creatures. It evades its enemies by diving and remaining concealed, just raising its head and bill at intervals to take a breath and look around. All it requires for a nest is a small floating platform of rotting plant material. Its habit of rapidly covering the eggs with wet nest material when it leaves the nest, even when in a hurry, is an additional aid to successful breeding and survival in a hot climate. The breeding season in eastern Arabia is protracted. Eggs have been seen in nests as early as mid-February; but small chicks have been seen with attendant adults as late as mid-September.

Once an area of water exists, but before much vegetation has grown on its edges, birds which utilize the bare margins of waters may colonize it. The species concerned tend to be those that take small fish or crustaceans; or pick flies or other small creatures from the surface of land or water. The Kentish Plover (*Charadrius alexandrinus*), in addition to inhabiting the coastal sands, will occupy bare and sandy areas by the edge of fresh water, or even a little distance from it. Each breeding pair establishes a territory, although several pairs may often be found nesting in relatively close proximity.

The Black-winged Stilt (*Himantopus himantopus*) is a successful colonist of open shallow water with marshy edges, usually betraying its presence by noisily and persistently mobbing any intruder near its breeding area. It is slender and ridiculously long legged, tending to wade in water and take small creatures at the surface. It nests on the ground, often using small islets formed as the water level drops. The long legged downy chicks can follow the parents soon after hatching.

Where waters flow away through dune areas, as at al-Hasa or Abqaiq, they tend to absorb minerals and become increasingly saline the further they flow. Some of the birds attracted are those that can use saline or semi-saline water. The Avocet (*Recurvirostra avosetta*) is such a bird, another black and white wader related to the Stilt, but having a slender upturned bill. It normally feeds in semi-saline lagoons, swinging its bill laterally through shallow water to catch small prey. It has attempted to breed in the Eastern Province and its failure to colonize, like the Black-winged Stilt, may be due in part to these more specialized requirements.

The Little Tern (*Sterna albifrons*), which in other parts of its extensive range is a bird of sea coasts as well as of river and lake margins, occurs here only as an inland breeder, leaving the coast to Saunder's Little Tern (*S. saundersi*). It feeds on small fish, shrimps and similar creatures and nests on the shores of inland lakes and islets resulting from falling water levels. Both eggs and newly fledged young may be seen in the Province in June, though some juveniles are already on the wing by late May.

Ducks also use these inland waters. Most of the surface feeding species listed as occurring on the coast also occur on inland waters to some extent, and Garganey may be very numerous when migrating. There is little deep water but it attracts such diving ducks as occur in the Province.

Apart from wintering Pochard (*Aythya ferina*) and Tufted Duck (*A. fuligula*), Ferruginous Ducks (*A. nyroca*) breed regularly in the Abqaiq area. The nest is hidden in thick vegetation by the water, and the first intimation of successful breeding is usually the sudden appearance of ducklings, which have been seen between the end of April and early June.

The largest breeding bird of inland open waters is the Ruddy Shelduck (*Tadorna ferruginea*), a waterfowl normally found in steppe regions. It nests typically in a burrow, although it might perhaps settle for a hollow under thick scrub, as will its relative the Shelduck (*T. tadorna*). At Abqaiq, the only place where it is known to have bred, chicks have been seen in early May, and well grown ducklings on 29 April (JP, DR, LR).

The presence of fresh water promotes a lush

growth of reeds and other grasses, sedges, rushes and bushes such as tamarisk. This combination of water and cover and the food chain it stimulates encourages the presence of other bird species.

It is at this stage that the rails tend to move in. Like the Little Grebe these are birds that do not look like long distance travellers, but they turn up in widely separated places and quickly colonize a new area. The Coot (*Fulica atra*) is aggressive, noisy and successful, feeding mainly on plant material taken both in the water and on land. It is prepared to nest in fairly exposed sites. The Moorhen (*Gallinula chloropus*) is a more skulking species, taking advantage of any cover that is present and usually hiding its nest in thick patches of waterside vegetation. The Coot prefers the larger, deeper and more open waters, while the Moorhen can make do with any small marshy area and is a good deal commoner as a result. In both species the fluffy black chicks are adept at hiding from enemies. The Moorhen's breeding season is protracted, with half grown chicks having been seen near Hofuf in late March and eggs near Dhahran as late as August.

The last group of inland waterbirds are those which move in to take advantage of the taller and thicker growth of vegetation that gradually takes over the shallow water. The Water Rail (*Rallus aquaticus*), although it may occur at times in more sparsely vegetated habitats, is a breeding bird of this thicker cover, preferring the larger reed beds and more likely to be heard than seen. It is possibly double brooded in the Province: chicks have been seen in late April (GB) and eggs in June (JHM). Other species of rail, Spotted (*Porzana porzana*), Baillon's (*P. pusilla*) and Little Crakes (*P. parva*), also occur on passage. They are easily overlooked where vegetation is thick, and may also be found in wet irrigated areas at times.

The Little Bittern (*Ixobrychus minutus*) is another species requiring tall thick reed beds when breeding, although it may come out into more open places to feed at the water's edge. It is more likely to be seen, usually in flight, than the Water Rail, but its calls are a still better indication of its presence. The larger herons and egrets that pass through the Eastern Province tend to occur on the coast, but the Bittern (*Botaurus stellaris*), Night Heron (*Nycticorax nycticorax*), Grey Heron (*Ardea cinerea*), Purple Heron (*A. purpurea*) and Squacco Heron (*Ardeola ralloides*) all visit inland waters.

The reed beds have their own songbird fauna. The Graceful Warbler (*Prinia gracilis*) is a waterside species rather than a reed bed bird, but in many of these areas the two categories are synonymous. It is usually found where there is a mixed growth of tamarisk and reeds; a small dark streaked bird with a weak fluttering flight which disappears into the undergrowth with its tail cocked high. Its domed nest is usually built in tamarisk shrubs, tangled reeds or juncus. Song and pair formation begin in February. The breeding season is protracted with two, possibly three, broods (RJC).

The *Acrocephalus* warblers are skulkers, and since males may be present and singing in places where nesting does not finally occur it is difficult to be certain of their status. The dark-capped Moustached Warbler (*Acrocephalus melanopogon*) has so far been proved to breed only in the al-Hasa reed beds, though it has been seen and heard singing elsewhere. Song starts in February but only lasts until the birds pair up, after which they are less obvious. The Reed Warbler (*A. scirpaceus*), even more closely associated with thick reed beds, is sometimes present in summer, producing its monotonous plangent song, but breeding has never been proven. The large and noisy Clamorous Reed Warbler (*A. stentoreus*) is also present and singing in summer in reed beds at a number of places, and is suspected of breeding.

In addition to supporting these known or suspected breeding species, the waterside reed beds and vegetation also serve as a refuge and feeding place for passing migrants and other species that are attracted by the presence of water, such as the Marsh Harrier (*Circus aeruginosus*) which frequently establishes itself for periods of several weeks at a time.

JABALS AND ESCARPMENT

For half the nesting species of the arid parts of the Province, the *jabals* and the rocky escarpment of the Summan plateau are of primary importance. The *jabals* represent islands in a waste of level land, comparable in some respects to the islands used by nesting seabirds. Unlike the latter they do not swarm with a crowded mass of birds, for the food potential of the surrounding land is low. The birds populating them are generally very sparsely and widely dispersed; but the importance of these rocky outcrops in the provision of secure and sheltered nest sites cannot be stressed too highly.

In general the limestone outcrop of the Summan

escarpment and its outliers, with drooping surface crust, downward sloping ledges, deep fissures and caves, is little used by nesting birds. Rock Doves (*Columba livia*), wild birds with a typical and consistent plumage pattern, are locally abundant though they may travel some distance to feed and, like other pigeons, need to be within flying distance of fresh water. An occasional Eagle Owl (*Bubo (b) ascalaphus*) will nest in an eroded hole or a cavity immediately under the surface crust. The White-crowned Black Wheatear (*Oenanthe leucopyga*), the only breeding wheatear of the Eastern Province, is well represented in the rocky gullies. It nests in cracks or fissures, often at the entrance to a cave, or amongst fallen rocks at the base of a cliff, thereby gaining additional protection from the elements. The Brown-necked Raven (*Corvus ruficollis*), opportunist as ever, will build its nest in any suitably inaccessible niche.

However, it is the Trumpeter Finch (*Bucanetes githagineus*) that has adopted these outcrops as its own, and in the Eastern Province is rarely encountered elsewhere. It is quite well camouflaged with pink-tinted, buffy-grey plumage that harmonizes well with its surroundings; but it advertises its presence by a long-drawn, harsh, buzzy song-bleat.

Above: *Trumpeter Finch (ALL)*

Below: *Eagle Owl nest with a full clutch of 3 eggs in a cavity under the cap rock. (ALL)*

Its nest is placed deep in a fissure, and is generally quite inaccessible.

It is the free-standing sandstone *jabals* with more sharply defined ledges and cavities that provide a more attractive nesting habitat. The mere availability of a ledge is not an adequate assurance of successful nesting. In hot and arid areas, shade and shelter are equally important and the sites chosen are those which meet this requirement. They also need to be out of the reach of mammalian predators, since the desert fox is as much a potential threat to birds nesting on open sites on *jabals* as it is to those nesting on the ground in open desert.

The Egyptian Vulture (*Neophron percnopterus*) is the largest raptor likely to be found nesting in the Eastern Province. It requires a deeply recessed ledge or small cave where it builds a straggling nest of dry sticks and twigs copiously lined with sheeps' wool, animal skin and odious refuse of all descriptions. The stinking mass of the nest is in startling contrast to the immaculate black and white under surfaces of the bird in flight; but on the ground it looks bedraggled and dirty, giving rise to the often used name 'Pharaoh's Chicken'. Vast areas of the Eastern Province are devoid of habitat suitable for the nesting of the species and it has almost certainly contracted its range, due in no small measure to the industrialization of the region and a reduction in traditional animal husbandry by nomadic Bedouins. It readily tolerates the presence of man but is now confined to *jabal* outcrops south of Yabrin and the fringes of the Summan escarpment west of a line drawn from 'Uray'irah to as-Sarrar. At present the breeding population is small, but appears to be securely established.

The Long-legged Buzzard (*Buteo rufinus*) usually nests in much more open situations than the Brown-necked Raven; in a large wind-eroded 'bowl' or on a sheltered ledge which affords a wide view and permits an easy flight to and from the nest. Most *jabals* have a rounded top formed by a similar secondary crust to that present on the main plateau, and quite large cavities erode into this top where one layer slightly overlaps another. These are favoured as nesting sites by the Eagle Owl. Owls do not build any sort of nest, and lay their eggs in a scrape amongst the rock dust and wind-blown sand already present in the hole. Half-grown young have been seen in nest cavities as early as mid-December, which suggests a laying date in early November; though recently fledged young have also been seen as late as early May, indicating a variable laying period. Indeed, one pair occupying the same hole nested progressively earlier over three successive years, laying their eggs approximately one month earlier each season. Desert Eagle Owls have few natural enemies but often nest in places that are accessible to the desert fox and it would be surprising if both adults and young did not occasionally fall prey to it. Bedouins regard this owl as a bird of ill omen and have been known to shoot it (RJC).

Long-legged Buzzards and Eagle Owls do not appear to compete and the two are frequently found breeding in close proximity on the same *jabal*. Near Arab villages the remains of rats have been found in Long-legged Buzzards' nests, but away from human habitation prey remains are predominantly reptilian, usually the tails of Spiney-tailed Lizards (*Uromastyx aegyptius*). Eagle Owls, however, hunting largely at night, take mostly small nocturnal mammals, although the remains of a Black-winged Stilt (*Himantopus himantopus*) were found at one nest near 'Ain Dar (GKB) and a nest near Abqaiq was festooned with the remains of Rock Doves (RJC). Gerbils (*Gerbillus sp.*) are frequently found in nests that contain chicks, or are cached in holes near habitual perches. Around the entrance to a favoured nesting hole there is usually a layer of mammal bones and beetle shards from pellets that have disintegrated. Large beetles are evidently eaten in significant numbers in the Eastern Province, and this contrasts markedly with the diet of European Eagle Owls for which insects of any kind are a decidedly uncommon food item (Cramp 1985). Like many species dependent upon a fluctuating food supply, fewer Eagle Owls breed if conditions are unfavourable. Conversely, when there is heavy rainfall in the autumn, resulting in increased numbers of gerbils and other small mammals on which the owl preys, it responds by laying larger clutches. Hence in normal years three eggs are usually laid, but following heavy rains four to five eggs. Mature Long-legged Buzzards on the other hand regularly produce clutches of three, occasionally four, eggs regardless of the amount of rainfall, further emphasizing that during the breeding season these closely associated species are largely dependent upon different food supplies (RJC). Hume's Tawny Owl (*Strix butleri*) seems to be at the extreme limit of its eastern range in the *jabal* formations deep in the desert to the west of al-Wannan. A nest found in 1988 (RJC) is the first record for the Eastern Province. On present evidence the species is very rare and thinly distributed. It is reasonable to suppose that in terms of its feeding requirements it would be in competition with the highly successful and more powerful Eagle Owl.

At the start of the breeding season apparently paired Little Owls (*Athene noctua*) have been seen in occupation of small holes on *jabals* north of 'Uray'irah (RJC, ALL) but evidence of actual breeding in the Eastern Province is still awaited.

Eroded cavities on the down curving capping slopes, crevices and overhung ledges are used for nesting by the Brown-necked Raven (*Corvus ruficollis*). Their twig nests may subsequently form the base of a nest for another species. A pair of Lanners (*Falco biarmicus*) bred in an old Raven's nest on a *jabal* to the west of Abqaiq in the early 1980s (GKB, RJC), but the only falcon now likely to be found breeding is the Kestrel (*Falco tinnunculus*) and even that is very thinly distributed.

As a breeding species the Rock Dove does not occur in such high numbers on the isolated sand stone *jabals*, largely because the rock formations do not produce many caves suitable for nesting.

Pallid Swifts (*Apus pallidus*) nest in colonies on *jabal* formations in the Hofuf area and north of 'Uray'irah. They glue their scanty nests, of feathers and wind-blown plant fibres, snatched in flight, into a vertical cleft in a cliff face. They are present within the Province all year but have not been seen at the colonies before March, so, like the more northerly Swift (*Apus apus*), presumably roost on the wing at high altitude.

The Pale Rock Martin (*Ptyonoprogne fuligula*) makes a half cup shaped nest of mud pellets, which it sticks to some vertical rock surface. It usually uses a site where there is a well formed rock overhang, fixing its nest to the inner surface of the overhang in preference to the main rock face. The nest is lined with wind-blown material such as hair, animal wool, feathers etc. Once constructed it may be used for several years but, in some areas, mud is only available for a short period after rain; hence nest building or repair may take place some appreciable time before eggs are laid in April (RJC). This results in a greater gap between building and egg laying than is usual in this family. There is some evidence that nests are also used for resting and roosting.

The White-crowned Black Wheatear (*Oenanthe leucopyga*) does not occur so frequently on isolated sandstone *jabals*, preferring the more broken rocky gullies of the Summan plateau.

The Desert Lark (*Ammomanes deserti*) has already been mentioned as an exception to the larks as a whole in its choice of habitat and nest site. It lives in rocky areas and shows a close adaptation in colour to the type of rock. When R. E. Cheesman named the local subspecies of the Eastern Province *Ammomanes deserti aziz* he described it as being of the same pinkish-white tint as the local limestone. Birds in basalt rock areas bordering northern Saudi Arabia have blackish plumage that conceals them against this environment. It is inadvisable for such birds to stray from their chosen area. The species is generally inconspicuous in song and behaviour, and lazy in flight, but performs short song flights that attract attention. The nest is usually tucked into a recess under a low projection. This may be at any height, and is sometimes on the top of a *jabal*.

The House Sparrow occurs where suitable groups of holes and crevices occur in *jabals*. It forms small social units, usually feeding around the outcrop, nesting in it, and appearing isolated from other small groups elsewhere.

COASTAL SHORELINE

The shoreline of the Eastern Province is a narrow specialized zone along which the Gulf seabirds and arid-country inland birds meet. In most areas the shore presents a barely significant barrier between the two.

Breeding seabirds make limited use of the shore: in some areas a few White-cheeked Terns breed at or about the high tide line (RJC). Small numbers of Saunders' Little Tern breed on the upper levels of mixed sand and mud islets in channels and lagoons, thereby gaining protection from mammalian predators. In the Eastern Province its close relative, the Little Tern, has only been found nesting by inland waters. Eggs of Saunders' Tern have been found from April on nearby Bahrain to late June on Abu 'Ali in the Eastern Province (RJC).

The widespread Kentish Plover (*Charadrius alexandrinus*) nests on the shore, as well as on the bare margins of inland waters. The sand surfaces of the beach can be lethally hot in summer, temperatures of over 70°C, well above the 46°C critical for birds, having been recorded. The plover, like other waders, can presumably cool itself in the nearby water, and with wet belly feathers also moisten and cool eggs and small young.

The Western Reef Heron (*Egretta gularis*) bred in the past in low mangroves near Qatif; and still breeds on small mangrove covered islets north of

Abu 'Ali which may be regarded as fragmented extensions of the coastal marshes. A small colony also nests on the seaward aspect of the low cliffs at Jinnah island. It feeds along the shore, wading in shallow water.

The apparent absence of any breeding gull species in the Arabian Gulf is a little surprising. The only records are old ones of former breeding by Slender-billed Gulls (*Larus genei*) on islands off Kuwait and Abu Dhabi. As a group, gulls are not over-fussy about a breeding site and there would appear to be an adequate range of food items. Terns are notoriously intolerant of potentially predatory intruders, and the concentrations of breeding terns on offshore islands might be sufficent to prevent gulls from establishing themselves on these; but there would nevertheless appear to be potential sites on parts of the shore zone. It is possible that past predation, human as much as animal, may have played some part in such an absence.

The birds of inland areas may also take advantage of the shore during the hotter part of summer days. Crested Lark, Hoopoe Lark, Black-crowned Finch Lark and Bar-tailed Desert Lark are all known to use the shoreline as a cooler refuge at times, and the first two have been seen squatting along the tideline on damp sand and mud. Small parties of various lark species will stand, at intervals, facing into the wind. They stand high on their legs with head and neck extended forward and with the closed wings held out and raised level with the back; the posture suggests a bird poised to take off and glide. The presence of numbers of birds and of family parties with recently fledged young suggests a deliberate shoreward movement, and the occasional appearance of other species such as Quails and Cream-coloured Coursers on or by the beach at such times may be more than merely coincidental.

However, the primary importance of the shoreline may be as a halting place or wintering area for birds from further north, which use this zone in larger numbers than is usually recognized. Some individuals, or parties, of several of the various species involved may also be present during the summer; such birds are usually immature non-breeders which have not experienced the strong urge to return to the summer breeding range. They are mainly exploiters of the mud, sand, or mixed sand and mud sectors of the intertidal zones of the shore, resting when not feeding on the higher marshy and salt marsh zones.

The feeding zones are rich in small crabs and isopod crustaceans, molluscs, worms and other invertebrates which are exploited by birds ranging in size from Little Stint (*Calidris minuta*) to Curlew (*Numenius arquata*) (about 13 to 58 cm in average overall length) with an impressive range of size and shape of bill that enables them to exploit fully what is available at various depths.

They range from the long decurved probing bill of the Curlew, through the straighter long probe of the godwits (*Limosa sp.*) and various shorter straight bills, down to the stubby surface-snatching type of bill possessed by plovers. Other specializations in this group include the chisel bill of the Oyster-catcher (*Haematopus ostralegus*) that can open bivalve molluscs, the heavy crab-crushing bill of the Crab Plover (*Dromas ardeola*), and the slender, upward-curved bill of the Terek Sandpiper (*Xenus cinereus*) though the precise reason for the shape of this last one is not obvious, as the bird does not feed by side to side sweeping of the bill as does the Avocet, but largely by probing.

Excluding vagrants this group comprises some twenty-five species, including twelve species of scolopacid waders, six plovers, Oystercatcher, Crab Plover, three gulls, Gull-billed Tern (*Gelochelidon nilotica*), and White-winged Black Tern (*Chlidonias leucopterus*), the last usually snatching small food items from the surface of the water while in flight.

Another major group of exploiters of the food source offered by the shore zone are the surface-feeding duck species. Their greatest concentration, prior to present destruction of the habitat, was in Tarut Bay where a mixing of fresh and salt water increases the amount of plant and animal food available. Largest totals recorded for both Wigeon (*Anas penelope*) and Teal (*A. crecca*) were up to a thousand birds; with several hundred each of Pintail (*A. acuta*) and Shoveler (*A. clypeata*), and concentrations of up to about fifty Mallard (*A. platyrhynchos*) and Gadwall (*A. strepera*). Wigeon may graze the herbage of salt marshes but the others feed mainly at or just below the water level. Such an abundance of birds attracts raptors. The shore represents an occasional stopping place for most passage migrants, and is regularly used by wintering northern Peregrines (*Falco peregrinus*). Spotted Eagles (*Aquila clanga*) and Marsh Harriers (*Circus aeruginosus*) regularly winter on the coastal fringe between Dammam and Tarut Bay, particularly in the vicinity of Qatif.

One large and striking visitor to the shore is the

Greater Flamingo (*Phoenicopterus ruber*). Its curious bill is designed for filter-feeding with the head inverted and the bill just immersed. The tongue pumps water through the fine ridged structure of the bill where the minute food is filtered out. It is fussy about the saline water in which it feeds, and is limited to two or three coastal lagoon type sites in bays, and one inland location to the west of the Second Dammam Industrial City on the Dhahran – Abqaiq Road (RJC).

The European Cormorant (*Phalacrocorax carbo*), which is a non-breeding visitor to the Gulf, also qualifies as a shore user rather than as a deep sea bird. Unlike the Socotra Cormorant (*P. nigrogularis*) it prefers the shallow coastal waters for feeding and raised perches such as trees or rocks for resting and roosting. As well as the Western Reef Heron (*Egretta gularis*) which fishes along the shore, other heron species use the area as non-breeding visitors. Tarut Bay attracts Great White Egrets (*E. alba*) and Little Egrets (*E. garzetta*), the latter being both numerous and regular. Grey and Purple Herons (*Ardea cinerea* and *A. purpurea*) are also present, the former all year as a non-breeder and the latter on passage.

GULF ISLANDS

Although the Gulf islands of the Eastern Province have been formed in two different ways, from coral reefs or the inundation of low lying areas on the shore, thereby isolating the slightly higher ground (see pp. 22–3), they have certain features in common, each being low, flat and sandy with a beach. The offshore coral islands have beach areas of sand and powdered coral mixed with crushed sea shells. Islands of coastal origin usually have narrower beaches and are muddier; this enables them to support a thicker and more varied plant growth than the coral islands where the dominant vegetation is a reduced number of salt bush species.

Four species of terns nest on Saudi offshore islands, and one, Saunders' Tern (*Sterna saundersi*), on islets amongst tidal mudflats, etc, near the shore. As with the larks they show a range of bill sizes and minor variations in bill shape which ensure a more efficient partitioning and exploitation of food sources. The food, mostly fish, is taken by plunge diving, sometimes from a height sufficient to raise a plume of spray when the bird hits the water. One species, the Bridled Tern (*Sterna anaethetus*), is exceptional in fishing at dusk and during the night. It may take a greater amount of food such as squid, which surfaces then.

Terns are generally sociable species nesting in colonies, though the five different terns that use the islands show some degree of segregation in their choice of sites.

Breeding of the Caspian Tern (*Sterna caspia*) in the Eastern Province has not been established; but during visits to Samamik island in December of several successive years, a few pairs of the species were invariably present and reacted aggressively to the intrusion. Small numbers breed on the Hawar islands south-east of Bahrain. Eggs were found on 3 and 21 October 1980; and chicks on 20 October and 10 December 1981 (RJC). It is a species that nests during the spring in more temperate climates and this may account for its autumn and winter nesting on the Hawar islands. Its nesting period sets it apart from other terns that occur in the Gulf.

The other species are terns of tropical seas, and here they breed in spring to early summer. The Swift Tern (*Sterna bergii*) and Lesser Crested Tern (*S. bengalensis*) differ in size but are otherwise similar in appearance, behaviour and nesting. They nest on the larger, bare sandy areas amongst vegetation on top of islands, or on the tide berm above the beach. They tend to form separate nesting colonies, but birds of the other species may nest around the periphery in small groups. The tendency of these birds to nest close together confers a protective advantage in areas where avian predators or small mammals might be deterred by a concerted attack. The nesting birds sometimes appear to be almost touching, but the birds' basic aggressiveness keeps them separated by the distance of a bill stab. These two species do not make a nest. The birds incubate eggs and brood chicks with their backs to the sun. With the high temperatures on the islands in summer the birds are understandably reluctant to uncover eggs or young for long, an important point for observers to remember during visits to colonies. When feeding, or even briefly leaving the nest, the adults tend to allow legs and feet to hang down and to dip them into the water to cool them; birds returning to the nest also wet the feathers of the underside to moisten eggs and small young as they brood them. Once the chicks have grown a little they tend to leave the nest; at first hiding when disturbed, later moving towards the tide-line in large crèches to await the parents, each parent and chick recognizing its own.

There is usually a marked synchronization of

nesting behaviour in these two terns, all the birds of one species tending to show the same stage in the cycle at the same time—although this may apply only to sub-groups within a large straggling nesting colony rather than to the entire assemblage. North of 26°N most eggs of Lesser Crested Tern are laid from 25 to 31 May, but in 1981 on the island of az-Zakhnuniyah in the south newly hatched chicks were observed on 29 May; the Swift Tern generally starts breeding a week or so before the Lesser Crested (RJC).

Unfortunately, even the Lesser Crested Tern, the most numerous tern in the Gulf, could be threatened by the unrestricted collection of eggs for food and, where colonies are easily accessible, by human disturbance in the breeding season; this applies even more strongly to the Swift Tern. Colonies where eggs are heavily collected, or the birds seriously disturbed by human or other predators, are deserted en masse and the birds remove themselves to another site.

The White-cheeked Tern (*Sterna repressa*), smallest of the terns nesting on the offshore islands, is the only one that lines its nest scrape with small pieces of dried vegetation, sometimes forming a quite substantial pad. The one or two eggs, laid during the last two weeks of May (RJC), are fairly inconspicuous against their background. The young however are very variable, with a down colour ranging from white to ginger or drab grey-brown, and from almost unmarked to heavily blotched with black. At first the young crouch in the nest-hollow if deserted or disturbed. Though they normally remain in the vicinity of the nest until fledged, when they grow older they may run and tuck themselves beneath any available vegetation if threatened. On some islands in the Gulf egg losses are high due to human interference while at other sites the eggs are repeatedly washed away by high tides with the consequence that replacement clutches may be found as late as August (RJC).

Nesting Bridled Terns (*Sterna anaethetus*) disperse more widely than the other species. They select a sheltered site, usually tucked into a small hollow under a salt bush, although elsewhere in the Gulf, for example on the Hawar islands, birds nest in holes and crevices in low rocky cliffs (RJC). A single egg is laid, the first ones about 18 May, continuing into early June. During the day the off duty bird often perches on the bushes above the nest. The

Anxious to resume incubating its single egg, a Bridled Tern perches uneasily on the top of the salt bush that protects its nest scrape. (BS)

Socotra Cormorants (BS)

downy chick remains hidden at the nest site under the vegetation, and fledglings have been found in nests as late as the first week in August (RJC).

Apart from these terns, the big colonial nester of the islands is the Socotra Cormorant. Areas which this species has used for breeding in the recent past stand out quite obviously: devoid of vegetation, the surface is a dusty layer of guano with a scattering of flattened and shrivelled dead chicks; the site may also be bordered on one side by a windrow of moulted and rotting feathers.

Most nesting in the Eastern Province has been recorded through November to January though birds have also been found nesting in May. For details of recent visits to colonies, see p. 79. Breeding within a colony may be relatively synchronized, but the period may differ from one island to another and sites are not re-used in predictable sequence. Nesting appears to coincide with, or initiate, an enormous multiplication of large numbers of blood-sucking ticks which may infest the site rather than the birds and might cause the intermittent shifts of breeding sites. Ticks have also been blamed for otherwise inexplicable mass desertion of eggs or of chicks at various stages of development at some colonies. However, we are uncertain even of the factors which trigger off the mass breeding of these cormorants. If it is related to a temporary abundance of food then it is also possible that a sudden decrease in the food supply might just as easily cause desertion. The colonies may number at times up to hundreds of thousands of pairs. It is obvious that the birds cannot all find food in the immediate vicinity of the nests, and large flocks are seen fishing well away from the colony.

There is virtually no nest. The eggs are laid in a shallow scrape, and pairs are close together. The down of the young is white, not dark brown like that of the northern Cormorant, perhaps as a device to keep body temperature as low as possible. As they grow the young may be less tied to the nest site. On one visit to a very large colony, R. J. Connor found the mass of well grown young contained by a line of adults. As these moved away they appeared to chivvy the young along in front of them, the whole mass of birds raising a small dust storm. Large downy young at small colonies may go to the beach to await the returning adults.

The Socotra Cormorant appears specialized in behaviour as well as in other adaptations, and our knowledge of it is still very incomplete. There are no studies of its breeding biology and although the breeding islands are difficult of access, work on a ringed population would be invaluable.

The two other nesting species of the islands are the Western Reef Heron and the Osprey. Both are confined to the islands along the coast and are absent from the small coral islands further out. In both instances the method of hunting may well be the critical factor limiting distribution. The Reef Heron needs shallow waters in which to wade and fish and an underwater substrate rich in animal life. It is possible that the beaches of the small islands are too steep, with a relative paucity of food making them unsuitable for nesting colonies to rely upon. When nesting the Osprey requires an abundant source of sizeable fish loafing at or near the surface of the water, preferring to snatch up its prey but capable of plunging to seize food at about half a metre's depth. Again, one might presume that the seas around the smaller coral islands fail to provide what is needed. Alternatively it may be that as neither of these species is essentially marine, they simply do not locate these tiny outposts far out in the Gulf.

Kentish Plovers (*Charadrius alexandrinus*) almost certainly breed on the larger offshore islands (RJC) and the Crested Lark (*Galerida cristata*) may also nest. In some respects the islands are fragmented extensions of the sandy shoreline, and may be frequented by any of the shore birds that visit the Gulf. In addition, the islands provide a temporary resting place or refuge for almost any bird passing over the Gulf on passage.

Osprey (BS)
A female stands guard over its nest on Samamik island. This nest, like most in the Arabian Gulf, was built on the ground.

MAN AND BIRDS IN THE EASTERN PROVINCE

Traditional Activities

BIRD-HUNTING AND EGG-HARVESTING

As recently as 30 years ago, birds of all types were exploited as food, and shooting was not confined to larger birds. R. E. Cheesman (1926) referred somewhat caustically to the fact that the White-cheeked Bulbul was the 'game-bird' of the al-Hasa oasis. He mentioned men wandering around the palm groves of Hofuf looking for birds to shoot and suggested that this was the reason for the relative paucity of species present. With the advent of a plentiful supply of fresh meat and fish, such hunting is no longer necessary. Government directives now ban the use of firearms for hunting, but illegal and indiscriminate shooting of birds still takes place.

Bedouins have traditionally regarded owls as birds of ill omen, and such beliefs are still commonly held. Because the Eagle Owl (*Bubo (b) ascalaphus*) often uses the same perch and permits a close approach, it is particularly vulnerable to depredation by man. The traditional antipathy to owls may help to explain the scarcity of the Barn Owl (*Tyto alba*) around settlements and oases, but a more likely cause is the absence of suitable nesting sites. In recent years, old buildings and towers have been almost entirely demolished to make way for modern buildings that are totally unsuitable as nesting sites.

Falconry, though now referred to in more romantic sportive tones, was, in the past, pursued mainly for food. Birds were also killed with weapons, snared with nooses, and caught in small traps. A primitive spring trap was used, with two half-circles, one kept in tension. When the bait was taken, the two halves sprang together with sufficient force to kill a small bird or weigh down a larger one. Other more elaborate traps utilizing drop perches and spring twigs were also used within the region. With the exception of the activities of children, serious snaring and trapping of birds is no longer widespread.

In addition to birds, eggs were an obvious source of food, but the few scattered nests of most species and the effort entailed in finding them made egg-harvesting seldom more than a haphazard pursuit. Colonies of nesting reef herons and terns were an obvious exception, and even to this day island colonies are sometimes visited by fishermen who carry away as many eggs as they can. However, such forays are now largely opportunistic, and since both species invariably lay replacement clutches, it is unlikely that any long term ill effects ensue.

Eggs were not normally taken from Socotra Cormorant colonies, although nesting assemblies are frequently large and conspicuous. Colonies are usually heavily infested with ticks which carry a fever virus, and this has possibly made them a species to avoid.

While occasional egg-harvesting may not have a serious impact on island colonies, the accessibility of seabird colonies on mainland coasts makes them more vulnerable to repeated visits; and past disturbances may have resulted in the coast being abandoned by the birds for the relative security of the islands.

FALCONRY

Before modern firearms became available, hunting in the desert was difficult and dogs and falcons were widely used. These hunting animals would not necessarily kill the prey but harass or trap it until the hunter arrived.

Large desert birds which would provide food were often the target of the hunt. The principal prey

Barbary Falcon (ALL)
This bird had been used for falconry and the leather jesses can be seen attached to its legs.

was the Houbara Bustard. In earlier times it was present in large numbers in the Eastern Province, especially in winter when the local breeding population was augmented by wintering birds from Iran, Pakistan and other more northerly countries. Saker Falcons were used mainly for hunting the Houbara. It was not easily killed, however, and at times the falcon could only disable or delay the Houbara until the falconer arrived to effect a kill. Another quarry species was the Stone Curlew which could be hunted and killed by falcons alone.

Falcons were trapped on passage for use in falconry. It was believed a bird should have flown and hunted for itself in the wild before being used. Many birds were imported. The traditional method used for catching falcons is still employed locally. It involves tethering a live dove fitted with a harness carrying a number of nooses. The feet of the falcon become entangled when it attempts to seize and carry off the dove. H. R. P. Dickson has described other methods used in Kuwait involving a raised net, baited with dove or jerboa, which is pulled over the falcon when it attacks the bait; or a clap-net baited with a live dove. Sometimes a decoy raven with a ball of black wool attached to its legs, making it appear to have prey of some kind, is used as a lure.

The largest falcon regularly passing through the region was the Saker (*Falco cherrug*) and this was regarded as the most desirable for hunting. Sometimes birds were trapped or caught while wintering in eastern and northern Arabia. However, in the past, as today, many of the birds were imported from Iran or Pakistan. The hunters' preference for the largest falcons resulted in natural selection of the female, which is noticeably larger than the male. Local hunters were generally unaware of the sex of the birds and referred to all large hunting falcons as male.

The second falcon in order of preference was the

Peregrine Falcon (*F. peregrinus*). Individuals of a large northern race wintered on the Gulf and were trapped in various parts of the Eastern Province as an alternative to the Saker. The female Peregrine was often bigger than the male Saker and had the reputation for being a fierce hunter, thus making it a prized possession during the hunting season.

The Saker and Peregrine were both large enough to be used to hunt the Houbara. Techniques used in the hunt have changed little over the centuries. Four wheel drive vehicles have replaced animals, but the hunting style has not varied. The hunter approaches the quarry as close as possible before releasing the falcon for a short rapid attack. Often the sight of even a captive falcon causes the Houbara to remain motionless in an instinctive protective crouch common to many birds of the open country. Thus immobilized, the Houbara can be quickly dispatched with a firearm or other weapon.

If the Houbara takes to wing, the falcon is released in hopes that it will out-fly the Houbara and force it to land by harassing it. Once on the ground, the Houbara assumes a defensive posture, spreading its tail and erecting its feathers to look as large as possible. An experienced falcon might kill a Houbara by seizing its head as it swoops. If the Houbara is not killed outright, the falcon is at risk of being temporarily blinded or incapacitated by a storm of liquid faeces which the Houbara is capable of ejecting at an opponent. The falconer has to be alert to follow up and finish the kill.

Lanners (*F. biarmicus*) are smaller still and less vigorous in attack than the Peregrine. They were usually used in conjunction with salukis in the hunting of the Desert Hare. The even smaller Barbary Falcon (*F. pelegrinoides*), the desert counterpart of the Peregrine, was used for hunting the Stone Curlew (*Burhinus oedicnemus*), an easier prey.

It was customary to release birds at the end of a hunting season. Bringing them through the moult in captivity was not easy and only a few individuals were retained. Since moulting in Peregrines is to some extent adapted to the region in which they normally nest, northern Peregrines did not usually moult satisfactorily as captive birds in Arabia.

Recently, falconers have been faced with a scarcity in the number of choice hunting birds available. One consequence has been an increase in the taking of young from the nest to be reared and trained for falconry. In a region such as Saudi Arabia, where pairs of nesting falcons tend to be few and far between, this could seriously deplete local wild populations. There has also been a much greater tendency to keep birds, often in large air-conditioned cages, and have them moult in captivity so they can be used in subsequent seasons, rather than release them. Another consequence of this scarcity has been the development in the Asir region of a Government-sponsored breeding program that is successfully reintroducing falcons into the mountainous western regions of the Kingdom. There are similar programs to re-introduce the Houbara to areas where overhunting has depleted their numbers.

In addition to birds released, there were always a large number lost during the course of falconry. To a lesser extent this remains true today. There is evidence to suggest that some of these birds may cover considerable distances and return to areas from which they were originally taken. There is no evidence that they have augmented the local breeding stock in Saudi Arabia. Birds lost by falconers may be responsible for a number of unlikely observations of single falcons in the wild. Often they can be recognized by their jesses, the woven or leather straps falconers attach to the birds' legs for tethering to a leash when not being flown.

A bird that has suffered indirectly from falconry is the Steppe Eagle (*Aquila nipalensis*). The Steppe Eagle is a fiercer bird than its African relative, the Tawny Eagle (*A. rapax*). It will take food from other birds and may attack a Saker to deprive it of its prey when a Houbara is grounded. Such behaviour angers falconers; and hunting parties have been known to kill any eagles encountered during the hunt. With the advent of efficient firearms, this has led to considerable slaughter of wintering Steppe Eagle. It is to be hoped that present restrictions on the possession and use of firearms will relieve pressure on this eagle.

Some Changes and Effects of Present Activities

Exploitation of the oil wealth of the Eastern Province has led to rapid changes in the environment, some of which are likely permanently to affect the region's wildlife. In general these changes are related to the sustained spread of structures associated with the oil industry, power distribution and road networks. Development has seen the once empty tracts of desert crossed by roads, pipelines and power lines. The number of pipelines criss-crossing the desert has grown greatly in recent years. Raised above the surface or buried under a mound of oil consolidated sand, the pipelines can benefit wildlife by providing patches of shade in areas where it was absent and by restricting the movement of vehicles. Pylons built to carry power lines and cables are of limited use to birds. They serve as resting posts or lookout points for wintering eagles and other raptors. The Brown-necked Raven (*Corvus ruficollis*) sometimes nests on them and resident birds seek shelter in the shadows they cast during the heat of summer, but generally they are little used by desert birds. These limited advantages are more than offset by the destruction of broad tracts of vegetation during construction of the line and the building of access roads.

The desert represents a fairly fragile biotope which can easily be disturbed by man. The sedentary grazing of livestock permitted by the advent of water tanker trucks has been a mixed blessing for wildlife. Persistent grazing has resulted in the destruction of plant life and neither bird nor man benefits when the natural desert flora deteriorates or disappears.

The growing use of motor vehicles which can travel off the road has not only caused damage to the surface vegetation but has also permitted expansion of grazing areas which put further pressure on the ecosystem through wind erosion. Desert driving has disturbed wildlife in areas infrequently visited in the past.

Hunting with firearms, coupled with the use of motorized transport, has dealt a devastating blow to desert animals. Traditional game birds such as the Houbara Bustard (*Chlamydotis undulata*) have been especially hard hit. The increasing rarity of several kinds of large birds, including various species of vultures that were once commonly referred to by visitors to the Eastern Province, suggests that they may have also provided convenient targets.

The Arabian Gulf coastline, where much of the commercial and industrial development has taken place, is another highly vulnerable locale. Human activity is concentrated along the shore, and planners who think in terms of houses, industrial estates, jetties and harbours often see mudflats and stands of mangroves in terms of development prospects rather than bird sanctuaries.

The shoreline collects considerable flotsam from materials cast off by Gulf shipping. Northerly facing beaches are often considerably littered with lumber, plastic, bottles and tins and other debris that has been improperly discarded by ships transiting the Gulf. Since a major part of the bird population using the Gulf depends on it during the winter or on migration, it is possible that widespread changes on the edge of the Gulf could impact on bird populations which breed elsewhere.

Tarut Bay, located between the commercial centre of Dammam and the oil refining and terminal centre of Ras Tanura, provides one example of the effect of modern development on the coastline. The bay, which has long hosted large assemblies of wintering shorebirds and ducks, is considered to be one of the richest biotopes of its type along the entire coast; but it is already partially filled in due to land development and its shoreline could be permanently affected. There are now moves to control landfill projects and to require environmental impact assessments for coastal development. The Kingdom is also grappling with the problem of balancing development with conservation by identifying conservation management areas. Such moves may save the environmental riches of Tarut Bay and similar areas if implemented before irreversible harm is done.

Residents are turning more and more to the shore

area for recreation, and some of that activity threatens local wildlife. The small islands of the Gulf are particularly affected. Visitors can easily travel to them on motorized dhows, swim off their beaches and wander about on them, frequently staying overnight. Such intrusions can result in harm to wildlife, especially to nesting seabird colonies. Disturbances in the nesting period may cause the wholesale desertion of nests, with huge losses of eggs and nestlings. The islands are also resting and roosting sites. Repeated disturbances can leave them barren of birds, which may have no other haven. As yet the islands seem to be surviving the visitors as well as the fishermen, but this is an area to watch for early indications of changes in breeding habits and locations.

Although the Gulf is the major oil producing region of the world there appears to be little direct effect of oil pollution on the seabirds as evidenced from the scarcity of oiled birds found along the shoreline. The seabirds have benefited from the numerous offshore oil well platforms which are used as safe roosts away from predators. Birds living in fresh water have also benefited from man's activities. Due to the lack of rivers and streams in the region treated sewage effluent is normally disposed of in open ponds rather than discharged to a river as is done in wetter climates. Such effluent ponds are soon surrounded by vegetation supporting resident, migrant and wintering bird populations. Schemes to reuse the effluent may alter these man-made habitats by drying up the ponds but such schemes will no doubt open a different habitat for opportunistic birds to fill.

In general, an increase in cropland and garden irrigation, along with the establishment of shade trees, has resulted in an increase in the number of birds and the range of species. The use of insecticides and herbicides by farmers and gardeners will not have the same devastating effect on birds that has been seen in other countries due to the strict Government control on pesticide imports and the complete banning of most pesticides that have proved so harmful elsewhere in the world.

The growing trade in imported exotic parrots and, to a lesser extent, small seed eating waxbills and similar birds is another factor to be considered. Individuals and small groups of various species that have obviously escaped from captivity can be seen from time to time. The conditions around villages and cities suit some imported birds, and many imported Australian parrots and cockatoos are adapted to conditions similar to those found in Saudi Arabia. It is possible that the accidental introduction of several individuals could add another species to the avifauna of the region.

Looking very far into the future is difficult in the fast changing Eastern Province but, in the near term, rapidly expanding industrialization and a growth in population pose an increasing threat to the area's natural habitats and wildlife. Increased mobility may make *jabals*, escarpments and islands even more vulnerable; birds of the desert *jabals* are threatened because of the limited number of breeding sites available to them. During the past ten years (1978 to 1988) there has been a significant withdrawal of species from *jabals* that are now easy of access.

Birds inhabiting the limited freshwater sites and cultivated areas in and around settlements are tied largely to the man-modified environment for survival. Any long term sustained change in man's activities will directly affect them.

In the long term, birds of the open desert are most likely to survive successfully. Shore birds appear to have the least chance of retaining the habitats they need to feed, breed, and nest. Island nesting species are the most clearly threatened.

SYSTEMATIC LIST OF SPECIES

One of the problems encountered when compiling a regional list, and one that takes up an inordinate amount of time in correspondence and research, is deciding what reported sightings have been satisfactorily identified. Inquiries regarding the authenticity of some unprecedented records, particularly in the case of 'difficult' species, have produced little or no supporting evidence. We have avoided the temptation to exclude *all* those records for which supporting evidence has not been forthcoming. A foremost consideration has been the experience and reputation of the observer; his familiarity with the species in question, or closely related forms more commonly encountered; and the circumstances of the reported sighting. Nevertheless the decision-making process has inevitably been subjective and, since we have tried to err on the side of caution, perhaps at times arbitrary.

Until 1988 the Arabian Gulf region was not well served by field identification guides, but the publication of *Birds of the Middle East and North Africa* by P. A. D. Hollom, R. F. Porter, S. Christensen and Ian Willis has done much to fill this void and supplement *The Birds of Britain and Europe, with North Africa and Middle East* (Heinzel *et al* 1972) which, in the absence of a more specifically regional work, was for many years the stand-by of field workers in the Gulf.

In the interests of uniformity the sequence of the list follows Voous (1977) whose work on the Holarctic bird species is widely accepted. Departures from the conventional English names have been made in only a very few instances to avoid confusion if the same English name has been applied to different species.

Until sufficient specimens, obtained in the Eastern Province of Saudi Arabia, are available for scientific study, some of the difficult taxonomic questions that now face us will remain unanswered; consequently the use of trinomials has generally been avoided.

Unless some indication is given to the contrary, status summaries have been made from a compilation of unpublished data. Additional notes and unusual records are followed by the observer's initials (see p. 11).

Each species is given a 'status symbol'—a quick indication of its overall status in the Province. For these the following abbreviations are used.

RB	Resident breeder:	present throughout the year, and breeding.
MB	Migrant breeder:	breeds and normally departs after the breeding season.
CB	Casual breeder:	breeds only sporadically.
FB	Former breeder:	not known to have bred for at least ten years.
PM	Passage migrant:	normally only present while en route between breeding grounds and a regular wintering area.
WV	Winter visitor:	this term is retained since it is widely understood. It might be re-phrased 'non-breeding' visitor for this is what it means. Non-breeding visitors remain in the region during immaturity and often throughout the year. Adults spend the period between breeding seasons in their 'winter quarters'.
	Vagrant:	a species usually recorded less than annually. At the present time, this normally means less than about ten records in total.

Brackets ( ) around an abbreviated status symbol indicate irregularity of occurrence, and a question mark (?) indicates some uncertainty about status. The symbol given first, where two or more are shown, indicates the more significant status on present evidence.

Attempting to describe degrees of abundance in faunal works is unavoidably hazardous, especially when trying to cover as large an area as the Eastern Province of Saudi Arabia. It is admittedly an impossible task even to approach accuracy but nevertheless *some* indication of numerical status seems desirable. Since most species included here are passing migrants, usually seen in fairly well-defined vegetated areas surrounded by desert, it is generally possible to give a simple designation. The degrees of abundance used in the species accounts and appendices are thus confined as much as possible to three hopefully unambiguous categories:

'Abundant'—hundreds or more in a given area
'Common' —tens
'Scarce' —less than ten.

Moreau (1934) wrote: 'The terms I have used . . . to indicate relative density are very vague indeed. It is inevitable that our quantitative ideas on such a subject must be for a long time ill-defined. It is particularly difficult to observe and record migration phenomena with a proper degree of objectivity, seeing that we lack standards. Indeed even with the same observer it is certain that his estimate of migration density must be greatly affected by the environment of his observation. A passage of given volume will make itself obvious in a narrow well-defined belt of vegetation with an extensive barren hinterland; less obvious where the vegetation is larger, because bird concentrations will be less; least obvious where the vegetation is too scanty to attract migrants to descend.' This statement is particularly relevant to observations in the Eastern Province and is no less true 55 years after it was penned.

Family STRUTHIONIDAE

Struthio camelus · OSTRICH FB

Now almost certainly extinct in Arabia. The last recorded occurrence is of one shot in northern Saudi Arabia, not far from the international frontier with Iraq, between October and December 1939 (Vincent 1966–71), an incident also described in Wallace Stegner's book *Discovery* (1971). Until the 1930s it was to be found on the fringes of the Nafud desert and in the Rub' al-Khali (Ticehurst & Cheesman 1925), inhospitable regions that are seldom visited even today. The former range almost certainly extended to the Dibdibah in the same general area as the last recorded example and to those parts of the Rub' al-Khali that lie within the Eastern Province. Within our region a long-abandoned sand-covered nest with six unbroken eggs and a scattering of shell fragments was found in the Rub' al-Khali in about 1964 (JPM). An egg, of unknown origin, was sold in Hofuf market in 1947 (Ripley 1951) and another was found, unbroken, in Oman (18°N 52°E) in March 1979 (Walker 1981).

Family PODICIPEDIDAE

Tachybaptus ruficollis · LITTLE GREBE RB

A locally common species breeding on inundated areas associated with irrigation projects and sewage lagoons. These areas are often only temporary waters and several quite important sites have recently been drained, notably near Hofuf at al-'Uyun; just west of Dammam; and the ponds of the Imhoff sewerage disposal system at Dhahran. Builds an inconspicuous nest of floating vegetation in reed beds, or amongst the branches of a partly submerged tree or bush; occasionally in quite open situations but usually attached to submerged vegetation. From the beginning of April onwards lays 4–5 pale bluish eggs, thickly encrusted with a chalky white coating that becomes stained dark brown as incubation progresses. Shape variable, but often pointed at each end. The incubating bird covers the eggs with wet weeds when leaving the nest. Double or treble brooded (RJC). There is evidence of some post-breeding dispersal when juveniles, and some adults, are regularly seen on small waters not normally used for breeding. Increased numbers are regularly noted on breeding waters and elsewhere from September to January when the population is presumably swollen by the progeny of the breeding stock, there being no evidence of immigration as yet. Examples of some autumnal counts are 500+ near al-'Uyun, 250 at the former Imhoff ponds and at least 600 on four lakes at Abqaiq. It has yet to be seen on the sea.

Little Grebe (GKB)

Podiceps cristatus · GREAT CRESTED GREBE WV

A regular but usually scarce visitor chiefly to coastal waters from October through March, though small numbers have been seen as early as August and as late as May. Numbers are highest in November when birds are regularly seen on waters away from coasts. There was a large influx in November 1979 when birds were widely distributed on inland waters and an unusually large concentration of 130 was seen in Half Moon Bay about 30 km south of al-Khobar. It is rare and irregular during the summer months, though three in breeding plumage were present from March to August 1982 on the shore just south of al-Khobar. On 1 June 1984, a total of 82 (all in breeding plumage) were counted in a large coastal bay just to the north of Qurayyah (GKB); such numbers at this time of year are difficult to explain.

Podiceps grisegena VAGRANT
RED-NECKED GREBE

Three in Half Moon Bay, 29 December 1978 (DJBra). One 5 km south of al-Khobar, 28 November 1979 (GB). One on the sea, south of al-Khobar 12 December 1985 (JP).

Podiceps nigrocollis · BLACK-NECKED GREBE WV

A regular visitor from late August through March but generally scarce in April and May. Adults in summer plumage remained until late May at two localities in 1980; while in 1984 at least one bird in breeding plumage was present at Abqaiq throughout the period April to August. It is usually local in coastal waters but counts of over 40 are not unusual in Half Moon Bay south of al-Khobar. Small numbers are regular away from the coast at lakes near al-Qarn, Dammam, Dhahran and notably near Abqaiq where assemblies of up to 45 have been noted.

Family HYDROBATIDAE

Oceanites oceanicus · WILSON'S PETREL WV

Probably a regular visitor to the eastern Arabian Gulf from April to August (Bundy & Warr 1980). Petrels which are very probably this species are not

White Pelican (GKB)

infrequently observed offshore in Saudi waters during this period although never close to the coast. Recent examples of these occurrences are of about 50 birds near Jana island on 19 July 1980 (BS), and 11 off Ju'aymah on 17 July 1980 (PWGC). One was seen off Jurayd island in early June 1981 (LR), and small flocks were seen regularly at sea in Saudi waters during late July and throughout August 1985 (DMS).

Family PHAETHONTIDAE

Phaethon aethereus VAGRANT
RED-BILLED TROPICBIRD

Two at Ras az-Zawr, 9 October 1981 (JCB).

Family PELECANIDAE

Pelecanus onocrotalus · WHITE PELICAN (PM)

Possibly a more regular migrant than records suggest at present. 17 at Imhoff ponds, 30 June 1974 (KJF) and single birds at Dammam marsh on 5 December 1975 and 27 September 1976 (GKB). An adult over the desert camp at al-Musannah in the north, 1 August 1979 (GJR). Nine at Abqaiq lagoons, 28 September 1979 (GB). In 1980 there were individuals over the Shedgum plateau on 3 April (PJI), at Qatif on 3 November (RH), and soaring over Dhahran on 24 November (DC). One at Shedgum pools, 26 January 1982 (GB). One at Qatif on 18 November 1983 (JAH, TSH).

Family PHALACROCORACIDAE

Represented by two species: the Cormorant is a common winter visitor, and the Socotra Cormorant has a world range that is almost restricted to the Arabian Gulf. There are also several unconfirmed reports of Pygmy Cormorant (*Phalacrocorax pygmeus*), a freshwater species that breeds as close as Iraq. The two regular species are superficially similar and may cause identification problems. CORMORANT is the larger but size is of limited value when identifying distant birds on the sea. Immatures are alike, brown above and whitish below, but SOCOTRA is generally paler and less 'pied-looking' with an area of noticeable buffish freckling over the wing-coverts. In Cormorant, the bill is deeper at the base and rather heavy looking, and usually pale with a yellowish area close to the gape. In the slightly smaller Socotra, the bill is dark, more slender and relatively longer.

Cormorant (GKB)

Socotra Cormorant (BS) *The bird in the centre is still carrying filamentous plumes, below and to the rear of its eye. These are believed to play a part in the display that accompanies pair formation, but are usually shed before the birds come ashore to nest.*

Socotra Cormorant chicks (BS) *While the photographer was in the hide, the small dark chick in the foreground solicited food from a larger chick in a neighbouring nest. The larger chick responded by opening its bill. Here the smaller chick is inserting its own bill into that of the larger one, seeking regurgitated food. Such behaviour has rarely been observed in other species, but not enough is known of the breeding biology of the Socotra Cormorant to state whether such behaviour is typical or abnormal.*

Phalacrocorax carbo · CORMORANT WV

Common, sometimes abundant in coastal waters from September through March, a few immatures sometimes remaining through the summer. Birds are occasionally seen inland at ponds near Abqaiq, Hofuf and al-Qarn. It has been noted exceptionally at Haradh where there is no open water—two individuals having been seen there in September (JCD). From 1978 to 1981 during the months of November to March, before the Imhoff effluent evaporation ponds at Dhahran were drained, there was a large roost in the lakeside tamarisks with birds flying to and from the sea at dawn and dusk. The maximum count at the roost, in December 1980, was of 1,100 individuals (JP).

Phalacrocorax nigrogularis RB
SOCOTRA CORMORANT

This little-studied species is well represented in the Arabian Gulf. It breeds in closely packed colonies, sometimes of enormous size, and lays 2–4 pale bluish eggs, thickly encrusted with a chalky white coating, in a scrape in the sand. Contrary to published reports, the eggs are not marked but occasionally show traces of blood (RJC). In recent years breeding has been recorded on at least four Saudi Arabian offshore islands. It formerly bred on al-'Arabiyah island: in April 1938 there were about 250 nests with eggs (Loppenthin 1951) but the site has now been abandoned (BS). The breeding season is either a protracted one or somewhat irregular, since at different colonies eggs have been laid from late September to May. For this reason details of recent island visits are given site by site. Kurayn. 21 December 1979: approximately 100 nests with eggs in all stages of incubation. 23 May 1980: about 50 nests mostly containing chicks in all stages of development; also a few eggs being incubated. 13 November 1980: about 150 nests containing fresh or partly incubated eggs. az-Zakhnuniyah. 4 December 1980: many thousands of very large chicks present although a few nests contained fresh eggs or very small chicks. Samamik. 18 December 1980: approximately 500 nests with incomplete clutches of fresh eggs. 'Unaybir. 4 December 1980: approximately 1,000 nests with very large young (RJC).

Small numbers are commonly seen close to the mainland coast, especially from April through August, but from October through March it is always outnumbered by the Cormorant in coastal waters. However, at times enormous concentrations are seen from the mainland. Such assemblies, occurring from December to May and sometimes in other months, number up to around 25,000 and probably more. Larger concentrations have been photographed from the air by RJC in the neighbourhood of the Hawar islands (Bahrain).

The large offshore assemblies seem to comprise chiefly black adults. The flocks are usually seen flying in large packs low over the surface with birds plunge diving into the sea at regular intervals, then rising and circling in hurried flight to repeat the dive as though a very abundant food source was only temporarily available. It was formerly thought that these large offshore concentrations were 'movements' but they almost invariably coincide with mass plunge diving activity and, significantly perhaps, occur when most young are being fed at the colonies. This species has a very restricted world range and within the Gulf suitable breeding sites are being subjected to increasing disturbance. Although some colonies remain very large, with from approximately 10,000 to 25,000 pairs or more, the colonies are rather few in total and some islands have been deserted altogether.

Family ARDEIDAE

The herons are represented by ten species of which only two breed, seven are more or less regular visitors, and one is a vagrant. There are two unconfirmed records of Goliath Heron (*Ardea goliath*). The numbers of the two breeding species have recently been reduced due to the destruction of reed beds and mangroves. At the drainage lakes north of Hofuf, large areas of reeds were eliminated as a result of re-channelling irrigation water in 1980. Similarly, small but significant reed beds near the Abqaiq sewage ponds were destroyed in the same year and both events caused a loss of breeding habitat for Little Bitterns. Just north of Qatif a small colony of Western Reef Herons disappeared after the clearing of an important area of mangroves.

Most species are readily identified but caution should be exercised when separating LITTLE EGRET and WESTERN REEF HERON. The Reef Heron has two morphs, a dark grey and a white, the latter being very similar to Little Egret. Generally Little Egrets are found by fresh water but they are regularly seen on the littoral, while Reef Herons are confined to the coast. In favourable light conditions the Reef Heron's heavier bill can be seen to be brownish, sometimes yellowish or even pinkish-brown; it is deeper at the base than Little Egret's, making the forehead less obvious. The relatively longer bill of Little Egret is black, sometimes paler and greyer at the base of the lower mandible. Little Egrets have slightly longer wings that look more pointed in flight and the wing-beats are shallower and quicker. The much larger GREAT WHITE EGRET has a more massive bright yellow bill, a relatively longer 'snakier' neck, and black (not yellowish) feet.

Botaurus stellaris · BITTERN VAGRANT

Individuals recorded at Hofuf lakes on 21 May 1976 (GKB), at Imhoff on 24 November 1978 (GB), and at Jawb, on the northern edge of Rub' al-Khali on 25 September 1980 (GJR); at Abqaiq one from 11 to 17 December 1982 (GKB, DR, LR), a party of three on 19–20 October 1983 (JAH, TSH, CVP, WHP), and one on 14 and 21 December 1984 (GKB).

Ixobrychus minutus · LITTLE BITTERN RB

A locally common breeding species in a few suitable areas, notably in the extensive reed-beds north of al-'Uyun about 25 km north of Hofuf. A few pairs breed at Qatif when conditions are suitable, and at Abqaiq breeds annually (at one lake probably since 1976). Nests are usually built of dried stems and lined with dried leaves of phragmites, about 25 cm above the water level in an extensive area of mature reeds, often where there is a secondary growth of tamarisk. In the Eastern Province egg laying begins in early April and five immaculate white eggs form the usual clutch (RJC). It is present all year at breeding grounds; elsewhere it occurs fairly regularly from March through to early June and from August through October, and the individuals seen away from breeding sites are almost certainly on passage. The population in Iran departs after the breeding season (Scott *et al* 1975).

Nycticorax nycticorax · NIGHT HERON PM (WV)

Usually a scarce migrant, noted more often in autumn than spring. From September through November, when juveniles predominate, gatherings of up to 12 were almost regular in the environs of the Imhoff sewerage evaporation ponds near Dhahran and a few remained until February. It tends to be inconspicuous and may have been over-

Little Bittern (GKB)
Cattle Egret (GKB)

Squacco Heron (GKB)

looked in spring when its occurrences have been rather irregular in April and May. There is one June record, and a single immature bird was present at the Abqaiq lagoons from 22 July to 22 August 1983.

Ardeola ralloides · SQUACCO HERON PM (WV)

Sometimes locally common from March through May but usually scarce by June. Small numbers are regular from August through November in scattered wetland localities and a few sometimes overwinter. This species is a well-established trans-Saharan migrant (Bundy 1976) and the occurrence of about 200 at Haradh in September suggests that it crosses the Arabian desert in good numbers as well. A pair of adults summered on flooded grassland surrounded by trees at the Imhoff sewerage effluent evaporation ponds, Dhahran, in 1978.

Bubulcus ibis · CATTLE EGRET PM (WV)

As a migrant it occurs chiefly from March through May and from August through November mainly in the coastal zone, but also inland, especially at Abqaiq. Although somewhat irregular in its appearances, it is recorded annually. There are records of odd individuals in June and July, and from December through February. It occurs singly or in small parties of up to ten. Sightings of single birds at Haradh in July, August and October suggest that some birds may cross the desert to the south.

Egretta gularis · WESTERN REEF HERON RB

This is the common and conspicuous heron of the littoral. It nests colonially on suaeda bushes at Samamik island; on low suaeda and mangrove-clad islets north of Abu 'Ali; and on low cliffs at Jinnah island. About ten nests containing eggs were seen in mangroves near Qatif on 18 May 1979 but this area has since been reclaimed. Nests are very frail structures of slender twigs with a shallow, saucer shaped depression to contain the eggs. The clutch is of two or three, occasionally four, very pale blue eggs. In the Eastern Province laying begins at the end of March and continues through to August (RJC). Along the mainland coast it is most numerous from August through April although small numbers are frequently seen in the remaining months—especially on the shores adjacent to the breeding colonies. This species is dominant over the slightly smaller Little Egret where the two overlap, but curiously the latter is far more numerous in Tarut Bay, possibly due to the outflow of fresh water from the Qatif oasis complex. White morphs usually outnumber dark birds by two to one on the mainland coasts in winter, although further east in the Gulf grey morphs outnumber white (Bundy & Warr 1980). At the breeding colony on Samamik island in May 1981 dark and white morphs were present in approximately equal numbers and were often paired (RJC).

Reef Heron: dark morph (BS)

Reef Heron: white morph (BS)

Reef Heron: nest and eggs (BS)

The statement in Cramp & Simmons (1977) that this species feeds alone with each individual maintaining a feeding territory is certainly not borne out by experience in this region. Here groups of up to 40 birds have been noted in favoured areas, feeding close together in small shore pools and in muddy creeks, not without animosity but not in well-spaced territories either.

Identification: see pp. 79–80.

Egretta garzetta · LITTLE EGRET WV PM

A regular migrant from March to early June and from September through December, it is usually encountered in small numbers although migrant flocks of up to 40 have been noted at inland sites away from regular wintering places. It overwinters in Tarut Bay and the Dammam area, large numbers frequenting the littoral and mangrove flats where Western Reef Herons are curiously scarce.

Identification: see pp. 79–80.

Egretta alba · GREAT WHITE EGRET WV PM?

A regular visitor to Tarut Bay and the coastal areas south to around Dammam, it has been recorded from September through March (and occasionally as late as May), with a maximum count of 30. Away from the coastal zone presumed migrants have been recorded in March at lakes north of Hofuf and in October at Abqaiq, where three birds were seen to depart to the south-west.

Identification: see p. 80.

Ardea cinerea · GREY HERON WV PM

Common locally from August through April with the majority in the coastal zone and close to the littoral. Non-breeding immatures are often present along the coast throughout the summer. Occurrence away from the coast is only regular during the period August through October, suggesting a southerly passage over the desert. During this period it occurs in small parties at Abqaiq and Hofuf, sporadically at Haradh and elsewhere. At Jawb on the northern edge of the Rub' al-Khali up to four birds occurred from 15 to 18 September 1980 (GJR). It is very scarce away from the coastal zone after November and there is no evidence for any overland passage in spring.

Little Egret (GKB)

Grey Heron (GKB)

Ardea purpurea · PURPLE HERON PM

A regular spring migrant, although always scarce, from March to June. In autumn it is more numerous and occurs from August to November, occasionally until the end of December, with juveniles predominating.

Family CICONIIDAE

Ciconia nigra · BLACK STORK VAGRANT

Single individuals at Dammam marsh 30 April to 3 May 1974 (GKB, KJF), at Abqaiq 12 December 1975 (GKB, DMH), and one flying south-west at Abqaiq, 20 November 1981 (GB, JP, DR). Two birds at Abqaiq lagoons 8 July 1988 (TSH, JAH).

Ciconia ciconia · WHITE STORK PM

A scarce and irregular migrant, though probably passing over the area unseen more regularly than the records suggest. It migrates by soaring on thermals and observations in the Eastern Province have often been of migrant flocks coming down in the evening to roost. Most of the records are in autumn, from August to mid-October, with a well-marked

Purple Heron (GKB)

Glossy Ibis (GKB)

White Stork (GKB)

peak in late August, though there is a record of a sighting about 15 km north of Haradh on 2 November 1965 (JPM). The largest number recorded was a flock of 71 which came in to roost at Abqaiq on the evening of 9 October 1982 (LR). Most of the migrants move on quickly, though a flock of 21 at Haradh on 28 September 1984 was still present a week later (JHM, JP). Spring occurrences are of single birds in the Jubail area on 30 April 1983, heading north (AD), and at 'Anak on 5 May 1983 (JAH, TSH, CVP). During 1986, when conditions were exceptionally favourable small numbers frequented an inundated area to the west of the Dammam Second Industrial City on the Dhahran/Abqaiq Road during January, February and March, suggesting they may have overwintered in the area (RJC).

Family THRESKIORNITHIDAE

Threskiornis aethiopicus · SACRED IBIS VAGRANT

9 birds at a small lake of treated sewerage effluent, Aramco compound, Dhahran, 7 July 1988 and a single bird at the same location 14 July 1988 (TSH, JAH).

Plegadis falcinellus · GLOSSY IBIS PM

A regular but generally scarce migrant from March to early May and from August to November. It is rare and irregular from December through February and during June and July. One migrant was seen flying south-eastwards over the Jawb camp in the Rub' al-Khali on 19 September 1980 (GJR).

Platalea leucorodia · SPOONBILL (WV)

Winters in West Africa, Mediterranean region, Nile valley, Red Sea (where also resident), southern Iraq and Iran, and south-east Asia. A rare and irregular visitor, with about 12 records, usually involving immatures, which have often stayed for several weeks if undisturbed and feeding conditions are suitable. There is no well-marked pattern to the records, though November–December, April and June account for most; usually it occurs only singly,

Spoonbill (GKB)

but at Qatif/Tarut Bay, there were 5–6 in December 1979 (GB), 4 on 7 April 1983 (CVP), and a party of 11 on 13 December 1984 (GKB). Almost all sightings have been confined to the coast, especially Qatif and Tarut Bay, but also the former Dammam marsh, Abu 'Ali and al-Khobar. The only inland record is one at Abqaiq on 30 September and 1 October 1976 (GKB).

Family PHOENICOPTERIDAE

Phoenicopterus ruber · GREATER FLAMINGO WV

There are regular wintering assemblies in a few suitable coastal areas, notably at Abu 'Ali, just south of al-Khobar, and near al-'Uqayr. Numbers vary from year to year, though counts of the flock near al-Khobar from 1974 to 1984 have shown a steady increase: in the period 1974–7 the maximum was 190 in December 1974 and January 1975; then 260 in March 1980, 560 in March 1981, 610 in February 1983, and 690 in December 1984. Usually only small numbers (mainly immatures) remain during the summer. In 1984, however, a quite different pattern

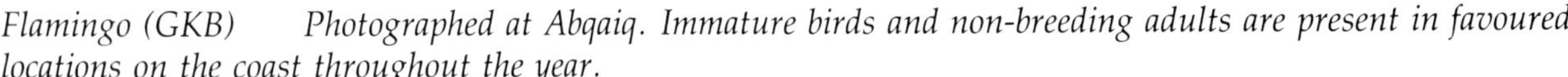

Flamingo (GKB) Photographed at Abqaiq. Immature birds and non-breeding adults are present in favoured locations on the coast throughout the year.

emerged, when 250–300 birds, of which at least 95% were adult, remained during May to July. It was formerly rarely found away from the coast, the only records being from Abqaiq, where there were 10 immatures in November 1977, 1–2 immatures in November 1981, April 1983 and April 1984, and up to 14 in December 1984. However, since 1985, a small flock of about 30 mainly immature birds has established itself during the winter months on an inundated area to the west of the Dammam Second Industrial City on the Dhahran/Abqaiq Road. There is also a report of 4 dying inland at Haradh in September 1984 (per JHM and JP).

Family ANATIDAE

Of the eighteen species represented here, only the Ruddy Shelduck and Ferruginous Duck are known to breed; ten are winter visitors, one is a trans-desert migrant, and five are vagrants. Of the species breeding in the central and western Palearctic only one, the Garganey, winters exclusively outside and large numbers pass through eastern Arabia bound for tropical Africa. At least four other species of duck from the Palearctic winter south of the Sahara but large numbers of these winter in northern latitudes as well, including the Arabian Gulf region.

Anser anser · GREYLAG GOOSE — WV

One at Dammam, 7 December 1973 (KJF, JAW). Two at Dammam marsh, 14 February 1977 (GKB). Seven, of the Eastern form *rubrirostris*, on a small lake of treated sewerage effluent in the Aramco compound at Dhahran, 7 November 1985; two of these overwintered and left about 20 March, 1986 (TSH, ALL, JP). During the winter of 1985–1986 small parties were regularly seen on inundated land to the west of the Dammam Second Industrial City, on the Dhahran/Abqaiq Road (RJC).

Anser albifrons — VAGRANT
WHITE-FRONTED GOOSE

Two immatures were seen on a small lake of treated sewerage effluent in the Aramco compound at Dhahran on 14 November 1985, and left the same day. They were probably attracted by the presence on the lake of two Greylag geese (TSH, ALL).

Greylag Goose (ALL)
An example of the race rubrirostris *showing the rich pink bill characteristic of the Eastern populations.*

Ruddy Shelduck (male) (GKB)

Wigeon (female) (ALL)

Tadorna ferruginea · RUDDY SHELDUCK RB WV

Breeds only near Abqaiq with up to four pairs present in each year from 1976, though it has not been established that all the pairs have attempted to breed each year. The appearance of ducklings is the first indication of successful breeding. No nest has been examined in Saudi Arabia. Elsewhere, nests in a hole in a bank or cliff, often at some distance from water, and lays 6–10 ivory white eggs in a depression warmly lined with white down from the female (RJC). The birds are generally absent from the breeding areas from June through most of September, presumably moulting. Between late September and March, up to 50 have been noted in the high dunes and on the pools throughout the main breeding area. Elsewhere it tends to be very scarce and irregular even in coastal localities.

Tadorna tadorna · SHELDUCK WV

Usually the scarcest of ducks in coastal localities, only small flocks occurring from November through March. In early 1981 there were up to 20 near Abqaiq, some 40 km from the littoral, from January through March, and one at the Imhoff sewerage effluent ponds near Dhahran as late as 7 May (RJC).

Nettapus coromandelianus VAGRANT
COTTON TEAL

A female, or immature, at Abqaiq, 14 November 1981 (GB).

Anas penelope · WIGEON WV

Regular and numerous only in Tarut Bay, from November through March (and occasionally as late as April), with up to 1,000 spending this period there on the tidal flats fronting the Qatif oasis. Extensive reclamation of the main area north and south of the Tarut causeway since 1981, however, has placed the future of this valuable wintering habitat in jeopardy and the immediate prospects are uncertain. Small numbers are fairly regular inland at Abqaiq and elsewhere during this period, with occasional inland records of 'pairs' as late as mid-May, the later birds suggesting some trans-desert passage.

Anas strepera · GADWALL WV

It is generally rather scarce in the coastal zone, frequenting the few suitable pools near the shore as well as tidal creeks. It is probably only regular in Tarut Bay where normally about 50 (though once 90 in January 1983) occur from late October through March, sometimes into April. The only inland records are from the small lake of treated sewerage effluent in the Aramco compound at Dhahran, the Abqaiq lagoons and Shedgum pools, up to 65 km from the littoral; small numbers have been noted there from November through February.

Anas crecca · TEAL WV

Regularly present from late August through April but most numerous from November to March. Occasional records of single birds seen in May and June probably refer to injured birds. The largest concentrations are usually in the creeks that empty into Tarut Bay from the Qatif oasis. Away from the coast it is also regular at Hofuf, Abqaiq, Shedgum and formerly at the Imhoff sewerage effluent ponds, Dhahran, and the Dammam sewage works. The wintering assemblies do not normally exceed 1,000.

Anas platyrhynchos · MALLARD WV

Appears to be regular only in the Dammam and Tarut Bay areas where it has been recorded from August through May but more especially from September to March. At the Abqaiq lagoons small numbers occur during the period from late August to early May; a small peak in numbers during the

Gadwall (male) (ALL)

Gadwall (female) (ALL)

Teal (male) (ALL)

Pintail (female) (GKB)

period late September through November suggests that some may be on passage for it becomes scarce and irregular after November away from its coastal haunts. In its regular wintering areas flocks seldom exceed 60.

Anas acuta · PINTAIL WV

Wintering flocks in the coastal zone concentrate in a few favourable localities, notably at Tarut Bay and near Dammam. Away from the coast it tends to be commonest at the Abqaiq ponds and near al-Qarn; there are few other remaining localities that are suitable. Wintering concentrations seldom exceed 100 although at the former Dammam marsh and at the lakes just west of the town, there were often 350 birds present. The Imhoff sewerage effluent ponds near Dhahran were also favourite wintering places before they were drained in 1981. Birds arrive in late September and most depart during March. There are records for individual birds or small groups in August and during April to June. This species has a large Palearctic range and many birds cross the Sahara to winter in eastern Africa. At Haradh, although there is only a wet ditch at the most, up to 16 have been noted (RH, JP), suggesting that some birds are crossing the southern Arabian desert.

Anas querquedula · GARGANEY PM

Occurs from mid-February with a peak in numbers during the first half of March, numbers in April declining rapidly until early May. It is usually absent from May until late August, after which it becomes twice as numerous as in spring. It occurs mainly on freshwater pools and lagoons away from the littoral, but especially in autumn it is regular in small numbers on shore, and even occasionally on the sea. The autumn peak is usually during September but, if flocks are undisturbed and ecological conditions are right, some remain until December.

Anas clypeata · SHOVELER WV

A locally common visitor from September through April with occasional individuals recorded from May to August. Numbers fluctuate, depending no doubt upon local conditions; up to 700 have been counted at the former Imhoff sewerage effluent ponds but the wintering population there was normally around 350 between 1977 and 1981. It is a regular winter visitor to the Abqaiq sewage run-off ponds and possibly still to the few remaining lakes north of Hofuf. There is a regular assembly in Tarut Bay, birds frequenting those areas where fresh water empties into the tidal system from adjacent oasis cultivation; flocks of up to 200 have been noted at this coastal site. It has been recorded in August and September at distant Haradh, suggesting that some birds may pass through. It is a common winter visitor south of the Sahara.

Marmaronetta angustirostris VAGRANT
MARBLED TEAL

One, a male, at Abqaiq lagoons on 31 August 1979 (GB).

Netta rufina · RED-CRESTED POCHARD VAGRANT

Four females Dhahran 31 July 1985 (TSH, JP, CP).

Aythya ferina · POCHARD WV

Suitable waters for diving duck are few and it is now only regular at the Abqaiq sewerage effluent evaporation ponds. Until 1981 it was a regular visitor to the Imhoff sewerage effluent ponds, Dhahran, and in February of that year a winter maximum of 155 birds was recorded. It was also once regular at the extensive lakes north of Hofuf; a maximum count of 500 has been recorded for that area (MCJ). It occurs chiefly from October through March but has been seen exceptionally from April to early June and in August and September.

Shoveler (male) (ALL)

Pintail (male) (ALL)

Aythya nyroca · FERRUGINOUS DUCK RB (PM)

Chiefly a resident breeding species at the Abqaiq lagoons, and rather a scarce winter visitor elsewhere in small flocks rarely exceeding 20. Its migrant status is difficult to assess. Its nest is usually well concealed in a natural depression amongst vegetation, not far from water, lined with whatever dried material is in the vicinity and copious amounts of down from the female. The normal clutch is of 8–12 eggs, very pale 'café au lait' in colour (RJC). At Abqaiq, breeding was proved in 1983 and 1984; in earlier years, its appearance in July (as far back as 1977) may suggest that it has bred at this locality undetected prior to this. Its preference for overgrown, secluded pools means that it is easily overlooked. During 1982, up to 5 birds were continuously present from April to August (GKB), and in 1983 7–11 young were seen at the end of April and early May (JP, LR). In 1984, broods of 4, 8 and 8 (estimated at 1–2 weeks old) were seen on 11 May (GKB, JP), with a total of 28 fully-grown young on 1 June (GKB); a peak total of 76 on 20 July doubtless comprised mainly birds of the year, and the numbers then dropped away during August, though some remained till November at least. Although otherwise irregular in June and July there are a number of further records, with up to 48 at Abqaiq in July. These mid-summer occurrences are not easily explained—they possibly refer to early migrants or failed breeders from Iran.

Aythya fuligula · TUFTED DUCK WV

Chiefly present from late October through March but very occasionally from April to August. Usually absent in coastal waters and seldom numerous even on the few lakes where it seems to be regular. At the once extensive lakes in the drainage system north of al-Hasa 400 were recorded in late December 1975 (MCJ) but at the former Imhoff sewerage effluent ponds near Dhahran the maximum winter count seldom exceeded 100.

Mergus serrator VAGRANT
RED-BREASTED MERGANSER

A female at the Abqaiq lagoons on 31 March and 1 April 1984 (JAH, TSH, CVP, JP, DR, LR).

Family ACCIPITRIDAE

Represented here by twenty-four species, of which only two, Egyptian Vulture and Long-legged Buzzard, certainly breed. Six species are regular winter visitors to the region, four are mainly passage migrants, and twelve may be no more than vagrants. Moreau (1972) listed only three species that breed in the central Palearctic (45° to 90°E) and winter south of the Sahara, species that presumably cross Arabia en route. One of these, Honey Buzzard, is only a vagrant in our region; two others, Steppe Eagle and Buzzard, winter sparingly in the Eastern Province so that their migrant status is somewhat obscured. Two further species that breed in the central Palearctic, Pallid and Montagu's Harriers, are regular migrants.

There is no concentrated and therefore conspicuous passage of soaring raptors in the eastern half of Saudi Arabia. At the head of the Gulf in Kuwait quite large numbers of Steppe Eagles have been seen passing south-westwards from September to November. Recently a large passage, consisting of a number of species, has been seen in autumn passing south through western Arabia. The largest concentrations were in the south-west, evidently of birds moving towards the narrowest crossing to Africa from Bab al-Mandab at the southern end of the Red Sea.

In the Eastern Province, the area around Qatif attracts wintering Spotted Eagles but the higher numbers in October and November of this and other raptor species suggest that some might be passing through the region. Also in autumn, especially in September, there are frequently large numbers of harriers over the recently developed agricultural projects, notably at Haradh.

In eastern Saudi Arabia identification problems centre mainly on the female and immature ('ringtail') harriers, the two buzzard species, and the *Aquila* eagles. Raptor identification has recently been greatly assisted by the studies of Porter *et al* (1981) and Cramp & Simmons (1980), but the following summary is included so that observers in eastern Arabia may be assisted in the identification of species regularly occurring there.

Caution should be exercised when trying to identify the three ringtail harriers—PALLID, MONTAGU'S and HEN. A very close view of the head is required to see the Pallid's pale collar, lacking in the generally darker Montagu's.

The Holarctic buzzards form a complex taxonomic group; in the western and central Palearctic three species range from the Arctic tundra to the deserts of North Africa and Arabia. South of the tundra the Buzzard (*B. buteo*) ranges from the Atlantic to about 140°E in Siberia (Cramp & Simmons 1980). Northern populations especially are notoriously variable and east of Scandinavia and the Balkans the race *vulpinus*—the so-called Steppe Buzzard—intergrades into a form that closely resembles the Long-legged Buzzard of the arid lands to the south.

Moreau (1972) estimated that some six million migrant Steppe Buzzards leave the central Palearctic for eastern Africa in the autumn, many presumably passing over Arabia and the Middle East. In the Caucasus and possibly Asia Minor a slightly larger and more rufous race of Buzzard, *menetriesi*, occurs and may be a link between Buzzard and the larger Long-legged Buzzard. Alan Vittery (1980) has recently questioned the identity of the buzzards breeding in central Turkey, boldly suggesting from his field experience that the population there is the *menetriesi* race of Buzzard, and not Long-legged Buzzard as was previously supposed. The central Russian Long-legged Buzzards are migratory and some birds of the species reach eastern Africa (Cramp & Simmons 1980), although many past accounts of migrants are bedevilled with the identification problems of this species and the similar Steppe Buzzard.

The identity of the breeding buzzards of the Eastern Province is retained here as Long-legged Buzzard although doubts have been expressed about this small, rather isolated population. In late February 1924 Major Cheesman took three chicks from a nest south of Hofuf and kept one alive until 23 March in order to confirm its identity. This bird, now in the British Museum (Natural History), was tentatively identified as '*Buteo vulpinus*' (Ticehurst & Cheesman 1925). The specimen is not full grown and its identity impossible to confirm with any confidence since there are no constant and reliable structural or morphological characters with which to separate Buzzard from Long-legged Buzzard at this age. Even some adult specimens overlap in size and are difficult to identify with certainty.

The eastern races of Buzzard have larger white patches on the underwing than western forms; their pale gingery tails usually have some light barring but they are very like the Long-legged Buzzard's. Morphological characters are very variable in buzzards and allowance should be made for variations. Generally Long-legged is larger (a dubious field character) and longer-winged, suggesting a Golden Eagle in wing shape, but, although shape and outline are useful points, previous experience of many buzzards is probably required for it to be of instant value. Long-legged Buzzards differ from Steppe Buzzards by usually having a paler, sometimes almost white, head and a zone of dark striations across the lower belly—the latter forming what often looks like a quite noticeable blackish patch. Long-legged usually has a paler overall appearance with unbarred tail and paler, more contrasting upperwing-coverts—the latter being much paler than the dark flight-feathers while in most Steppe Buzzards the upper surface of the wing appears almost uniform brown. Steppe Buzzards are much less variable morphologically than Long-legged and the nominate (western) race of Buzzard. However, the breeding buzzards of the Eastern Province do not always conform with the 'classic' Long-legged Buzzard in appearance—see p. 99.

Given a good view in favourable light, *Aquila* eagles can normally be identified from below by their underwing features. Three similar species are regular in this region: Imperial, Steppe and Spotted. Both adult and the more distinctive juvenile (first-winter) Imperial Eagles occur—chiefly the latter. From below the juvenile Imperial could be mistaken for juvenile Steppe but the latter always has a quite conspicuous white line along the edges of the wing-coverts while the heavier-looking Imperial shows a distinctive greyish panel between the blackish primaries and secondaries. In eastern Saudi Arabia almost all of the wintering Steppe Eagles are dark immatures or sub-adults; pale juveniles are relatively scarce. These immatures are as dark as adults but usually retain some white along the underwing-coverts and on the rump. Spotted Eagles are seldom seen away from the coastal palmgroves and mangrove flats north of Dammam, and nearly all of the wintering birds are juveniles: dark heavy-looking eagles, they show a quite conspicuous white U-shape on the rump, whitish freckling on the upperwing-coverts, and white lines along the edges of the upperwing-coverts and the rear edge of the secondaries.

Adults of these three species are less distinctive and much less often encountered; they are all mostly uniform brown. Imperials have a two-toned grey and dark brown tail and quite noticeable buff areas on the crown and scapulars. Adult Spotteds often retain some white on the rump but are perhaps best distinguished by the two-toned underwing: the dark coverts (forewing) contrast slightly with the paler, sometimes greyish, secondaries. This underwing pattern is reversed in the similar Lesser Spotted Eagle—a vagrant in eastern Arabia. The underwing in adult Steppe is usually paler than the dark brown body, more uniform-looking than Spotted with darker-looking areas around the carpal joint and the ends of the primaries. The greyish-brown secondaries often show some darker barring when they can be seen sufficiently well.

Most Spotteds also have a buff area on the vent which is lacking in adult Steppe. Imperial and Steppe usually glide and soar on straight and level wings; the two spotted eagles soar on flat wings but characteristically glide with the wings slightly drooping. Steppe Eagles will, however, glide with

Black Kite (GKB)

spread primaries held below the level of the wings, so this oft-repeated character should not be considered diagnostic. Further subtle differences in shape and outline (Porter *et al* 1981) need not be elaborated upon here.

Pernis apivorus · HONEY BUZZARD VAGRANT

Single birds have been recorded as follows: at Dhahran, 4 March 1976 (GKB); at Dhahran, 6 October 1978 (GB); over the Rub' al-Khali at Jawb, 23 March 1980 (GJR); at Dhahran, 27 October 1980 (GB, RH); at Qatif, 19 October 1981 (GB); at Dhahran, 13 March 1983 (GKB, JP).

Milvus migrans · BLACK KITE PM (WV)

Generally scarce. There are records for all months from January through June but most are seen from March through May. A group of eight birds was present and roosting in the Nariya area on 7, 17 and 24 March 1983 (JP, DR, LR). It tends to be rather rare and irregular at other times although one or two possibly winter in some years in the coastal areas between Dammam and Qatif. In the autumn it has been noted only twice in September but more regularly from late October through January, especially in the coastal localities mentioned above where perhaps the same individuals are involved. At Haradh presumed trans-desert migrants have been seen in July (JCD) and September but not in spring.

Haliaeetus leucoryphus VAGRANT
PALLAS'S FISH EAGLE

Two adults near Qatif, 2 November 1979 (RH).

Haliaeetus albicilla VAGRANT
WHITE-TAILED EAGLE

One between the mainland and Bahrain, 27 July 1950 (Ripley 1951). An adult near Qatif, 26 October 1978 (RJC).

Neophron percnopterus · EGYPTIAN VULTURE RB

Now has a very restricted distribution and recent records are mostly from desert *jabal* areas around the eastern edge of the Summan plateau from late January through July (GKB, RJC).

Vultures, very probably of this species, were commonly seen around Abqaiq rubbish tips until the early 1950s (JCM). A pair were seen at a nest on Jabal al-Arba', al-Hasa, on 1 March 1924 (Ticehurst & Cheesman 1925), and a pair were said to have bred on a *jabal* near Yabrin in 1979 (per RR). During the period February through August 1979 to 1982 individual adults or pairs were seen fairly regularly

Egyptian Vulture (GKB)

above the escarpment in the vicinity of Judah and 'Uray'irah and it is probable that one or more pairs nest in that general vicinity. On 13 March 1986, an occupied nest attended by a pair of adults was found on a deeply recessed cliff ledge near Nata'. It was a broad and flattened mass of dried twigs, copiously lined with animal skin and sheeps' wool, and contained two white eggs heavily smeared and capped with liver brown. That same day an immature was also seen in the area. The Nata' nest was again occupied by a breeding pair in 1987 and 1988; and a wider ranging survey during those years disclosed that the species was securely established, albeit in small numbers, and breeding successfully in *jabal* areas to the west of al-Wannan (RJC). The only recent record for the coastal zone is of a single sub-adult near Dammam on 12 January 1979 (DJBra).

Gyps fulvus · GRIFFON VULTURE VAGRANT

Two around camel carcasses between al-'Uqayr and Hofuf, 19 November 1923 (Ticehurst & Cheesman 1925). One about 20 km south of Dhahran, 17 October 1975 (GKB). An immature at al-Musannah in the north, 26 September 1979 (GJR). An immature at Haradh, 23 July 1980 (JCD). An immature near Nariya, 24 December 1980 (RH). An immature on the Dibdibah on 4 November 1983 (CVP, WHP, JP, LR).

Aegypius monachus · BLACK VULTURE VAGRANT

One, Dibdibah 18–19 December 1986 (MAE, CSH).

Circaetus gallicus · SHORT-TOED EAGLE PM

It has only been recorded since 1979, this no doubt reflecting the better observer coverage since the late 1970s. There are now 21 records, in all months of the year except July and August. A concentration of sightings in March (five), October (four) and November (four) suggests that most birds are merely passing through the area. Single records in the period December to February, however, indicate that perhaps a few winter here. Sightings, almost always of single birds, have been widely distributed, from the Dibdibah, Nariya, and Manifa in the north, to Haradh and Jawb, on the edge of the Rub' al-Khali.

Short-toed Eagle (GKB)

Circus aeruginosus · MARSH HARRIER WV PM

Small numbers are regular, especially in the coastal zone, from late August through May. It is especially conspicuous over the reedy channels and mangroves between Dammam and Tarut Bay during the winter. It also winters inland at suitable localities, especially Hofuf and Abqaiq; at the latter, a few have wintered each year from 1981 to 1984. Some onward passage is suggested by the regular occurrence of individuals in May, September and October at Haradh and the isolated Jawb camp on the edge of the Rub' al-Khali.

Circus cyaneus · HEN HARRIER (PM)

Possibly a scarce but regular migrant. A female was shot near Dhahran on 29 April 1946; the specimen is now in the Californian Academy of Sciences (J. Gasperetti per FEW). It has otherwise been recorded annually only since 1979, reflecting the better observer coverage during the late 1970s. The records, all referring to adult males, are as follows: one north of Salasil, 29 March 1979 (RJC); one flying west over the Gulf at 28°N 49°E, 21 October 1979 (DMS); one at Qatif, 1 February 1980 (GB); two at the Hofuf lakes area, 18 April 1980 (RJC); one at Jawb on 25 October, with two probable females there from 23 to 25 October 1980 (GJR); one at Haradh (12 March 1981 (GB).

Circus macrourus · PALLID HARRIER PM WV

There is a regular passage from late February to early May, and again (with immatures predominating) from September through November. It is especially conspicuous in autumn over the Haradh cultivation when up to 80 birds have been seen in September. From December through February nearly all the records refer to adult males, birds being regularly noted over the cultivated areas but also in semi-desert throughout the region. Males are generally outnumbered by ringtails during the spring passage.

Pallid Harrier (female) (GKB)

Circus pygargus · MONTAGU'S HARRIER PM

Migrants are regular in April, September and October, occurring throughout the region. Up to eight have been noted in a day at Haradh in September. Juveniles in autumn are almost certainly overlooked—unless seen well they are difficult to separate from Pallid Harrier.

Accipiter gentilis · GOSHAWK (WV)

This species is regular in a few well-vegetated coastal areas, notably around Qatif and Dhahran. Most records are from late October through February although it has been recorded also in March, April and September.

Accipiter nisus · SPARROWHAWK WV

A regular visitor in small numbers from October through April. Most birds have departed by late March, and individuals seen in late April and May at Haradh and Hanidh farms, areas where it does not normally overwinter, are perhaps passage migrants.

Accipiter brevipes VAGRANT
LEVANT SPARROWHAWK

One about 15 km west of Abqaiq, 10 April 1977 (GKB).

Buteo buteo · BUZZARD PM (WV)

In spite of the large numbers that pass between the central Palearctic and its winter quarters in southern and eastern Africa, it is generally very scarce in eastern Arabia. Individuals are fairly regular, especially in the coastal zone, during February and March while immatures are sometimes noted from April to early June. It has been recorded once each in July and August and more often from September through January. Although usually seen singly, there have been consistent small peaks of occurrences in February and November suggesting some passage movement at those times. Adults (which are rare) are of the race *vulpinus*; the immatures are most likely from the same central Palearctic region but they are indistinguishable from western immatures. For a discussion on buzzard identification and taxonomy as it affects the Eastern Province, see pp. 92–93.

Buteo rufinus · LONG-LEGGED BUZZARD MB WV

The breeding population is small in numbers and thinly distributed. It nests in eroded cavities and on recessed ledges on isolated *jabals* and rocky escarpments. One nest, in a remote desert area, was situated only about 1.5 metres above the surrounding desert on a low, rocky outcrop. Others have been found in very high and precipitous situations, but most nests are relatively easy of access and situated about 5–8 metres above the scree slope. The nest is usually very rudimentary, sometimes only a few dried twigs on the outer aspect of the ledge, with a shallow 'bowl' for the eggs, lined with whatever material is available, i.e. discarded rags, paper, plastic sheeting, rope, sheeps' wool and, characteristically, a few dried rooted tufts of very coarse grass. A breeding pair is loyal to the same territory, year after year, though any one of several nests within it may be used. One female, identified by a distinctive egg type, has bred annually for at least seven years. Eggs are laid from the beginning of February onwards, and most clutches are complete by the middle of that month, though some not until well into March. The usual clutch in the Eastern Province is 3, occasionally 4, eggs. When fresh they are a very pale bluish white, sparsely blotched with reddish brown. Some eggs show a few ashy shell markings. They are visibly smaller than eggs of *B. rufinus* from more northern parts. If some mishap befalls the first clutch before incubation is well advanced, a 'repeat' clutch will be laid in about 3 weeks. The frontal aspect of young just about to

Common Buzzard (GKB)

leave the nest is a rich orange-brown. Adult breeding birds are markedly variable when seen from below and not all exhibit the features of classical *B. rufinus*—they sometimes lack the whitish head and often the dark lower belly as well; the upperparts too are often less contrasting than text-book Long-legged—one bird seen was uniform chocolate-brown above though patterned normally below. Of eight breeding pairs located in arid desert between 25° and 27°N, two females were dark morph. One female viewed in flight from below was almost pure white with only vestiges of the usual dark carpal patches. One female in sub-adult plumage bred successfully. It is by no means clear what happens to our breeding birds after the post-breeding dispersal. By the early autumn the picture is complicated by the arrival of migrants that range over the desert and are almost regular in the coastal zone (RJC). In the south, at Haradh, it is most numerous from September through November when it will walk about the stubble fields in search of locusts.

Aquila pomarina VAGRANT
LESSER SPOTTED EAGLE

A sub-adult at Haradh, 21 November 1980 (GB, JP).

Aquila clanga · SPOTTED EAGLE WV

Present annually in coastal areas from September through March, mostly between Dammam and Safwa. There has been a small consistent rise in numbers during November, notably in the Qatif area, followed by an apparent decline in December, and it is thought that some birds may be passing migrants. Evidence for onward passage is slight but first-year birds have been noted at Jawb on the northern edge of the Rub' al-Khali in November (GJR) and at Haradh where an individual remained for about four weeks during the same month. Away from the usual coastal haunts, it has been noted once at Nariya in January and at Abqaiq in October, November and May. Immatures have also been seen at Qatif in May and June.

Identification: see p. 93.

Long-legged Buzzard (GKB)

Long-legged Buzzard (BS)
One of a pair that nested to the north-east of Salasil. This bird is more boldly marked than many occurring in the Eastern Province.

Below: *Long-legged Buzzard chicks (ALL)*
This nest was on virtually level ground at the top of a low cliff, and could easily be approached on foot. The two chicks disappeared prior to fledging, probably taken by a predator.

Spotted Eagle (GKB)

Aquila nipalensis · STEPPE EAGLE WV PM

This species has been noted passing south-west through Kuwait from September through November and it presumably crosses the northern half of our region in higher numbers than current records suggest. It winters commonly to the west, around Riyadh, al-Kharj and on the plains of the north-central Najd. In the Eastern Province it is regular in smaller numbers from late October through March on the northern plains from Nariya westwards to the Dibdibah and south to around Hanidh.

Once over 60 were seen in one steppe area 'in winter', evidently attracted to the carrion near Bedouin camps (RR); and in October 1984 there were 66 at Haradh feeding on rodents disturbed by ploughing operations (JHM, JP). Elsewhere it tends to be scarce and irregular. Wintering birds in the Eastern Province are almost invariably dark sub-adults. In April however, a small passage has been noted across the northern steppe areas which consisted of predominantly pale first-year birds. *Nipalensis* is considered by many authors to be specifically distinct from *A. rapax* (Tawny Eagle) on account of differences in size, structure, colour of iris and the age at which immature and adult plumages are reached (see Cramp & Simmons 1980). Birds seen in Saudi Arabia are of the sub-species *'orientalis'*. For identification notes, see p. 93.

Aquila heliaca · IMPERIAL EAGLE WV

A regular visitor to the northern half of the region, occurring chiefly north of Hanidh and on the steppe around Nariya from November through March and occasionally in early April. Up to 14 have been seen at a winter roost near Nariya with juveniles (first-winter birds) predominating. It is generally absent from the coastal zone but occasionally juveniles have been seen in the vicinity of Dammam and al-Khobar in September and November through February. Birds briefly visiting the more isolated southern localities of Haradh and, some 300 km further south, the Jawb camp between September and December have presumably been migrants.

Identification: see p. 93.

Imperial Eagle (GKB)

Booted Eagle (ALL)

Osprey (BS) *Female with 3 half-grown chicks on Samamik island.*

Aquila chrysaetos · GOLDEN EAGLE VAGRANT

An immature was found dead at Nariya in March 1974 (GKB), and two immatures were seen in the same area in January 1979 (RR). One bird was seen at Haradh on 4 December 1981 (GB); and an immature 25 km north of 'Uray'irah 16 January 1986 (RJC). An eagle's nest with two eggs was discovered in the Rub' al-Khali at 21°N 51°E in 1931 (Thomas 1932). The eggs, when examined at the British Museum (Natural History) by Kinnear, were thought to be those of *A. rapax*. Since the Golden Eagle has since been found nesting in Saudi Arabia and has recently been proved to breed sparingly in Oman, the eggs have been re-examined by R. J. Connor, but no conclusive identification can be made.

Hieraaetus pennatus · BOOTED EAGLE VAGRANT

Individuals have been noted 30 km north of Hofuf town on 22 March 1974 and near al-Khobar on 27 December 1974 (GKB). One was at Abqaiq on 4 May 1979 (GB) and one over the Dibdibah on 26 March 1982 (JHM, JP). One north of 'Uray'irah mid February 1987 (RJC, ALL).

Hieraaetus fasciatus · BONELLI'S EAGLE VAGRANT

A first-year bird at Dhahran from 2 to 9 January 1981 and what may have been a different individual at the same locality from 4 to 27 February 1981 (GB, RH, JHM, JP, DR). One captured in an exhausted condition 20 km south of Safaniya on 14 July 1984 (RJC).

Family PANDIONIDAE

Pandion haliaetus · OSPREY RB

Present throughout the year along the Gulf coast but generally scarce. In the Eastern Province of Saudi Arabia it has been found breeding on only two offshore islands—although most potential sites have been visited in recent years (RJC). At Samamik island a nest with birds in attendance was found on 4 December 1980. It was on the ground, a huge and well established pile of dried suaeda and driftwood nearly 2 metres across and 1 metre high, with a flattened top of dried and disintegrating seaweed. By 14 December the nest contained 3 eggs from which young fledged successfully. On the island there are also three other nests in varying states of decay, indicating that it is a traditional site. This island is only some 35 km from the nearest point of the Hawar islands (Bahrain) where up to 15 pairs regularly breed. An occupied nest with an apparently incomplete clutch of 1 egg was found on a ruined house on Jinnah island in mid-January 1982. This is also a traditional site (RJC). On the Hawar islands and elsewhere in Gulf waters egg laying starts in November. Young Ospreys acquire adult plumage during their second year and first breed when 3 to 5 years old (Cramp & Simmons 1980). The 'pairs' at Abu 'Ali—where it is almost invariably present—and other individuals seen along the coast are most likely to be immatures. There is a consistent increase in sightings from August through March which suggests some immigration. Birds sometimes visit waters close to the coast but are rare inland.

Family FALCONIDAE

The falcons are represented in the Eastern Province by nine species. The Kestrel definitely breeds; the Lanner bred until recently. There are three unconfirmed records of Red-footed Falcon (*Falco vespertinus*), a species that breeds in the central Palearctic and winters exclusively in southern Africa.

Most large falcons seen in the Eastern Province in winter are dark brown immatures and some are undoubtedly escapes from falconers. Immature SAKER and LANNER are alike and only identified with difficulty. Saker is the more likely visitor to the Province and tends to be larger and heavier than Lanner with broader-based wings. Look for the underwing if possible: Saker shows almost white flight-feathers that contrast with dark wing-coverts. In the immature Lanner the tail may look longer and more distinctly barred than Saker. Porter *et al* (1981) is an essential reference, but many large brown falcons will still remain unidentified.

The breeding population of Lanners in Arabia belongs to the pale grey and white race *tanypterus*. These birds may be confused with the so-called BARBARY FALCON (*F. pelegrinoides*), which, in the opinion of many ornithologists, is conspecific with the Peregrine. In flight, it reveals the typical PEREGRINE outline, broad-based, pointed wings and rather short, tapering, square-cut tail. Lanners have

Kestrel (GKB)

longer, more angled wings and invariably look longer in the tail. Barbary Falcons always look darker from below with buffish (not white) underparts and darker-looking tail. Immature Peregrines are sometimes encountered in the Eastern Province in the winter months and are dark brown above with heavy moustachial stripes contrasting with conspicuous white cheeks. Apart from the outline already described, they differ from immature Lanners and Sakers in having the undersides of the wings densely barred throughout.

Two other falcons that occur widely throughout the region on passage are KESTREL and LESSER KESTREL: the males are easily identified if seen well but the females cause problems, especially if unaccompanied. Lesser Kestrels are often encountered in small parties which include the bright little males, and these occasions provide a useful opportunity to gain experience of the females. Female Lesser Kestrels are slimmer than the better-known species, with a more wedge-shaped tail, generally paler underparts and underwing, and a more active flight. The brownish striations on the underparts are sometimes in a narrow zone across the breast while the underwing can look almost uniform white in some examples; the wing-coverts are only sparsely spotted. If an exceptionally close view can be obtained the colour of the claws might be looked for: Lesser Kestrel's are whitish or at least pale, while Kestrel's are black. The larger bird almost invariably shows a fairly bold moustachial stripe which is often very thin and inconspicuous in the Lesser Kestrel.

Falco naumanni · LESSER KESTREL PM

Usually a rather scarce migrant but small flocks are regular in spring. It occurs from mid-February to early May throughout the region. In autumn it seems mainly to have been noted in October: twice in the coastal zone but frequently at Haradh where up to 15 have been seen in the cultivated areas. By far the largest number seen on migration was on 6 April 1983, when a minimum of 300, and perhaps as many as 600, were encountered in the desert near, and to the north of, Abqaiq (JAH, TSH, CVP). An immature male was present at Dhahran during July and August 1984.

Identification: see above.

Falco tinnunculus · KESTREL WV RB

A very thinly distributed resident. In March 1979 a pair frequented a small cave in a cliff face at Jabal Shadgam, north of 'Uray'irah, but the site was not examined (RJC). A pair with four recently fledged young frequented the Aramco compound at Dhahran in June 1984, and had probably bred there (NB, RJC). A pair bred near Judah in 1986 (JP). In the Eastern Province holes in rock faces are the most likely nesting sites. No nest is made, the eggs merely being deposited on loose debris within the hole. Three or four may be expected. They are white, virtually covered with blotches and spots of deep reddish brown.

A winter influx is apparent throughout the region from late September through March with birds occasionally seen near the coast in August (once), April and May. Numbers are consistently higher in October, November, February and March, suggesting passage. This is particularly obvious at isolated Haradh where large numbers of birds are seen

Hobby (GKB)

during the autumn months exploiting the abundance of locusts in the cultivated areas. At Jawb, 300 km south of Haradh, females have been noted as early as 21 July and in October (GJR), presumably trans-desert migrants.

Identification: see opposite page.

Falco columbarius · MERLIN VAGRANT

One was obtained near Hofuf in 1924 and assigned to the race *pallidus*, a form breeding in south-western Siberia and wintering south to Iraq. This example was said to have been obtained on 1 February but the label on the skin, preserved in the British Museum (Natural History), states that it was collected on 2 January (FEW). Further birds were seen at Zarnuqa on 11 February and near Yabrin on 21 February 1924 (Ticehurst & Cheesman 1925). There was an adult male at Haradh on 6 February 1981 (GB, RH), a male over the Dibdibah on 25 March 1982 (JHM, JP) and an adult male near Qatif on 17 February 1983 (GKB).

Falco subbuteo · HOBBY PM

Generally a scarce migrant but noted annually in April and May. It has been noted twice in June and a one-year-old immature remained at Dhahran for several weeks in July 1982. A few occur in most years from September through November. Although wintering birds are exceptional in the western Palearctic (Cramp & Simmons 1980), a bird was apparently seen as well at Ras Tanura on 19 January 1979 (DJBra).

Falco concolor · SOOTY FALCON VAGRANT

An adult at Abqaiq, some 40 km from the Gulf coast, 16 July 1977 (GKB). An adult flying east at Jawb camp in the northern Rub' al-Khali, 22 July 1980 (GJR). One at Abqaiq on 13 August 1982 (JHM, JP) and another on 29 April 1983 (JP, DR, LR). This species breeds on the Hawar islands and may be expected in Saudi coastal waters.

Falco biarmicus · LANNER FB?

As a breeding species it seems to be extinct in the Eastern Province; the eastern half of Saudi Arabia has probably only ever possessed a fringe population. A pair were located breeding on a *jabal* south-west of Abqaiq in 1977; they were photographed and thought to belong to the race *tanypterus* (GKB, PJI, DMH). Saudi falconers have informed RJC and PJI that birds bred on the *jabal* from 1978 to 1980 and that chicks were removed in 1978 and 1980. This pair apparently had an alternative site in the same general area. As a winter visitor its status is equally obscure since large falcons in the coastal zone have seldom been specifically identified, for brown immature Lanners resemble Sakers. Some birds have certainly been falconers' escapes. One at Manifa in July 1983 was chasing Lesser Short-toed Larks (AD).

Identification: see p. 103.

Falco cherrug · SAKER (WV)

Probably an almost regular, although scarce, winter visitor to coastal areas between October and March. One remained at Haradh farm from mid-July to 8 August 1980 (GB, JCD, RH). One was seen at al-Khobar on 1 May 1984 (GKB) and a juvenile at Dhahran 27–29 August 1984 (GKB, JAH, TSH). Most large falcons (except Peregrines) seen in winter are immatures, and some are undoubtedly escaped or liberated falconers' birds.

Identification: see p. 103.

Falco peregrinus · PEREGRINE WV

Regular but solitary and scarce, occurring chiefly from October through March. It is less regularly encountered in April and May although it has been seen in late May at Harqus island where there is a large breeding population of terns (RJC). It has mostly been seen in the coastal zone but also occasionally near Hofuf and the Abqaiq lagoons where there are concentrations of wintering ducks and waders. Wintering birds are thought likely to be *F. p. calidus*, a large pale race from the Eurasian tundra.

Identification: see p. 104.

Falco pelegrinoides · BARBARY FALCON VAGRANT

This species breeds along the Tuwayq escarpment near Riyadh but past reports of its being resident in the Eastern Province are very probably due to confusion with and misidentification of the pale race of Lanner (*F. p. tanypterus*). The only recent records are of single birds near Dammam from 1 to 5 May 1974 and at Abqaiq on 14 May 1977 (GKB).

Identification: see p. 103.

Family PHASIANIDAE

Francolinus francolinus · BLACK FRANCOLIN FB?

Possibly a rare and elusive resident in the al-Hasa oases although it is more likely to be extinct there now. A male was seen there 6 January 1924 (Ticehurst & Cheesman 1925), a female on 20 November 1977 (GKB); and a female, possibly of this species, was seen 20 October 1978 (AB).

Lanner (GKB) Photographed at a traditional site, no longer occupied, south-west of Abqaiq. This species is not now known to nest in the Eastern Province.

Coturnix coturnix · QUAIL MB PM

Breeds at Haradh in the extensive areas of irrigated crops, arriving there in February. In 1981 it was estimated that there were three pairs for each pivot (areas of regularly watered alfalfa and rhodes grass), with a minimum of 60 pairs. The first chicks were seen on 19 April (JCD) suggesting a laying date in late March. Nests on the ground, usually in thick grass or growing crops. The nest is a scrape or natural depression lined with whatever dried vegetation is available. Eggs number 8–13 or more; they are creamy yellow, spotted and usually heavily blotched with chocolate brown. Elsewhere it is a scarce migrant, mainly from August through November. One at Abqaiq in sparse desert vegetation in early January was presumably an early migrant. At Dhahran 2–3 were continually present, and sometimes calling, from June to October 1984 (JAH, TSH).

Family RALLIDAE

There are seven species of which three breed locally in the Eastern Province. The three Porzana crakes and the Corncrake are trans-desert migrants, the western Palearctic populations all wintering south of the Sahara. The two smallest species, Little and Baillon's Crakes, are superficially alike and need to be seen well; the identification problems are, however, well covered in field guides and the *Handbook of the Birds of Europe, the Middle East and North Africa* (Cramp & Simmons 1980). Attention should be paid if possible to the leg colour, barring on the flanks, and to the extension of the folded primaries beyond the tertials.

Rallus aquaticus · WATER RAIL RB (WV?)

Breeds in a few suitable localities, notably in the reed beds north of Hofuf and around al-Qarn. It also breeds at Abqaiq (at one lagoon since 1976). The

Spotted Crake (GKB)

Little Crake (ALL)

nest is a well defined cup of dried leaves and plant stems, usually well concealed in a tangled mass of rushes or reeds growing in shallow water. 6–11 eggs are laid, blunt oval in shape, creamy white or stone coloured with a few blotches and spots of reddish brown. It is present throughout the year in the breeding localities but it has been noted elsewhere in June, July, and October through April, suggesting the possibility of some immigration of winter visitors.

Porzana porzana · SPOTTED CRAKE PM (WV?)

A scarce but regular migrant; like other crakes it is almost certainly overlooked on account of its skulking behaviour. It has been noted especially at lakesides and marshy surrounds near Hofuf and Abqaiq but also at Haradh in irrigated crops of alfalfa. It occurs from March through May, mostly in March. In autumn it has been recorded from September through December but chiefly in October and November. A few overwinter, though possibly not every year: one remained at Imhoff from December through February 1981–2; two were at al-'Uyun on 25 December 1982 (GKB), and one was still there on 25 February 1983 (GKB, JP, DR, LR).

Porzana parva · LITTLE CRAKE PM

A scarce but annually recorded migrant with small numbers in marshy places and tangled vegetation near pools, from February through April and in September and October. Up to three at both Abqaiq and al-'Uyun through December 1982 (GKB, JP, LR) suggests that some may overwinter. It has been seen most commonly during the autumn period at Haradh where surprisingly high numbers have been located in irrigated grassy crops (JCD).

Porzana pusilla · BAILLON'S CRAKE PM

Although on present evidence it is scarcer than the last species it is almost certainly overlooked. Has been recorded in March and from August through October.

Crex crex · CORNCRAKE PM

In spring it is scarce and possibly overlooked; like other crakes it keeps itself hidden in dense ground cover. It has been noted in April at Dhahran; north of Nariya (RR), and at Haradh. In September there have been scattered records of single birds at Abqaiq, Dhahran, al-Musannah and at Jawb in the northern Rub' al-Khali (GJR). In the grass crops at Haradh during September and October it is sometimes quite numerous with possibly several hundred present (JCD).

Gallinula chloropus · MOORHEN RB

It breeds commonly wherever suitable habitat exists, and must have spread during the last 30 years where man's activities have created pools and run-offs of open water. The nest is usually placed in a reed bed, or amongst rushes, etc, growing in shallow water, but quite frequently is amongst the branches of a tree that has fallen into the water. It is built of whatever materials are available locally, usually slender twigs, rushes and leaves and stems of phragmites. In Saudi Arabia eggs are laid from March onwards. Clutches of 5–13 eggs have been recorded. They are blunt oval in shape, larger than those of the Water Rail which may nest in similar situations, and likewise spotted and blotched with reddish brown on a light stone coloured ground. Away from the breeding places it is rare, but presumed migrants have occurred at Haradh in irrigated crops during September and October (JCD). These records and one at Jawb, 300 km further south on the fringe of the Empty Quarter, in mid-September suggest that some individuals disperse widely and may even attempt a desert crossing.

Moorhen (ALL)

Fulica atra · COOT **RB WV**

A few pairs breed at Hofuf, numbers there having been drastically reduced since 1980 due to drainage and development. It breeds in largest numbers at Abqaiq, where, on the most favoured lagoon, at least 25 pairs are resident. The foundations of the nest are placed on the bottom in shallow water amongst reeds or other emergent vegetation, often in a more open situation than would be chosen by the Moorhen. Above water level, it is a bulky structure, built of live and dead plant stems encompassing a deep 'bowl' which is usually lined with finer material. The eggs number between 6 and 10. They are oval in shape, smooth and slightly glossy, evenly speckled with dark brown or black on a stone coloured ground. It is also a winter visitor, flocks of varying size occurring in the first two localities named from August through March with the main arrival in November. Odd stragglers (or migrants?) have even been recorded in September at Haradh (JCD) and at a desert camp south of Salwah (RR).

Coot (ALL)

Family GRUIDAE

Grus grus · CRANE **VAGRANT**

About 30 cranes, probably this species, flew over Haradh in September 1979 and there was a single adult there on 14 November 1979 (JCD). Also an adult at Haradh on 21 February 1980 (GB).

Anthropoides virgo **VAGRANT**
DEMOISELLE CRANE

A single bird was seen in a small pool at al-Hafiah near Yabrin on 6 March 1986 (JP).

Family OTIDIDAE

Chlamydotis undulata **MB? (WV)**
HOUBARA BUSTARD

In favourable years still breeds in small numbers on the eastern fringe of the Dahna (per JB). The nest is merely a slight depression, scratched in the ground by the female, and usually sheltered by a small shrub. 2 or 3 eggs are laid. They are a blunted oval in shape, usually a glossy, pale olive brown with lilac or ashy coloured shell markings overlaid with elongated blotches and spots of rich dark brown. Three eggs given to Major Cheesman in 1924 were said to have been taken between Hofuf and Riyadh (Ticehurst & Cheesman 1925). Its present status, even as a winter visitor, is uncertain although falconers as recently as the 1960s are said to have taken up to 20 in a week. Literary references to large numbers occurring in Bahrain and the Eastern Province seem to be a feature of the past rather than the present: Meinertzhagen (1954) recorded up to 70 being killed in a single day in Bahrain on 'autumn passage'. Elsewhere in Arabia it is still hunted with falcons during the winter months. Up to 700 are said to have been taken in 1979–80 in the north of Najd Province. In spite of increased observer coverage during the 1970s, recent records for this species in the Eastern Province are very few although some desert-dwelling Arabs declare that it still occurs sparingly from November through March (per PJI). Recent records are of one flying over the sea towards the Saudi coast at 26°N 50°E on 31 October 1976 (PWGC), one at Haradh for a week in early February 1980 (JCD), one near Abqaiq in December 1980 (RR), and one by the shore south of al-Khobar on 27 December 1983 (JP).

Black-winged Stilt folding its long legs as it settles to incubate its clutch of eggs. (GKB)

Family HAEMATOPODIDAE

Haematopus ostralegus · OYSTERCATCHER WV

This species tends to be rather local along the littoral, usually in small numbers though up to 40 together can occasionally be found. It is present chiefly from September through April but small numbers of white-collared immatures remain annually from May to August.

Family RECURVIROSTRIDAE

Himantopus himantopus RB PM?
BLACK-WINGED STILT

As a breeding species it is an opportunist, nesting locally when ecological conditions become suitable. It formerly bred at the extensive Dammam marsh (GKB, KJF) but that area was reclaimed in 1978. When the area was partially re-flooded in 1980 at least one pair bred and although a pair was present again in 1981 breeding was not confirmed.

At Abqaiq it has bred or attempted to breed in most years (probably annually) since 1975. In that year a young bird unable to fly was seen; in 1976 seven nests were found and about 20 young reached the flying stage; in 1977 4–5 pairs bred successfully (GKB). In 1981 a pair were present, though breeding was not established; in 1982 at least 6 pairs nested, and a few young reached the flying stage; in 1983 perhaps as many as 15 pairs bred, and in 1984 there was a total of about 30 pairs at two separate sets of lagoons (GB, GKB, JP). During the years 1985 to 1988 the number of breeding pairs fluctuated annually, but it now seems to be firmly established in this area (RJC).

Up to two pairs frequented a small pond on Dhahran airport before the site was filled in late 1979. On 18 April 1980 nine nests with eggs in various stages of incubation were found on islands of silt in a large shallow inundated area north of Hofuf (RJC) but this locality too was doomed to drainage within months of this discovery. A pair bred on a sewerage effluent pond in the Aramco

Above: *Black-winged Stilt's nest and eggs, Abqaiq. (GKB)*

compound at Dhahran in 1981 (RJC). In the spring of 1986, it was well represented as a breeding species on a large expanse of flooded desert to the west of the Dammam Second Industrial City on the Dhahran/Abqaiq Road, and over 50 nests containing eggs or newly hatched young were found. Nest counts were not made in 1987 or 1988 but there seemed to be no reduction in the number of breeding pairs (RJC). The nest is usually a scrape in drying mud, lined with small pieces of dried plant stalk; but occasionally, as at the Abqaiq ponds, eggs are laid on a flattened tussock in shallow water. Eggs are usually four in number, pointed oval or pyriform in shape, and pale olive buff in colour, showing some shell markings of lilac overlaid with dark liver brown blotches and streaks. Wintering flocks occur at the pools in the areas mentioned above and not uncommonly elsewhere if conditions are suitable. In March especially, the numbers in flocks at Dammam marsh lagoon, where the species wintered, rose to around 100 and suggest that some birds might be on passage.

Recurvirostra avosetta · AVOCET WV CB

Two pairs attempted to breed at Abqaiq in 1976 (GKB, DMH, PJI) and again in 1982, and three pairs probably attempted to breed there in 1983 (JP, LR). In 1984 one pair successfully hatched three young; halfway through the fledgling period, the adults disappeared (doubtless shot), and the chicks fended for themselves from then on; at least one reached the flying stage (GKB). The nest is a scrape in drying mud, lined with pieces of plant stalk and other vegetable debris. The eggs are usually 4 in number, pointed oval in shape, and slightly larger than those of the Black-winged Stilt which often nests in the same area; sparsely blotched and spotted with dark liver brown on a pale, stone coloured ground. It is generally a rather scarce visitor from August through March, occasionally in small flocks, but nowhere is it very regular or predictable in its appearances. Its presence, like its breeding attempts, is almost certainly linked to the varying water levels at certain localities. Odd records away from Abqaiq in April, May and June, mostly in the coastal zone, are presumably of non-breeding immatures.

Left: *Black-winged Stilt (GKB)*
A chick poses for the photographer.

Family DROMADIDAE

Dromas ardeola · CRAB PLOVER PM

This conspicuous coastal wader has been observed in largest numbers at Abu 'Ali, where up to about 150 have been recorded from late July through December. Flocks of up to about 60 have also been noted in August and September near Safwa, and occasionally single birds have been seen in May and June elsewhere, notably al-Khobar, and also between Tarut Bay and Dammam. In early August food-soliciting juveniles have been seen with adults at Abu 'Ali but there is no evidence that the species breeds in the Eastern Province.

Top: *Stone Curlew (GKB)*
Right: *Cream-coloured Courser (GKB)*

Collared Pratincole (GKB)

Family BURHINIDAE

Burhinus oedicnemus · STONE CURLEW (PM)

A scarce migrant although probably annual, especially at Haradh; it has occurred in widely scattered localities throughout the region. Most records have been in March and October but it has been noted from February to early May, once in July (GKB), and from September through November (JCD, GJR). Up to seven have been seen together but birds found are usually single, tame and tired.

Family GLAREOLIDAE

Represented by three species, one of which breeds sparingly. On Bahrain a fourth species, the Little Pratincole (*Glareola lactea*) of India and south-east Asia, has occurred as a vagrant in April and December (Bundy & Warr 1980). The two larger pratincoles form a superspecies only recently separated by taxonomists. Caution should be exercised when making identifications since field guides typically refer only to the different colour of the underwing-coverts. The reddish colour of the underwing area in Collared Pratincole often looks black when seen against the light. In ideal light, Collared Pratincole can be distinguished by its more contrasting upper surface to the wing and the pale line along the rear edge of the secondaries; Black-winged Pratincole typically looks almost uniform sooty-brown above. On two occasions, however, the writer has seen examples that can only be described as intermediates—birds with shared characters and possibly hybrids from a region where these two forms both breed.

Cursorius cursor MB
CREAM-COLOURED COURSER

Breeds on the northern plains and on the Dibdibah —north of about 27°N, and very locally north-east of 'Uray'irah and in the vicinity of 'Ain Dar and 'Udhailiyah (GKB, RJC). It shows a preference for lightly vegetated gravel or stony desert. Nesting takes place from February onwards. The eggs, invariably two in number, are laid in a slight scrape. Their ground colour is pale to warm buff, but this is virtually covered with interlacing scrawls and fine speckings of very dark brown. During the months of January and February a northerly movement of small flocks takes place across a broad front (RJC). In the post-breeding season it ranges widely, with juveniles often accompanying adults in small flocks.

Glareola pratincola · COLLARED PRATINCOLE PM

A regular migrant, usually in small numbers, from late March through May and in August and September. During the remaining summer months and in October it tends to be scarce and irregular. It is most frequently met with around pools and especially the dried-up margins of shallow lagoons. Migrant flocks hawk insects over the cultivation at Haradh in spring and autumn.

Identification: see opposite page.

Glareola nordmanni (PM)
BLACK-WINGED PRATINCOLE

Single birds have been recorded as follows: al-'Arabiyah island, 23 April 1921 (Ticehurst 1925); Dhahran airport pond, 25 August to 1 September 1978 (GB); Dammam lagoons, 27 May 1980 (GB, RH, JHM); Abqaiq, 23 April 1981 (JHM, DR); Abqaiq, 23 and 30 April 1982 (GKB). Also, there were three on the Dibdibah on 13 April 1983 (JAH, TSH, CVP, WHP) and a flock of 14 (with two Collared Pratincoles) at Abqaiq on 20 April 1984 (GKB, CVP).

Identification: see opposite page.

Family CHARADRIIDAE

The plovers are represented here by 14 species, only one of which breeds in the region; eight, possibly ten, are passage migrants, and 11 are present in winter more or less regularly.

Observers usually experience some difficulty in identifying the two sand plovers, Greater and Lesser, since these two species and Caspian Plover are inadequately dealt with in field guides. Both GREATER and LESSER SAND PLOVERS in winter plumage look rather like large, sluggish KENTISH PLOVERS, but Kentish usually shows a neat, well-defined white hind-collar, lacking in the two larger species. As its name implies the Greater Sand Plover is larger than Lesser but unfortunately there is some variation, especially with Lesser, and unless they are seen together size is not always sufficient for reliable identification. Greater is normally longer in the leg, relatively longer-necked, and the head always looks larger with a flatter crown, more angled forehead and a larger bill. The bill and head shape are probably the best characters when the birds are in winter or juvenile plumage. Lesser Sand Plovers often adopt a hunched, neckless posture, rather like Ringed Plovers; they have a more rounded head, usually a smaller, often tapering, bill and a gentler expression.

Immature CASPIAN PLOVER is superficially like the two sand plovers but, though about the size of Greater Sand Plover, it is easily identified by shape alone. On the ground Caspian may recall Golden or Lesser Golden Plover: it usually looks longer-necked than either of the sand plovers, with a small

Little Ringed Plover (GKB)

Kentish Plover: nest and eggs (GKB)
Frequently the eggs are virtually buried, point down, amongst an accumulation of mud flakes or tiny stone chips.

rounded head and a short, rather slender bill and long legs. Autumn birds have a white-faced appearance and show a quite striking white superciliary stripe which recalls a Dotterel. Another useful character is the fairly broad, dun-brown gorget which is much more obvious than in the two sand plovers. In flight it may cause trouble for the unwary observer as its general appearance may strongly suggest one of the golden plovers: it hardly shows a wing-bar, very little white in the tail and, especially in autumn juveniles, an almost spangled pattern on the upperparts. The underwing, usually described in the literature as white, often looks pale grey in the field and sometimes as dark as the underwing of Lesser Golden Plover. The underwing colour would also appear to be a dubious way of separating Caspian Plover from the very similar Oriental Plover (*Charadrius veredus*) of east-central Asia with which it may in fact be conspecific.

Charadrius dubius PM (WV)
LITTLE RINGED PLOVER

A regular migrant in small numbers from January through to early May. It is scarce and irregular from May through July and most numerous, although seldom more than ten together, in August and September with a few sometimes recorded until November and exceptionally December. It occurs on pools and lagoons away from the littoral.

Charadrius hiaticula · RINGED PLOVER WV

A common winter visitor along the coast from August through May, and scarce, but annually present, in June and July. Higher numbers at some inland localities in May and from August through November indicate that a proportion of birds are on passage. There are also a few inland records, notably at Abqaiq, in December and January.

Charadrius alexandrinus · KENTISH PLOVER RB

Occurs commonly along the coast and at inland pools and on the fringe of some of the better-vegetated *sabkha* areas. Breeding begins in early April. The nest consists of nothing more than a small, relatively deep scrape in dried mud or gravelly soil, sometimes lined with a few dried bents. Frequently the eggs are partly buried, point down, amongst flakes of dried mud or very small chips of stone. Usually three eggs are laid; they are pale stone coloured and profusely marked with large spots or scrawlings of blackish brown. Some inland sites are deserted after the breeding season, more especially from late November through February when birds are numerous along the littoral. However, 130 were seen on flooded *sabkha* at as-Sarrar on 9 December 1982, and over a hundred were at al-'Uyun pools on 28 October 1983 (RJC). Odd birds have occurred at isolated Haradh in February, April, May and October, though none are known to breed within 170 km.

Identification: see p. 115.

Charadrius mongolus WV PM
LESSER SAND PLOVER

Abundant along the coast from August through May, with smaller numbers of non-breeding immatures remaining during June and July. It is very rare away from the littoral. Larger numbers on passage

Kentish Plover (male above, female below) (ALL) *Note the small chip of stone in the male's bill. When relieving an incubating mate the off duty bird will frequently approach the nest with a stone in its bill.*

Greater Sand Plover (GKB) This bird has a relatively short bill, typical of the race columbinus.

from late July to September, and more especially in March and April, show the characters of the south Tibetan race *atrifrons*.

Identification: see p. 115.

Charadrius leschenaultii WV PM

GREATER SAND PLOVER

Less numerous than Lesser Sand Plover, wintering birds favour muddy shores where there is an abundance of small crabs. There is a regular arrival of juveniles in late June and July, birds presumably straight from breeding grounds in southern Asia; they are common until late September both on the coast and at inland sites. From October it is usually scarce away from favoured coastal stretches. Inland sightings have been most regular at Abqaiq, where it has been recorded February to May, July to August and in December. Up to 76 have been noted on flooded *sabkha* near as-Sarrar in December (JP, DR). Elsewhere, inland sightings become almost regular again in April and May, suggesting that birds are on passage.

It should be noted that two forms of *leschenaultii*, tentatively ascribed to the races '*columbinus*' and '*crassirostris*', pass through the Eastern Province. Of the two, the bill of *columbinus* is significantly shorter; and may be shorter than the longest billed examples of *C. mongolus*. This has given rise to much confusion in the past. An aid to identification in the field is the leg colour of these two very similar species, *crassirostris* and *columbinus* being greenish and *mongolus* so dark as to appear black.

Identification: see p. 115.

Charadrius asiaticus · CASPIAN PLOVER PM

A regular migrant, usually in small numbers, during March and April and again from late July until early September. The peak passage of adults is during March and again, after moult, in August when juveniles are also seen frequently. In late

Greater Sand Plover (GKB) *The bill of this bird, significantly longer than that of the bird opposite, is typical of the race* crassirostris.

March 1982, flocks totalling about 500 were seen on the northern steppes (JHM, JP).

It occurs away from the coast but often near inland water. This is a central Palearctic species which deserts the steppes in winter and travels to eastern and southern Africa; its reported wintering in Arabia (Meinertzhagen 1954, Raby 1981) requires confirmation.

Identification: see p. 115.

Charadrius morinellus · DOTTEREL WV

Until 1982, this species was considered to be a rare and irregular migrant, with a total of only six records in March, April and November. In November and December 1982, however, large numbers were observed on the Dibdibah, with maximum counts of 140 on 10 December (GKB, JP, DR) and 107 on 24 December (GKB); none were found there on 21 January 1983 (JP), but there was a great deal of human disturbance and they may have been overlooked. Again in 1983 it was found in large numbers on the Dibdibah, with 218+ on 25 November (JP), 300+ on 8–9 December (JAH, TSH, CVP), and 132 and 136 on 22 and 23 December respectively (JP); only 5 on 23 February 1984, however, 14 the following day (JP), and 18 on 16 March 1984 (CVP). Up to 1,000 wintered on the Dibdibah 1986/87. More observations are clearly needed to clarify the movements of these wintering flocks. Eleven were seen on recently cleared and levelled land in the Aramco compound at Dhahran on 18 November 1988 and five still remained on the 19th (JAH, TSH).

Pluvialis dominica · LESSER GOLDEN PLOVER (WV)

It was regularly observed only at the former Dammam marsh lagoons: at least four wintered there in 1980–81, and adults in summer plumage have been seen in May and June; maximum numbers (of up to 30) were in April, September and October. The majority of records away from Dammam have been in the coastal zone, of presumed migrants in March–April and September–October. It has been recorded inland at Abqaiq in September. There are very few recent records.

Pluvialis apricaria · GOLDEN PLOVER VAGRANT

At Dhahran airport, up to three birds said to be this species were present from November through February 1973–4 (KJF, JAW). One in partial summer plumage, at al-Khobar on 29 April 1978 (GB), and one at Qatif, 17 November 1981 (GB).

Pluvialis squatarola · GREY PLOVER WV PM

A common winter visitor along the coast from August through May with smaller numbers of immatures remaining in June and July. Away from the littoral it is usually scarce and irregular but individuals are occasionally noted at inundated areas near Hofuf and at Haradh and it has been known to winter at Abqaiq. Most inland appearances are in April–May and August–September which suggests some overland passage. In coastal areas too, numbers of fine summer-plumaged birds are at their peak during May, again suggesting that most may be migrants from further south.

Hoplopterus spinosus VAGRANT
SPUR-WINGED PLOVER

Single birds have been seen at Haradh on 24 October 1986 (MAE, TSH, JAH) and at Dhahran on 22 November 1986 (TSH, JAH, JP).

Hoplopterus indicus (PM) (WV)
RED-WATTLED PLOVER

This bird will probably prove to be a rare and irregular migrant, though there are only about 12 records so far. All are of single birds, mainly in the period October to December (especially November), but also in January, April and July. It has been observed at Nariya in the north, twice at Haradh in the south, 4 times at Abqaiq, and 3 times in the Dhahran area.

Chettusia gregaria · SOCIABLE PLOVER VAGRANT

An adult at Haradh farm on 25 February 1982 (GB).

Chettusia leucura PM (WV)
WHITE-TAILED PLOVER

Chiefly a migrant, with individuals and sometimes small parties occurring from late February through May and from August through November. It has occurred also in June and in late July. Six wintered near Dammam in 1979–80, remaining in the same locality (since drained) from November through February.

Vanellus vanellus · LAPWING (WV)

A scarce and somewhat irregular visitor with records from November to early April but chiefly from November through January. In 1970–71 up to 15 wintered at Dhahran (LJ), but this has proved to be exceptional.

Family SCOLOPACIDAE

This large family has been divided into six subfamilies by Voous (1977): Calidridinae, Gallinaginae, Scolopacinae, Tringinae, Arenariinae and Phalaropodinae. 31 species have been recorded in the Eastern Province: there are no breeding species and eight are currently considered vagrants. There are also unconfirmed records for Knot (*Calidris canatus*) (Eddy 1962) and Slender-billed Curlew (*Numenius tenuirostris*).

Of all the bird visitors to the Province, waders are probably the most conspicuous as well as the most numerous; large concentrations crowd along stretches of the coast and at some inland sites. Although generally thought of as winter visitors, the shores are by no means deserted during the hot and humid summer months; large numbers of non-breeding, mainly one-year-old birds remain on the littoral and on nearby pools. Many full-plumaged, Arctic-breeding waders, notably Sanderling, Curlew Sandpiper and Turnstone, arrive in good numbers in April and depart only in late May and early June. In late July and August some Arctic breeders return in summer plumage and most species are represented by adults, the bulk of juveniles apparently travelling further west as they predominate in western Europe at this period. The available field guides and other sources give adequate attention to identification problems for this family. Most species can easily be identified by voice alone, a technique perhaps best learned in the field

Grey Plover (GKB)

rather than by reading, although records and tapes can be useful.

As with all identification problems, the better one knows the commoner species the easier will be the recognition of similar, but rarer visitors. This familiarity is only acquired by regular field observation of birds in all plumages. The familiar Common Snipe, for example, is a common migrant and well-known to European observers. All snipe when flushed rise quickly from marshy grass and seldom is there time to focus binoculars on small plumage characters—it is necessary therefore to know what points to look for during a hurried view.

The Common Snipe usually, but not invariably, flies away with a twisting, erratic flight, rising all the time and often flying a considerable distance before pitching. On rising it utters a harsh, rasping 'sschaaap' note, often drawn out, with a sometimes poorly defined second syllable which rises in pitch. It shows quite noticeable buff lines down the sides of the back, a white border to the dark hind-wing which can often be seen at a distance, and a pale underwing. A snipe of similar proportions rising suddenly in front of the observer and uttering an obviously shorter, more clipped, higher-pitched 'chenk' or 'chet' note would at once attract attention and justify close examination. The Pintail Snipe lacks the white border to the secondaries, and the buff lines down the dark back are obscure and hard to see. It looks a darker bird and this impression is heightened, when it circles overhead looking for another landing place, by its dark underwing. It flies with less zigzagging than the common western species, having a more direct flight with regular, steady wing-beats and perhaps less of the jerky action of Common Snipe. There are some differences in the average sizes of the two sexes and some individuals can look bulkier than others; size is seldom a good field character unless birds can be compared side by side. Bulkier snipe might be Great Snipe or, although unknown so far in Arabia, another Siberian species, Swinhoe's Snipe (*Gallinago megala*). The latter is not well-known anywhere; it breeds to the east of 90°E and winters in southern Asia and Australia. It is said to be heavier and darker than Common Snipe with a more direct flight, and differs from the Pintail Snipe in having, like the Common Snipe, bold straw-coloured lines along the sides of the dark back; it differs from both in having more mottled pale barring on the coverts of the inner wing and in being rather more heavily barred on the underbody (thus, like Great Snipe, lacking an obvious pale belly). It is said to prefer drier habitats and have a different call from Pintail; see Madge (1980). The GREAT SNIPE is a plump, Woodcock-like bird in outline; its underparts are barred throughout and it usually makes only a short escape-flight on bowed wings. The upperwing of Great Snipe is boldly patterned: the greater coverts are almost black and are bordered by white tips which give a similar effect to that of a Mallard's speculum. Adult Great Snipes show white borders to the tail although this is less obvious in first-autumn birds which also tend to possess a less well-defined upperwing pattern.

Calidris tenuirostris · GREAT KNOT VAGRANT

Two immatures on the shore south of al-Khobar from 28 to 30 May 1984 (GKB, JP, CVP, WHP, JAH, TSH), with one still present on 9 June (GKB, JP, DJBro).

Above:
Little Stint (ALL)

Left:
Curlew Sandpiper (GKB)

Dunlin (GKB)

Calidris alba · SANDERLING WV PM

Small numbers winter along the littoral where it is present from August through May, and a few remain very locally on the coast during June and July. A very marked passage is conspicuous from late April to about mid-June. During this spring passage, birds appear at many inland sites as well as at pools near the coast.

Calidris minuta · LITTLE STINT WV PM

Abundant throughout the region in suitable areas, chiefly from August through May but with a few remaining in June and July in most years. Higher numbers occurring during August through November, especially at some inland localities, suggest that many are passage migrants. In May, adults in breeding plumage appear on pools upon which they do not winter, again suggesting that birds are on passage. Small flocks are quite regular at Haradh in April, May, September and October. A record of one bird at Jawb, some 300 km south of Haradh, in September (GJR) is also suggestive that onward passage is regular; presumably the desert is crossed in one long, unbroken flight. Some adults in May, but especially in late July and August, before summer plumage has begun to fade, are very red about the head and neck. These examples are very like the Red-necked Stint (*C. ruficollis*), with a reddish supercilium and sometimes white around the base of the bill. It may even be that these two species are actually conspecific, showing a cline of redness from west to east across Siberia.

Calidris temminckii · TEMMINCK'S STINT PM WV

A regular migrant in small numbers, almost always away from the coast. It occurs in April and May and again from September through November. At Abqaiq lagoons, and possibly elsewhere, there are records for every month, and up to 7 have remained there each winter since 1981.

Calidris subminuta · LONG-TOED STINT VAGRANT

One at Abqaiq lagoons, 28 August to 4 September 1977 (GKB).

Ruff (GKB)

Common Snipe (GKB)

Calidris melanotos VAGRANT
PECTORAL SANDPIPER

One at Abqaiq lagoons 21 to 22 April 1977 (GKB); another at the same locality 22–23 October 1981 (GB, JP); another 14 to 15 August 1983 (LR); one (probably an adult) on 5 and 12 October 1984 (GKB) and one 10 to 17 January 1986 (JP, TSH, CSH); one Qatif 22 July 1982 (JCB).

Calidris ferruginea · CURLEW SANDPIPER PM WV

Abundant on and near the coast in April, May and August. In May there are large numbers of migrating adults, but in June and July the majority are non-breeding immatures. It is less numerous from September, and much less so from October through March. In April, May, August and September birds occur on pools far inland during passage. One at Jawb on the fringe of the Rub' al-Khali in September also suggests a desert crossing.

Calidris alpina · DUNLIN WV

Abundant, especially along the coastline, from September through March; fewer in April and May and usually absent in June and July. The return movement is evident in August when numbers build up again. It is also locally abundant away from the littoral, notably at Abqaiq pools and, when conditions are suitable, on the inundated areas north of Hofuf. On 9 December 1982 there were about 150 on extensively flooded *sabkha* at as-Sarrar (JP, DR).

Limicola falcinellus PM (WV)
BROAD-BILLED SANDPIPER

Frequent in small numbers both on the coast and at inland pools, occurring chiefly in May, August and September. Though numbers fluctuate it is generally scarce in June and the first half of July. From October to March, it is perhaps a regular winter visitor, though in its winter plumage it is easily overlooked on the shore among much larger numbers of other small waders. Before Dammam marsh was reclaimed in 1977, larger numbers were noted there with up to 75 in May (GKB). On 13 September 1984 a total of 81 were counted on a rising tide at Qatif (GKB).

Great Snipe (GKB)

Tryngites subruficollis VAGRANT
BUFF-BREASTED SANDPIPER

Single birds at Abqaiq on 23 to 31 October 1975 (GKB) and at the former Dhahran airport pond on 27 to 28 May 1978 (GB).

Philomachus pugnax · RUFF WV PM

Common on pools away from the littoral and recorded in every month but mostly from October through March. Numbers of wintering birds were always highest at the former Dammam marsh (GKB) until that area was drained in 1977. From 1978 until 1980 no flocks of more than 50 were noted but from autumn of 1980, after the partial reflooding of the old Dammam marsh, concentrations of up to 600 were recorded. In more recent years the inundated land to the west of the Dammam Second Industrial City has supported equally large numbers (RJC).

Lymnocryptes minimus · JACK SNIPE (WV)

It is scarce in marshy areas away from the coast from late October to early April. Although it is not recorded annually it is an inconspicuous and skulking species and is probably overlooked.

Gallinago gallinago · COMMON SNIPE WV PM

A common species in marshy places around pools away from the littoral from August through April; in May, June and July it is scarce and usually absent. Higher counts in the better-watched localities near Dhahran and Abqaiq from late August through September suggest some onward passage. Some trans-desert migration is further suggested by the appearance of birds during autumn in a ditch at Haradh, and of one bird at Jawb, an isolated camp 300 km further south (JCD, GJR).

Identification: see p. 121.

Gallinago media · GREAT SNIPE VAGRANT

One at Abqaiq on 9 and 10 May 1976 (GKB, DMH); possibly as many as three there from 3 to 16 September 1977, and one on 12–13 October 1977; another single on 30 April 1982 (GKB).

Identification: see p. 122.

Gallinago stenura · PINTAIL SNIPE VAGRANT

Single birds at Abqaiq, 12 October to 4 November 1981 and at the Shedgum lagoons on 22 and 23 October 1981 (GB, JP). What was considered to be a different bird was present at Shedgum from 3 December 1981 to at least 12 March 1982 (GB, JHM, JP). One was at pools adjacent to the Aramco beach road, about 10 km south of Dhahran, on 4 and 5 March 1982 (GB). Single birds seen at Abqaiq on 31 August 1984 (JHM), and 12 October 1984 (GKB).

Identification: see p. 121.

Scolopax rusticola · WOODCOCK VAGRANT

One at Dhahran, early March 1971 (LJ). One at Dhahran on 17 December 1982, and also 4 and 18 February 1983 (CMS).

Limosa limosa · BLACK-TAILED GODWIT WV

It is scarce and generally irregular away from the Dammam area, although it has been noted occa-

Turnstone and Whimbrel (GKB)

sionally at Dhahran and Abqaiq; birds have been recorded in all months. Before the reclamation of Dammam marsh in 1978 it had been more regular with up to 46 wintering (GKB). This locality was partially flooded again in June 1980 and birds were present from August through to June 1981, up to 12 being seen together.

Limosa lapponica · BAR-TAILED GODWIT WV

An abundant species along the coast, mostly from August through May. Flocks tend to be localized in areas of higher productivity—those mudflats where food is abundant, notably around the Abu 'Ali islands, Tarut Bay and from Dammam to south of al-Khobar. There is an exodus of full-plumaged adults during May but flocks of non-breeding immatures remain during the summer months. Even during the period May to August flocks of up to about 400 have been noted near al-Khobar and at Abu 'Ali. There was often a large assembly at Dammam marsh lagoon, especially when the tide was high on the nearby shore, otherwise it is only exceptionally seen away from the littoral. Odd birds have been seen at Abqaiq in March, April, August and September.

Numenius phaeopus · WHIMBREL PM

Regular from late March to early June and from late July through October, with small peaks in numbers in April and August. Never numerous, it is usually noted in small parties. Odd individuals have been recorded, perhaps wintering, from November through January. Almost invariably seen on the coast but single birds have been noted at Abqaiq in April and from August through October.

Numenius arquata · CURLEW WV

A regular visitor to the coast from August through May, usually in small gatherings of under 50 but once about 200 in the al-Khobar area during March. Small numbers remain on the littoral during June and July. It is generally very scarce away from the coast but birds have been seen at Dhahran, Abqaiq and even at Haradh in January and from July through September. The race involved is evidently *orientalis* (Cramp & Simmons 1983), birds being quite decidedly longer-billed than those seen in western Europe.

Tringa erythropus · SPOTTED REDSHANK PM WV

Chiefly a rather scarce migrant from March through May and again from August through November at pools away from the coast. There are two records for July but no obvious peak at passage times. Varying numbers spend the winter at Abqaiq: in 1979–80 up to 60 remained during October through March but in the following winter the maximum count was only 15; in 1982–3 the maximum was 58 and in the following winter 76 (JP).

Tringa totanus · REDSHANK WV (PM?)

Common along the coast from August through March but it is generally scarce from mid-March until mid-June. From July through October parties are common on pools away from the littoral suggesting that some may be migrants. This apparent increase is obscured on the Gulf shores where numbers of waders are always difficult to assess satisfactorily.

Tringa stagnatilis · MARSH SANDPIPER PM (WV)

On pools away from the littoral it is a regular migrant appearing chiefly from March through May and again from August through October. It is usually scarce during the remaining winter months although it has been noted irregularly at Abqaiq. During the re-flooding of the Dammam marsh area in 1980 it overwintered there, up to 50 being counted during November through February. There are three June records including 16 birds near Dammam in June 1980.

Tringa nebularia · GREENSHANK WV (PM)

Small numbers, usually less than ten together, winter along the coast and around nearby pools. It is commonest from August through May, with odd non-breeding birds sometimes being seen in June and July. Peak numbers away from the coast are normally in April (scarce), May, September and October, suggesting some overland passage.

Tringa ochropus · GREEN SANDPIPER PM WV

Chiefly a migrant, appearing on pools away from the coast, especially at the sewage lagoons near Abqaiq, where there is a strong and conspicuous autumn passage from early July through

Spotted Redshank (GKB)

Redshank (ALL)

Marsh Sandpiper (GKB)

November; up to 25–30 remain annually from December to February. The spring passage is obscured by those overwintering, but a peak in March is almost certainly due to an arrival of migrants. It is generally very scarce from April through July until the first autumn birds arrive.

Tringa glareola · WOOD SANDPIPER PM WV

A common spring migrant at pools away from the coast, numbers reaching a peak in April and May after the main passage of Green Sandpipers. Individuals are not uncommonly encountered in June and July. The return passage starts in August and continues through November with a few wintering in suitable localities. The autumn peak is normally in September and October and about a month after the bulk of Green Sandpipers occur. Trans-desert or onward passage is suggested by its fairly regular occurrence at Haradh during migration periods, with parties of up to 15; there is very little water at this locality, often no more than a wet ditch. At Jawb, 300 km further south on the edge of the Rub' al-Khali, up to three have been noted during September (GJR).

Xenus cinereus · TEREK SANDPIPER PM WV

It winters commonly on the tidal flats of Tarut Bay and in lesser numbers elsewhere but seems to be chiefly a migrant. The spring passage is conspicuous from March through early June, mainly from late April, when birds appear in many wetland areas inland as well as close to the coast. During this period it has even occurred on wet fields at Haradh. What are presumably non-breeding immatures remain through June and July with concentrations in the Dammam area exceeding 100 in number. In August it becomes abundant on the coast, where it favours extensive mudflats: peak counts at Safwa (near Tarut Bay) were 350+ on 19 August 1982, and 425+ on 2 September 1982 (GKB). The numbers decline after September.

Wood Sandpiper (GKB)

Below:
Green Sandpiper (ALL)

Common Sandpiper (GKB)

Actitis hypoleucos · COMMON SANDPIPER PM (WV)

Small numbers winter along the littoral and nearby, but the bulk of records probably refer to migrants. There is an increase in occurrences during April, but more especially in September, although they are never numerous. There are three June records but it is usually absent between early May and late July. Onward passage is indicated by the appearance of a bird at Jawb in early September (GJR).

Arenaria interpres · TURNSTONE PM WV

Usually only small numbers winter in scattered parties along the littoral. In April and May especially, there is a large influx with birds appearing at all inland pools and even at unlikely ditches in the desert. Small numbers are noted annually during June and July. The return passage commences in August when again small flocks are commonly seen in localities away from the coast. Numbers decline after September.

Phalaropus lobatus · RED-NECKED PHALAROPE PM

Regular in varying numbers on marshy pools in spring but very scarce and irregular in autumn. It seems likely that the large number that winter in the Arabian Sea and northern Indian Ocean overfly the Gulf area. There is one report of a large concentration, estimated at about 10,000, some 40 km northwest of Bahrain and close to the Saudi coast on 27 March (Hallam 1980). In the Eastern Province it has been recorded only once in March, is scarce in April, and probably seen regularly only in May. There is one June record (GKB), and records from late July through October are very few. The peak inland count at Abqaiq was about 150 in May 1976.

Phalaropus fulicarius VAGRANT
GREY PHALAROPE

One in breeding plumage at Abqaiq on 15 and 16 June 1976 (GKB, DMH, PJI), and one in winter plumage there on 23 and 24 October 1976 (GKB). Three at a water hole in the Rub' al-Khali at 22°N 54°E, on 24 April 1980 (GJR).

Red-necked Phalarope (GKB)

Turnstone (GKB)

Terek Sandpiper (GKB)

Family STERCORARIIDAE

Stercorarius pomarinus VAGRANT
POMARINE SKUA

Two offshore between Dammam and Mina al-Ahmadi, 6 February 1954 (WJFMB). One or more at sea off Dammam, 21 to 22 April 1977 (WW). At least three at sea between late July and October 1985 (DMS).

Stercorarius parasiticus · ARCTIC SKUA (PM)

Recorded mainly at sea in the Arabian Gulf from September through April; all the records are from north of 26°N though this is doubtfully of much significance, since there has been little observation at sea. Up to four have been seen together, with the most sightings in November (DMS, KJF, WJFMB). From the mainland it has been noted twice: an adult light phase bird was seen chasing White-cheeked Terns at Jubail Port on 2 September 1983 (AD), and a dark phase immature was present on the shore of al-Khobar from 17 July to at least 26 August 1984, during which time it was observed chasing Slender-billed Gulls and Lesser Crested Terns (GKB, JAH, TSH, *et al*).

Family LARIDAE

The gulls are represented by ten species—five vagrants, and five more or less regular winter visitors to the Gulf coastal zone, large concentrations occurring locally. Gulls are generally scarce away from the coastal areas although some species regularly forage up to 30 km from the littoral—particularly on rubbish dumps.

Gulls, especially immatures, present identification difficulties; in this region at least two distinct races of yellow-legged HERRING GULLS occur and are sometimes confused with the LESSER BLACK-BACKED GULL. Adult Herring Gulls with slate-grey upperparts are the race *heuglini* from north-central Siberia; they usually outnumber the pale-backed *cachinnans* from south-west Asia. The primary-tips in the darker race are always black and thus darker than the mantle; in the race of Lesser Black-back which winters in Gulf waters, nominate *fuscus*, the mantle and upperwing are black throughout. Lesser Black-backs are frequently misidentified as Great Black-backed Gull (*Larus marinus*), although there are no confirmed records of that bird anywhere in the Gulf region. The brown immatures and sub-adults are more confusing still. Both Herring and Lesser Black-backed Gulls have a blackish area along the secondaries but Lesser Black-backed has an 'extra' wing-bar caused by black edges to the greater wing-coverts; it also has a darker underwing. The bill colour is a less reliable factor in Gulf waters since immature *cachinnans* Herring Gulls tend, unlike northern races, to have an all-black bill like young Lesser Black-backeds.

The taxonomy of the Herring/Lesser Black-backed complex of gulls is vexed in the extreme. There is no definitive classification of the many races involved, and the situation even as it affects the birds seen in the Eastern Province is not yet clear—some observers believe there may well be three forms of Herring Gull occurring. To complicate things, Cramp and Simmons (1983) have recently allocated *heuglini* to Lesser Black-backed Gull. However, in view of the large size and bulk (particularly the stoutness of the bill) of birds seen in the Province, it has seemed preferable to retain it here under Herring Gull. The GREAT BLACK-HEADED GULL is appreciably larger than both Herring and Lesser Black-backed Gulls and approaches Great Black-backed Gull in size. It has a rather distinctive, sloping forehead giving it a long-headed appearance, and the head shape tends to exaggerate the size of the deep, pale, dark-tipped bill. In its juvenile plumage (lost by about December) it has a distinctive brown gorget and, unlike other large gulls, it acquires a grey mantle and white underparts in its first winter. It retains a bold, black tail-band into its second summer, by which time its head and wing patterns make it as obvious as the adult.

The two smaller species, SLENDER-BILLED GULL and BLACK-HEADED GULL, are similar in winter plumage when the latter has lost its brown hood. They have a very similar wing pattern and the best distinguishing features are probably structural. The Slender-billed Gull is slightly larger with a longer-looking neck—even in flight this is apparent and shows as a bulge where the neck joins the breast. It has a long sloping forehead that exaggerates the bill length. Black-headed Gulls have higher, steeper foreheads, more rounded heads and shorter, dark-tipped bills. In flight they have a different outline with less head and neck projecting ahead of the wings, and a shorter tail.

Larus hemprichii · SOOTY GULL — VAGRANT

Two immatures on Dammam pier, 16 to 17 June 1974 (GKB, KJF). Two at sea off Dammam, 26 October 1979 (DMS).

Larus ichthyaetus — WV PM?
GREAT BLACK-HEADED GULL

Fairly regular in coastal waters from December through March, with sometimes up to 20 in one area; most recorded are adults, but it is likely that immatures are being overlooked. The only inland records are of single immatures at Abqaiq in March and a dead adult there in the same month (GKB) and near Nariya on 1 May 1981 (JP, JHM). Maximum numbers occur during March, when birds are probably on passage; once 120 were counted on Bahrain (Bundy & Warr 1980). Late birds in May have been observed in 1983 at Qatif (JP, DR) and in 1984 at al-Khobar (GKB).

Identification: see above.

Larus melanocephalus — VAGRANT
MEDITERRANEAN GULL

A first-winter bird at Half Moon Bay, about 30 km south of al-Khobar, on 6 January 1978 (GB).

Larus minutus · LITTLE GULL — VAGRANT

An immature at a desert camp, al-Musannah, on 29 September 1979 (GJR).

Larus ridibundus · BLACK-HEADED GULL — WV

Abundant along the coast and on nearby pools and rubbish dumps from October through April. The main arrival is during November and the majority depart in March although varying numbers of non-breeding immatures remain throughout the summer period. It is most numerous in the Dammam, Dhahran and al-Khobar areas, large numbers being present around dumps and sewage ponds, flying to regular coastal roosts at dusk. Further inland it is usually scarce but up to 150 have been noted at Abqaiq and at lagoons north of Hofuf. One was seen at Haradh in February 1981.

Identification: see opposite page.

Larus cirrocephalus VAGRANT
GREY-HEADED GULL

An adult, or sub-adult with a complete grey hood, near Qatif on 23 April 1981 (GB).

Larus genei · SLENDER-BILLED GULL WV

Abundant along the coast and often on nearby pools; usually the most numerous gull. The main arrival of adults is in late July and August, with most departing in March and April. Varying numbers of immatures remain in certain favoured localities, notably in the Dammam area, during the summer period, with concentrations of up to 1,000 not exceptional. Unlike Black-headed Gull it is usually scarce away from the coastal zone. Winter flocks comprise about 70% adults. On the shore, feeding birds keep apart from the similar Black-headed Gull, exploiting shallow water rather than wading at the tide line.

Identification: see opposite page.

Larus canus · COMMON GULL VAGRANT

Individuals near al-Khobar on 15 January 1975 and 28 January 1977, and at al-'Uqayr on 5 November 1976 (GKB). Two adults at Half Moon Bay, 7 February 1982 (GB). An adult at Qatif on 16 December 1982 (GKB). A first-year bird at Qatif on 2 March 1984 (JP).

Larus fuscus WV PM?
LESSER BLACK-BACKED GULL

A local winter visitor to the coast, sometimes common from October through March but occasionally recorded in April and August. It is generally less

A Great Black-headed Gull dwarfing its smaller cousins Larus ridibundus. *(GKB)*

numerous than Herring Gull and in some years very few are seen. One adult *heuglini* was present near al-Khobar as late as June in 1981, and another bird, apparently adult and apparently *heuglini* (but with pink legs) was at Qatif on 10 June 1984 (DJBro, GKB). Immatures, presumably trans-desert migrants, have been recorded well inland at Haradh in September and October, at Abqaiq in November, and at distant Jawb (23°N 50°E) on 10 September 1980 (GJR). Adults were seen preying on young Socotra Cormorants at az-Zakhnuniyah island in December 1980 (RJC).

Identification and taxonomy: see p. 134.

Larus argentatus · HERRING GULL WV

Locally abundant along the coast from September through April; numbers vary from year to year and most are present from November through March. Non-breeding immatures, but rarely adults, are scarce and irregular during May through August. It is generally absent away from the coastal zone although immatures occur at Abqaiq occasionally from August to early November and in March. Among the adults the darker race with the more northerly breeding distribution far outnumbers the pale-mantled *cachinnans*; immatures cannot be racially determined. A group at az-Zakhnuniyah island in December 1980 and January 1981 fed at a Socotra Cormorant colony and were responsible for the loss of many eggs (RJC).

Identification and taxonomy: see p. 134.

Family STERNIDAE

There are 13 species recorded, of which six breed. This total includes the very similar Little Tern (*Sterna albifrons*) and Saunders' Little Tern (*S. saundersi*) which are treated separately here for reasons of stability, following Voous (1977), though other recent authors have generally considered them conspecific, and even Cramp (1985), who also treated them separately, believed that they would be better combined.

The *Sterna* terns are mostly summer visitors to the Gulf and are consequently seen in breeding plumage, so there need be no identification problems apart from the little tern situation which is dealt with below. The migrant marsh terns *Chlidonias* can, however, be difficult in their juvenile and winter plumages. Both WHISKERED TERN and WHITE-WINGED BLACK TERN are regular autumn migrants and some birds remain for much of the winter period. The Whiskered Tern is slightly larger than the White-winged Black Tern with a more swollen looking bill, flatter head, and a more *Sterna*-like expression and general appearance. The White-winged Black Tern usually has a more active flight, a rounded head and smaller black bill; its facial expression suggests a Little Gull. In autumn juvenile White-winged Black Terns have dark brown mantles that tend to contrast with an almost white rump and greyish tail; they have a complete white collar (when it can be seen) and a less uniform appearance than juvenile Whiskered Terns. Juvenile Whiskered Terns have a paler brown mantle area, usually with some pale scaly looking vermiculations, no white collar, and a greyer, less contrasting rump and tail. First summer and winter plumage adults of the two species are also similar; first year White-winged Black Terns are whiter looking and could be misidentified as young Little Gulls; first year Whiskered Terns are more uniform grey in appearance and have less contrasting black markings along the secondaries and on the ear coverts. Some non-breeding Whiskered Terns seen in May and June have looked like adults with almost complete sooty caps but with whitish rather than dark grey underparts. White-winged Black Terns in their first year have a black bar along the secondaries and sometimes some dark feather edgings on the upper mantle and underwing coverts. Moulting adults in both species can sometimes show a dark 'shoulder' patch, thus possibly causing confusion with the Black Tern. Moulting adult Whiskered Terns, especially, can look uniform smoky-grey throughout the upper parts with mostly white looking underparts, and so recall autumn Black Terns.

GULL-BILLED TERNS are often locally common in coastal areas and may be confused with Sandwich Terns or even with some plumages of Whiskered Tern. Gull-billed Terns are superficially like Sandwich Terns but heavier bodied, with longer broader based wings, an almost square tail, and the shorter, stouter bill which gives it its name; juveniles are whiter looking than adults with a distinctive dark smudge behind the eye. Gull-billed Terns typically feed over land rather than water, dipping to pick up large insects, crustaceans and the like. Some observers have expressed difficulty in separating distant Gull-billed Terns from adult Whiskered Terns in winter plumage. They are superficially similar in general plumage characters especially in those examples that retain the sooty cap, but Whiskered Terns always look shorter winged and slighter, even at a distance when size is less easy to gauge. Gull-billed Terns have a more gull-like flight with deeper wing beats and the length of the wings is usually apparent; most also show an underwing with a fairly conspicuous black wedge along the primaries.

The situation regarding the two little terns is more complex. In Iran the two forms apparently breed separately, *S. saundersi* along the littoral, *S. albifrons* at inland sites (Scott *et al* 1975). This situation would seem to apply in eastern Saudi Arabia as well, although birds obtained in the Gulf have been termed 'intermediates' *S. albifrons 'praetermissa'* and are labelled as such in the British Museum (Natural History).

Typical *saundersi* is distinguished from *albifrons* in having the shafts of the three outermost primaries all black (not edged with grey). This does not reveal itself in the field but the outer primaries of *saundersi* are deeper black than *albifrons* and the back and upper wing are paler grey; the dark panel on the primaries thus contrasts more than in *albifrons*. In *saundersi* the rump and tail are concolorous with the pale upper wing and mantle, in *albifrons* the rump and tail are white and contrast with the grey back and upper wing. There is a difference in the area of white on the forehead of breeding adults and in the leg colour: under ideal conditions these features should be detectable in the field. Both species have a body moult in late summer; even by June the sharp edges to the white forehead patch are fading on some Gulf birds, and from July through October many adults can be difficult to identify by this means. In *albifrons* the white extends back over the eye, sometimes tapering almost to a point. In *saundersi* the white area forms a small inverted triangle, when seen from the front, ending in a straight line across the front of the crown; it does not reach back to the eye. The leg colour in the Gulf populations of *albifrons* is bright orange while in *saundersi* it is more variable, dark reddish-brown, pinkish-brown or dull flesh-brown, and it has also been described as dusky yellowish-olive and yellowish-brown (Ali & Ripley 1969), dull yellow to brownish-yellow (Meinertzhagen 1954).

Birds assigned to *albifrons* have been identified by their grey upper parts which contrast with the white rump and tail, by their orange legs and, to a lesser extent, the white of the forehead curving round the front of the crown below the black cap. The white forehead area varies and few examples have the white pointing back over the eye as suggested in some books. There is, however, invariably more white on the forehead in *albifrons* than in typical *saundersi*. Light conditions need to be perfect for the leg colour to be determined with any satisfaction: often the bird is shading its own legs and they look darker than they really are, or the sun is not directly behind the observer and the colour is distorted.

Birds assigned to *saundersi* on Saudi coasts are very white looking with a sharply contrasting black panel on the outer primaries. The upper parts and upper wing are very pale grey and in the field often appear to be concolorous with the rump and tail. In flight the secondaries look even whiter in bright sunlight, almost translucent in a triangular shaped wedge, making the bird look strikingly whiter than the grey and white *albifrons*. Attention should be paid to the colour of the upper parts and the presence or otherwise of any contrast between upper wing and rump, leg colour and to a lesser extent the small area of white on the forehead. There is little detectable difference in voice and it is doubtful whether juveniles can be identified in the field except possibly by the leg colour.

Gelochelidon nilotica · GULL-BILLED TERN WV PM?

Scattered through western Europe, Mediterranean region and central and southern Asia (and Americas). Winters in Afrotropics, around Arabia, and in south-east Asia and Australia. It has been recorded in all months and its status is not easily summarized. There would appear to be an influx in April of mainly first-year birds, notably to the coastal areas north of Dammam. These birds remain on the tidal creeks and adjacent mudflats in some years until July or August when there seems to be an exodus. In August and September it is usually scarce and often absent, and then becomes locally numerous during October when assemblies of up to 150 have been noted, especially in Tarut Bay. A high proportion of wintering birds are adult and most depart during March. In 1980 small numbers of adults, seemingly paired, remained in a coastal strip north of Dammam; they were unusually vocal but no evidence of breeding was obtained. They were still present around Dammam marsh lagoon in late June and were seen to mob potential predators. Inland records are surprisingly few; adults have been seen at Shedgum and Hofuf (al-'Uyun) on four occasions in March and April and at Abqaiq in May, August and October. On present evidence its migrant status is questionable.

Identification: see p. 136.

Sterna caspia · CASPIAN TERN WV

Present throughout the year along the coast, highest concentrations usually being in Tarut Bay and at Abu 'Ali where up to 80 have been seen assembled. There is no evidence that it breeds in Saudi territory but in December 1980 and 1981 small numbers were found breeding on the Hawar islands of Bahrain and young chicks were seen (RJC). A bird ringed as a chick on the Volga delta in the USSR at 46°N 49°E on 15 June 1975 was found dead at Abu 'Ali on 1 March 1976 (BTO), and during August to October 1984 several birds on the shore near al-Khobar were seen to be ringed.

Sterna bergii · SWIFT TERN MB

Breeds on islands in the Gulf but not always annually at each site. Nesting in Saudi territory was first established on 18 May 1979 when fresh eggs were found on the island of Karan approximately 65 km from the mainland coast and on Harqus further to the north (RJC). During 1979 about 1,000 pairs nested on Karan and a further 50 pairs made two unsuccessful attempts to colonize Harqus, each being defeated when high seas swept over the island and washed the eggs away. In 1980 400–500 pairs laid eggs on Harqus but their breeding success could not be monitored. There was no breeding on Karan in 1980 but about 1,000 pairs were found nesting on nearby Kurayn island (RJC). This species breeds in closely packed colonies, sometimes on its own, but on other occasions in association with the Lesser Crested Tern. No nest is made. One, very rarely two, eggs are laid on bare coral sand, but as incubation progresses scrapes are formed and accentuated by low ramparts of dried excrement. The eggs are extraordinarily variable. The most common type has a white or very pale stone ground colour, but others are varying shades of lilac, pink, drab olive or brown; blotched, streaked and scrawled with grey, red, brown or black. One unique example was bright blue, with interlacing scrawlings of black. Usually very scarce on mainland coasts but up to 120 adults were on the large island of Abu 'Ali

Slender-billed Gulls and a Caspian Tern. (GKB)

in late April 1981, probably loafing there until ready for nesting on the islands further offshore. Small numbers noted in the same general area of sea during November (DMS) and two at Abu 'Ali in October, December and February suggest that the winter exodus is not total.

Sterna bengalensis · LESSER CRESTED TERN MB

Present in coastal waters from March through October; less commonly until December with possibly some remaining in January and February. It is not known to breed on the mainland coast although, unlike the Swift Tern, it is commonly seen, and adults in late summer bring their fledged juveniles. It breeds regularly in large, dense colonies on the offshore islands of Harqus, Karan, Kurayn, Jana, Jurayd, az-Zakhnuniyah and Samamik; sometimes on its own, at other times in association with the Swift Tern. No nest is made. Towards the end of May one, very rarely two, eggs are laid on bare coral sand. As incubation progresses scrapes are formed and accentuated by dried ramparts of excrement. The eggs show little variation; the most common type has a very pale stone ground colour and small blotches of orange/brown, with the pigment tending to be diffused around the circumference.

Sterna sandvicensis · SANDWICH TERN (WV)

Scarce and irregular in coastal waters from November through February, and in April, June and July. There is no known breeding colony in the Gulf, so the apparent adults seen in June and July are presumably young non-breeders. In November birds have been seen 'commonly' at sea off Saudi shores (DMS) and it may well winter away from the mainland.

Sterna hirundo · COMMON TERN (PM)

Usually a scarce and irregular migrant. It has been recorded from February through June and once in September on the coast (GKB). Inland, migrants have been noted in April, May and August at Abqaiq and Hofuf. There are single records in February, June and July and once three birds in late September at Hofuf (GKB). At Haradh, some 150 km south of Hofuf, one in September (JCD) was possibly a trans-desert migrant.

Group of Swift and Lesser Crested Terns. (BS)

Sterna repressa · WHITE-CHEEKED TERN MB

This species is common along the coast from April through September. Most depart during October and it is very scarce in November. It breeds commonly on the offshore islands of Karan, Jana, Jurayd, Samamik and at Abu 'Ali (RJC) which is now linked to the mainland by road. It almost certainly breeds on other islands that are difficult of access, for example Za'l off Ras Tanura where large numbers were seen from the air on 23 May 1980 (RJC). Breeds in small, rather scattered colonies, frequently at some distance from the sea. The nest is a pronounced scrape in coral sand. In Saudi Arabia it is usually lined with small, dried pieces of suaeda, and particles of broken sea shells tend to collect at the bottom of the scrape. The clutch is of 1 or 2 eggs, very rarely 3. They are laid at the end of May, and show little variation. The most common types are pale stone coloured, or pale greyish green, sparingly spotted and blotched with various shades of brown. Adults with recently fledged young visit the mainland shores from late June; these must come from offshore sites since very few now breed on the Eastern Province mainland.

Sterna anaethetus · BRIDLED TERN MB

This tern arrives in Saudi waters in April and by September most have departed. It breeds in large numbers on the islands of Karan, Kurayn, Jana, Jurayd and Samamik. At the end of May, 1, very rarely 2, eggs are laid in a scrape under a salt bush. They are pale buff or greenish grey with ashy coloured shell markings; and are spotted and blotched, sometimes heavily, with deep, purplish brown. When incubating or covering chicks the parent leaves the nest scrape only with considerable reluctance, and consequently attempts to establish the size of a breeding population are likely to be inaccurate and estimates conservative. The following figures are no more than an indication of population size. In 1974: Jurayd 3,500 pairs (KJF). In 1979: Karan about 2,000 pairs, Kurayn 200 pairs, Jana 1,250 pairs, Jurayd about 2,000 pairs. In 1981: Samamik about 1,000 pairs (RJC). Considering the numbers breeding on the islands it is rare along the mainland coasts and must forage well offshore.

Sterna albifrons · LITTLE TERN MB

Small numbers arrive in late February and through March and breed by pools away from the littoral. Up to ten pairs have bred on the Dammam marsh and a few pairs inhabit pools at the Qatif oasis when water levels are suitable. Judging by the numbers of adults that frequent these areas after the young have fledged in June and July, especially the mudflats and creeks near Qatif and Saihat, there must be a considerable breeding population in the region. At the formerly extensive inundated area north of al-Hasa, there is a scattering of small colonies, most of the surviving sites being near al-'Uyun about 50 km from the Gulf coast. Numbers vary from year to year and birds seem to desert sites frequently, possibly due to changing water levels. The maximum number recorded at the al-'Uyun drainage system is 93 birds, with 22 nests, in 1982 (GKB). At Abqaiq 3 pairs were breeding in May 1982, though probably unsuccessfully; in 1983 at least one pair probably attempted to breed; and in 1984 a total of at least 19 pairs bred at two separate lagoon complexes and some young were reared. The nest is little more than a scrape or natural depression in drying mud. Fragments of shell or flakes of dried mud frequently collect at the bottom of the scrape, and occasionally small pieces of wind-blown vegetable matter are added. The eggs are usually 2 or 3 in number, pale stone coloured or greyish, with ashy grey shell markings and small blotches in varying shades of brown. This species' association with the littoral is limited mainly to areas where there is an outflow of fresh water from a nearby oasis or from cultivation. Thus it is common on or near the coast at Dammam, Saihat and Qatif, and in these places it has not been known to consort with Saunders' Little Tern. Where the breeding ranges of these two species overlap as in eastern Saudi Arabia and Iran (Scott *et al* 1975) they segregate themselves ecologically and appear to be 'good' species.

Identification: see p. 137.

Sterna saundersi MB PM
SAUNDERS' LITTLE TERN

In the past there has been considerable confusion over the status of this species and *S. albifrons* due to difficulties of field identification and taxonomy, and to some extent this persists. This species is much less common than was formerly supposed and in this region probably reaches the eastern extremity of its Indian Ocean range. It has been proved to breed only at Abu 'Ali and on the littoral near al-Khobar, though there are almost certainly more pairs scattered along the coast. Like *S. albifrons* it

White-cheeked Tern (GKB)

Little Tern chick soliciting food. (GKB)

Saunders' Little Tern (BS)

breeds in small, loose groups rather than in dense colonies. Birds arrive in coastal areas from about mid-February and most have departed by mid-November. Breeding begins at the end of May. The nest and eggs alone cannot be distinguished from those of the Little Tern (RJC). In 1980 there were two pairs on an islet at Abu 'Ali while in 1981 there was a minimum of five pairs present. On 25 June 1981, south of al-Khobar, two pairs had eggs and another a small downy chick, while on the following day a pair were attending a flying juvenile. It has not been found on any offshore island (RJC). Large post-breeding assemblies, sometimes numbering thousands, have been encountered on the coast: one such at Dammam marsh on 12 September 1975 numbered about 450, and another at Abu 'Ali on 7 October 1977 numbered 11,000+ (GKB). These concentrations are presumably migrants, probably from Iran where it breeds along most of the coast (Scott *et al* 1975). In eastern Saudi Arabia it is numerically the rarest breeding tern.

Identification: see p. 137.

Chlidonias hybridus · WHISKERED TERN — WV

Adults are regularly present in coastal localities between Qatif and al-Khobar from September through April, and some one year olds and occasionally summer plumaged adults remain throughout the summer on a few favourite pools near the coast. From August through December there is usually a number of juveniles at lagoons in the coastal zone although there is little evidence to suggest an onward overland passage.

Identification: see p. 136.

Chlidonias niger · BLACK TERN — VAGRANT

One at Qatif, 12 November 1982 (TSH). One at Abqaiq from 7 to 12 August 1983 (JB, JP, IR, LR). An adult at Qatif on 16–17 August 1984 (GKB, JHM). An immature at Qatif on 13 September 1984 (GKB). There are six further unconfirmed records of up to four birds at Dammam marsh between September and December 1974, 1975 and 1976.

Chlidonias leucopterus — PM (WV)
WHITE-WINGED BLACK TERN

A regular migrant in small numbers. Adults in breeding plumage occur from late April through to early June; numbers vary but concentrations of more than 20 are unusual. Coinciding with the arrival of migrant adults there is a small influx of one year olds, and these birds sometimes remain in suitable localities from April to August. In August there is a further arrival of distinctive juveniles and these birds are in evidence until December, in some years until early February. Especially in autumn, this species occurs more frequently away from the coastal zone than does Whiskered Tern. There are odd records from most inland pools and even one from isolated Haradh in September (JCD). Autumn concentrations are often larger than those of migrating adults in spring, especially in the Dammam marsh area. When that locality was more extensive assemblies of up to about 200 marsh terns were not uncommon (GKB).

Identification: see p. 136.

Family PTEROCLIDAE

The sandgrouse are represented in this region by one breeding species and two vagrants. The past history of this family in eastern Arabia is bedevilled by the uncertainty of field identification. Several sandgrouse in the Dhahran area in November 1960, where they are now absent, may have been Pin-tailed (*Pterocles alchata*) as stated by Eddy (1962) or Spotted, a species that still breeds in the Province. Unidentified sandgrouse were also seen at Abqaiq on three dates in August and September in 1976 and 1977 (GKB). Pin-tailed and Black-bellied Sandgrouse (*P. orientalis*) occur irregularly in Kuwait,

Black Tern (GKB)

and the former, a nomadic and opportunist species, has bred there (Bundy & Warr 1980). Although a map by Jennings (1981) shows Pin-tailed breeding throughout the northern half of the Eastern Province there are no satisfactory records.

Pterocles senegallus · SPOTTED SANDGROUSE RB

Present throughout the year at Haradh. An unknown number of pairs breed on the nearby stony desert and probably also on arid sections of the enclosed farm area. Two or 3 eggs are laid in a very shallow scrape, often amongst sparse vegetation. They are elongated, and equally rounded at each end. In colour, they are greyish olive or buff, lightly speckled and spotted with light brown and purplish grey. Chicks have been seen in both areas, attended by adults, between late March (JCD) and early May. Flocks of up to 400 are regularly seen on the Haradh cultivation arriving there daily from the north and north-west, though in late September 1984 up to 1,000 were counted (JHM, JP). Away from Haradh it was seen 'in small flocks' around Hofuf and Yabrin in 'winter' 1923–4, two birds being obtained (Ticehurst & Cheesman 1925).

Pterocles orientalis VAGRANT
BLACK-BELLIED SANDGROUSE

Possibly an irregular visitor when unusually hard winters occur in Iran and other neighbouring countries. On 10 December 1982 about 50 were seen on the Dibdibah steppes in the north; a flock of about 25 flew south and later two small flocks of seven and fifteen birds were observed (JP, DR).

Pterocles alchata VAGRANT
PIN-TAILED SANDGROUSE

About 130 at Mulayjah 28 November 1985 (JP); 150 to 200 at Mulayjah 27 November 1986 (JP, CSH, TC).

Family COLUMBIDAE

The pigeons are represented here by six species, four of which breed annually. The four breeding species appear to occupy different feeding niches and breed at different, although overlapping, periods. The two remaining species are vagrants. The COLLARED DOVES breeding in the region appear to be darker than those from south-eastern to north-western Europe, being earthier-brown with more contrasting grey primary coverts. European birds look greyish-fawn with more contrasting black primaries but with the greyish coverts hardly noticeable in the field. The summer visiting Turtle Doves (*Streptopelia turtur*) also show some atypical plumage characters that merit further discussion.

The RUFOUS TURTLE DOVE (*S. orientalis*), recorded only twice in this region, is a larger, darker dove with rather 'pigeon-like' proportions that breeds in the eastern half of the Palearctic, extending west to around 50°E in western Siberia and south to Baluchistan. Rufous Turtle Doves in the western part of their range belong to the race *meena*. They resemble *S. turtur* in having whitish tips to the dark tail, rather than the grey of the eastern race *orientalis*. Some easternmost *turtur*, including those breeding in eastern Saudi Arabia, often have bluish-grey neck patches like *S. orientalis*, rather than white like the Middle East populations of *S. t. turtur* and most *S. t. arenicola*. *S. t. arenicola* is paler than the nominate with a rather washed-out appearance and more pink-buff underparts. The eastern Arabian population of breeding TURTLE DOVES are closer in size and bulk to Collared Dove and are darker than most *S. t. arenicola* in having chestnut, rather than orange-buff, edges to the mantle feathers and wing-coverts, and generally darker pinkish-vinous underparts. The colour of the underparts varies in museum skins but *S. o. meena* is generally more orange in tone than *S. t. arenicola*: both forms shade to white on the belly and undertail coverts, *meena* being the only race of Rufous Turtle Dove to have white under the tail.

The presence of what appear to be overlapping morphological characters in these two species suggests that, in recent evolutionary times, they once intergraded where their ranges met. *S. t. arenicola* breeds through most of Iran (Scott *et al* 1975), where the Rufous Turtle Dove is also a vagrant, but the literature is at some variance regarding the eastern limit of *S. turtur*. Meinertzhagen (1954) treated the Palearctic turtle doves as one species, and while eastern Arabian birds seem to represent an intermediate form, the two species are known to overlap their breeding ranges in the north-western Himalayas, Turkestan and Kazakhstan without apparent hybridization (Voous 1960); thus they are currently treated as separate species.

The Turtle Dove may be distinguished from the more uniform, earthy-brown Collared Dove by the rufous, black-scalloped mantle and upper wing-coverts; grey rump and head; black, white rimmed tail and, even at a distance, flying birds should be quite easily separated by the sooty, rather than pale greyish-white underwing-coverts.

Columba livia · ROCK DOVE — RB

A sedentary species, found throughout the year on *jabals* and rocky escarpments. Although isolated pairs are sometimes encountered it is generally sociable and forms loose colonies of up to about 25 pairs (RJC). It exploits the newly cultivated areas at Haradh and some are present there throughout the year although it is not known to breed within about 50 km. Larger numbers have been observed at Judah, where up to 250 were seen visiting crops in the early morning during May 1984 (GKB). Here the proximity of a broken escarpment for nesting and crops for feeding have probably contributed to its increase, and it seems that the spread of agriculture in Arabia will benefit the species. In some large caves it nests colonially, utilizing ledges which become thickly encrusted with droppings. In such instances nesting material is often limited to a few feathers. The floors of nesting caves are frequently buried under an accumulation of droppings some 30 cm thick, indicating that the cave has been used for roosting or breeding for many years. Most breeding birds are found between 'Uray'irah and Hanidh, with smaller numbers frequenting rocky outcrops north and west of Hofuf and in the vicinities of Ain Dar and Salasil. On *jabals* where suitable caves are unavailable, especially near as-Sarrar and Nata', it breeds in small eroded holes, just large enough to contain a nest, on vertical cliff faces. In such instances the nest is well constructed of small twigs. Two slightly glossy white eggs are laid from February onwards, and there is evidence to suggest that it is double brooded (RJC). Although attracted to areas of intensive cultivation, it is not often seen away from its breeding haunts. It is very scarce on the flatter coastal plain and absent from the coastal zone. Feral Pigeons are present in small sedentary flocks in most settlements and towns, sometimes being encountered in semi-desert where rubbish is dumped near villages.

Streptopelia decaocto · COLLARED DOVE — RB

A common resident in the coastal zone around towns and villages, palm groves, farms and gardens. In the arid environment of the Eastern

Collared Dove (ALL)

Province, it is necessarily local but is quite widespread. It is present throughout the year as far south as Salwah on the Qatar border. Inland it becomes rather scarce but it has colonized Abqaiq, the al-Hasa oases around Hofuf and the Haradh farm area. At the latter, up to 400 have been noted in one cultivated area in the autumn. Display flights may be seen virtually every month of the year and the laying period is a protracted one, eggs having been found from December through September (RJC). The nest is placed at no great height in a shrub or low tree, frequently on a lateral branch. It is a very fragile platform of slender twiglets and grass stems through which the eggs are usually visible. They are invariably two in number, somewhat elongated, with a smooth, unmarked milky white shell (RJC). The peak laying time is towards the end of March and the beginning of April, before most Turtle Doves have arrived.

Identification: see p. 143.

Streptopelia turtur · TURTLE DOVE MB PM

It arrives during April and most have departed by late September although small numbers are seen annually in October. The breeding population is concentrated mostly in the coastal zone, notably in the cultivated areas between al-Khobar and Safwa. It extends south to al-'Uqayr, and inland as far as Haradh where there are possibly as many as 100 pairs. Its nest is similar to that of the Collared Dove, but usually more substantial. The eggs are likewise superficially similar, but of a more intense white. The earliest fledged juveniles have been noted before the end of May (RH), suggesting that laying commenced very soon after arrival. Eggs have also been seen at Dhahran in June and July and recently fledged young as late as 30 August. The breeding season is later on average than that of the Collared Dove. During the breeding season it has regular large scale movements between the nesting areas and favourite feeding places. These 'movements' are especially conspicuous from June through August and the flocks often include juveniles. Large numbers of presumed migrants are regularly seen away from breeding places, notably in April and September; these are often paler than the local breeding birds with, usually, white neck patches and are probably the race *arenicola* from the Iran–Turkestan region. The autumn passage was conspicuous at Jawb, 300 km south of Haradh, from 13 to 30 September 1980 with a peak of about 50 birds on 20 September (GJR).

Identification: see opposite page.

Streptopelia orientalis VAGRANT
RUFOUS TURTLE DOVE

One on a barge at sea, Zuluf oil field, 26 September to 2 October 1985 (DMS). Individuals at Dhahran, on 1 November 1974 (GKB) and 2 September 1978 (GB). The last example had slaty-grey tips to the dark tail and therefore was probably not the race *meena* from the western part of this species' range, but more likely the eastern nominate *orientalis*.

Identification: see p. 144.

Streptopelia senegalensis · PALM DOVE VAGRANT

Single birds at Haradh on 6 February 1981 (GB, RH), at Dhahran on 4 August 1982, and at Haradh on 30 September 1982 (GKB). One seen collecting grass (presumably for nest building) on northern outskirts of al-Khobar on 7 February 1983 (GKB); also seen on 10 February (GKB, LR). One present in al-Khobar from 21 February 1984 to October 1984 (JP). One at Haradh on 5 October 1984 (JHM, JP). Pair at Haradh 19 February 1987 (MAE).

Oena capensis · NAMAQUA DOVE MB RB?

In the Eastern Province breeding has only been confirmed at Haradh where there may be as many as 50 pairs in the farm area. Little is known of its movements but there seems to be an influx in late April and May. Numbers visibly increase at Haradh during May, reach their peak in September and October with the inclusion of juveniles, and decline during November. It tends to be scarce at Haradh from December through March although seldom absent. It is a late nesting species. The nest is unusually substantial for a dove and is constructed from thin twiglets, dried roots and grasses, with a shallow cup for the eggs. It is usually positioned in a low bush, but nests have also been found on piles of brushwood, bales of straw, etc. Invariably two eggs are laid; they are unmarked creamy yellow. At Haradh they have been seen between June and August. Both Collared and Turtle Doves breed in the same general area but Namaquas would appear to have a later breeding cycle and, although all three species are granivorous, they seem to maintain a harmonious relationship. Away from Haradh it is scarce and irregular in its appearances. Up to five have been seen at both Hofuf and Abqaiq in the period April to September. Males have also been noted near Dammam on the Gulf coast in May, August and September. A total of 65+ were observed in some neglected cultivation near Dammam on 31 July 1984; they seemed to be well established, and it seems likely that they had nested there (GKB, JHM). Flocks of up to 9 have been seen at Dhahran from July 1984, and this species is clearly spreading and establishing itself here.

Namaqua Dove (GKB)

Above: *Turtle Doves (BS)*

Below: *Rose-ringed Parakeet (GKB)*

Family PSITTACIDAE

Psittacula krameri WV RB?

ROSE-RINGED PARAKEET

Present locally throughout the year although its numbers vary and its movements are not well understood. It breeds on nearby Bahrain where nestlings have been noted from December through March (Bundy & Warr 1980) but breeding still remains to be confirmed for the Eastern Province of Saudi Arabia. Flying juveniles have been seen at Qatif in mid-May and from June at Dhahran. No nest is made. Three to four white eggs, broad oval in shape, are laid in a hole on an accumulation of powdered debris.

There is an influx into the Eastern Province during April through June in most years. Numbers remain fairly stable until September after which, until December, flocks of up to about 150 can often be seen flying noisily between feeding places. From January through April or May it is often scarce although during this period it has twice been noted at distant Haradh; small parties of up to 12 have been seen in March and April (JCD).

Family CUCULIDAE

Clamator glandarius VAGRANT
GREAT SPOTTED CUCKOO

One at Abqaiq, 17 February 1976 (GKB, DMH). One at Haradh, 1 to 3 March 1981 (JCD). One at Abqaiq, 11 March 1983 (GKB, JP, LR).

Cuculus canorus · CUCKOO PM

A scarce but probably regular migrant. In spring it has been seen once in February (GKB) but frequently in April and May. It is probably an annual visitor in August when adults have been seen in the coastal zone in recent years. There are a few records for September and early October.

Family TYTONIDAE

Tyto alba · BARN OWL RB

A pair were breeding at Qatif in December 1974; though the adults were never seen, the main prey item being supplied to the three small chicks was White-cheeked Bulbuls (GKB). It may well breed regularly in the coastal zone but is seldom seen. It has been reported at Dhahran in March and May (RH), near Abqaiq in March (RJC), at Ras Tanura (a bird that died) also in March (DJBra), at Haradh in September (JCD), and at al-'Aba oasis in August (GKB, JHM).

Family STRIGIDAE

Otus scops · SCOPS OWL PM

A scarce but annually recorded migrant; like most owls it is probably overlooked and more numerous than generally supposed. It has been noted chiefly in the coastal zone but this may well be due to an observer bias there. It has been recorded three times in February but the bulk of records are in March with fewer in April and September. Of special interest perhaps were two migrants on board a ship in the Gulf at 28°N 49°E on 16 October 1979 (DMS). Three records in December and one in January could conceivably apply to the closely related and very similar Striated Scops Owl (*O. brucei*) which breeds in scattered areas of the Middle East from Sinai and Yemen to Oman, Pakistan and south-central USSR; and as close to the Eastern Province as southern Iraq and the United Arab Emirates. It is migratory in the north but resident in Arabia (Cramp 1985). One has been obtained on Bahrain in October (Bundy & Warr 1980).

Strix butleri · HUME'S TAWNY OWL RB

On 25 February 1988 a female was flushed from 3 fresh eggs, deposited on a layer of rock dust in an eroded hole on the side of a *jabal* deep into the desert to the west of al-Wannan. This is the first record of breeding in the Eastern Province. The species seems to be very rare and thinly distributed (RJC).

Bubo (bubo) ascalaphus · EAGLE OWL RB

In its chosen habitat of broken escarpments and isolated rocky outcrops in the desert it is a generally well established, locally common, but inconspicuous species. Pairs are to be found in most suitable areas east of the Dahna, but not in the west in the vicinity of Riyadh and the Tuwayq escarpment. Eagle Owls are resident in their territory throughout the year. Nest sites are typically deeply eroded cavities under the cap rock or on steep scree slopes. The eggs are laid in a scrape amongst wind-blown sand or rock dust. The same hole is not necessarily used for breeding each year; most pairs will favour one of two or three different holes in the same general vicinity. One female chose to lay her eggs in a large cavity that had once been filled by a substantial stick nest; that of a Raven or Long-legged Buzzard. Viewed from the ground it appeared that the owl had taken over the nest, but closer examination revealed that most of the nest had disintegrated and that the owl was probably attracted by the cavity itself, rather than the remnants of the nest within it. Occasionally a female will lay eggs on an exposed ledge, and there is a well-authenticated record of one female laying eggs on the ground in a scrape under a salt bush in open desert. The laying season is prolonged and pairs may produce eggs at any time from November until the end of February, most frequently from the end of December through January. The usual clutch is 2–4 eggs, occasionally 5, unmarked white; generally blunt oval in shape though some are decidedly rounded. A frequently used nesting hole is easily identified by a veritable carpet of small bones from pellets that have disintegrated over the years. While the female is incubating the male usually occupies a perch in close proximity, a useful 'pointer' if the nest is being

Eagle Owl (ALL)

sought. When agitated, particularly if the female is flushed from eggs, the call is a low pitched 'hoo'. When young birds are disturbed at the nest they react with much angry clicking of the bill. This behaviour has also been noticed from adults when they have eggs or young, and may be coupled with a distraction display in which the adult tumbles down a slope or bounds along the ground with its wings spread, calling 'Hoo, hoo'. Occasionally a high pitched piercing scream is given (RJC). Pale birds, presumably from the local breeding population of *ascalaphus*, have occasionally been noted away from the vicinity of their breeding places, especially around the Abqaiq lagoons, Dhahran and Haradh where potential avian prey is relatively plentiful. Various authors have suggested that this form merits treatment as a species in its own right: it is geographically and ecologically isolated from the larger, dark birds of the northern forests and according to C. J. O. Harrison (pers. comm.) there are anatomical differences which may establish the desert forms at species rank; Cramp (1985) has also taken this view. Significantly larger, dark examples, presumably representing one of the northern races, have been noticed on Jinnah island on 18 May 1979, three together on Karan island on 23 May 1980 (RJC), and at Dhahran airport on 30 December 1977.

Athene noctua · LITTLE OWL RB?

A local species that seems to be confined to broken escarpments and rocky outcrops in the desert north of 'Uray'irah. First discovered to the east of as-Sarrar in early 1980 (Raby 1981), it has since been found in the vicinities of Abu Hadriyah, Nariya, Hanidh, 'Uray'irah and Judah. Information on its nesting

Eagle Owl chicks (ALL)

habits in the Eastern Province is lacking, but elsewhere 2–4 nearly spherical white eggs are laid on a bed of natural debris in a small hole.

Asio flammeus · SHORT-EARED OWL WV

One was found dead at Abqaiq on 12 December 1975 (GKB). One on a ship in the Gulf at 27°N 49°E, 18 October 1979 (DMS). One at Haradh, 29 November 1979 (JCD). One at Abqaiq, 3 December 1982 (GKB, JP, DR). Minimum of 8 near Wari'ah, Dibdibah 12–13 February 1987 (ME, CH, ALL).

Family CAPRIMULGIDAE

Three species of nightjars occur in eastern Arabia but only one is a regular visitor. One of the vagrants, Egyptian Nightjar, breeds in the central sector of the Palearctic between 45° and 90°E and winters in eastern Africa. Like so many central Palearctic migrants which winter in tropical Africa, it probably overflies Arabia in substantial numbers. As with the owls, nightjars are largely nocturnal, unobtrusive and very likely to be overlooked.

Barn Owl chicks (GKB)
At this nest there were many dead Bulbuls amongst prey scattered around the nesting area.

Short-eared Owl (ALL)

Caprimulgus nubicus VAGRANT

NUBIAN NIGHTJAR

One near Abqaiq, 7 September 1977 (GKB).

Caprimulgus europaeus PM

EUROPEAN NIGHTJAR

A scarce but probably regular spring migrant, with small numbers seen annually in April and May. It is even scarcer in the autumn, and there are currently only 10 records in the period September to November, always of single birds, except for two on 13 September 1982 at Imhoff.

Caprimulgus aegyptius VAGRANT

EGYPTIAN NIGHTJAR

Two at Abqaiq, 26 March 1976 (GKB, DMH). One at Haradh, late October 1979 (JCD). One Dhahran airport, 10 to 14 September 1981 (RRE). One about 10 km south of Dhahran, 10 April 1982 (GB). One at Abqaiq 3 to 10 December 1982 (GKB, JP, DR, LR).

Egyptian Nightjar (GKB)

Family APODIDAE

The swifts are represented by four species, one of which breeds on a few rocky *jabals* in the desert.

It is likely that the present status of the SWIFT (*Apus apus*) is confused and underestimated: in spring large concentrations of swifts consisting of this species and an uncertain number of the local breeding PALLID SWIFT (*A. pallidus*) are seen. When seen well under ideal light conditions these two all dark species can be identified in the field but a large assembly of both species causes problems to the observer attempting to calculate the numbers of each.

As its name implies, *A. pallidus* is paler than the migrant *A. apus*: it looks brown rather than sooty-brown or black, it has a larger grey throat patch and shows more contrast on the two-toned underwing. In good light the underwing shows a noticeably pale area along the secondaries that contrasts with the darker wing-coverts, while the underwing of *A. apus* looks almost uniform sooty-brown. The upper wing in *pallidus* also looks two-toned and much less uniform than in *apus*. When seen together, small and subtle differences in outline may be apparent: *pallidus* usually looks heavier with a larger head and broader-based, blunter-tipped wings.

Pied Kingfisher (GKB)

Apus apus · NORTHERN SWIFT PM

Careful scrutiny of large swift assemblies in March and April has revealed that this species is sometimes numerous; one concentration of several thousand over the Abqaiq lagoons in March 1980 proved to be almost entirely this species. Odd individuals in May and June have also proved to be of this species. It has not been satisfactorily identified in autumn when its occurrence on passage is probably obscured by large numbers of Pallid Swift.

Apus pallidus · PALLID SWIFT MB PM?

A local breeding species, frequenting rocky outcrops in the desert where there are suitable caves and fissures for nesting. The principal known colonies are north of Hofuf, near 'Ain Dar and in the *jabals* between 'Uray'irah and Hanidh. Birds attend these colonies from March onwards and presumably commence breeding soon afterwards. Birds have been seen entering caves and narrow crevices, usually at some considerable height on *jabal* formations, but no nests have been examined in the Eastern Province. Elsewhere it has been described as a shallow cup of straw, grasses and feathers, cemented with saliva. Two to three elongated white eggs are laid. After the breeding season, it is absent from the desert though little or nothing is known of its movements. Large assemblies occur over inundated areas and effluent evaporation lagoons, but it is always very scarce in the coastal zone. Odd individuals occur at distant Haradh in the south, mostly from March through June. From September through February small concentrations are not uncommonly seen over the Abqaiq lagoons and elsewhere. Larger numbers in March suggest some regular passage at that time.

Apus melba · ALPINE SWIFT (PM)

Single birds have been recorded as follows: near al-Khobar, 30 January 1975 (GKB); at Dhahran, 14 February 1975 (MSH); at Abqaiq, 27 February 1977 (GKB); at Dammam, 18 February 1979 (DJBra); at

White-breasted Kingfisher (ALL)

al-Musannah, 11 April 1979 (GJR); at Haradh, 13 March 1981 (RH, JP); near Dhahran airport, 4 June 1981 (JHM); at Abqaiq, 7 April 1983 (LR) and 17 September 1983 (JAH, TSH, CVP, WHP); at Dhahran, 3 April 1984 (GKB).

Apus affinis · LITTLE SWIFT — VAGRANT

One at Abqaiq on 11 March 1983 (GKB, JP, LR). One at Abqaiq on 12 August 1983 (JB, JP, LR, CVP, WHP). One at Haradh on 19 October 1984 (JHM, JP).

Family ALCEDINIDAE

Halcyon smyrnensis — VAGRANT
WHITE-BREASTED KINGFISHER

One at Dhahran on 4 and 5 October 1984 (GKB, JAH, TSH, CVP, WHP). One overwintered at a sewerage effluent pool in the Aramco compound at Dhahran from early November 1985 to early March 1986 (BG, JAH, ALL, JP).

Alcedo atthis · KINGFISHER — WV

An annual but usually scarce visitor from August through March, mostly encountered from August to November. It is commonest in tidal creeks and near pools close to the coast. A few reach the Abqaiq lagoons and Hofuf drainage lakes and irrigation canals, some 50–60 km from the Gulf coast.

Ceryle rudis · PIED KINGFISHER — (WV)

Very scarce and local but possibly an annual visitor between November and March in a few coastal localities, notably the tidal creeks near Qatif. One at Abqaiq on 4–5 November 1983 is the only inland record (JB, LR).

Family MEROPIDAE

Merops orientalis VAGRANT
LITTLE GREEN BEE-EATER

One about 5 km south of al-Khobar, 6 December 1974 (GKB). One at Jubail 24 October 1983 (JCB).

Merops superciliosus PM
BLUE-CHEEKED BEE-EATER

A regular migrant in varying numbers from March through May and from mid-August through October with small numbers sometimes in June, November and December. It is most numerous in March and October; it is often outnumbered by *M. apiaster* in spring but tends to be commoner than that species in autumn. It is not known to overwinter; December records were thought to be late migrants but one flying north at Hanidh on 18 January is difficult to explain.

Merops apiaster · BEE-EATER PM

A regular and conspicuous migrant from March through May and less commonly from August to early November. The main passage is in April and August, later than Blue-cheeked Bee-eater in spring but earlier in autumn. At least one 'pair' summered near Abqaiq in June and July 1980, without evidence of breeding. There are single unconfirmed records for January and February.

Family CORACIIDAE

Coracias garrulus · ROLLER PM

A regular migrant, annual but generally scarce from late March through May. In some years a small peak has been evident in late April. The return passage commences as early as July and reaches a peak during August, dwindling in September and October. At Jawb (22° 10'N 49° 51'E) single adults were seen on 7 and 27 September 1980 (GJR).

Coracias benghalensis · INDIAN ROLLER VAGRANT

One in the Dhahran area, December and January 1969–70 and another in 'spring' 1971 (LJ). One near Nariya, January 1979 (RR). One at Abqaiq on 25 March 1983 had probably been present since December 1982 (GKB, LR). This species could perhaps

Little Green Bee-eater (ALL)

be confused with immature *C. garrulus*. There are several unconfirmed records.

Family UPUPIDAE

Upupa epops · HOOPOE PM (WV)

Migrants are common from late February through April, usually absent from May through mid-July, but common again during a protracted passage from August through November. Peak numbers are generally recorded in March, September and October. It is scarce and irregular from December to early February.

Family PICIDAE

Jynx torquilla · WRYNECK PM

A scarce but annual migrant. A few birds are noted in April and early May. In autumn there is a more protracted passage with records from August through October and once in early November. A very unusual date for this species was a single bird on 18 February 1984 at Abqaiq (JP).

Blue-cheeked Bee-eater (GKB)

Indian Roller (GKB)

Hoopoe (GKB)

Family ALAUDIDAE

The larks are well represented in eastern Arabia; of fourteen species recorded, eight probably breed regularly. Terrestrial species, well adapted to arid conditions, they are widespread but seldom numerous. Two species are no more than winter visitors, two are passage migrants from southern Asia and a further two are vagrants.

Of the breeding species only four are well known, two are very local and two have distributions still to be worked out. The breeding seasons, as well as distributions, behaviour and ecology, are not well known. Outside the breeding season, some species are nomadic and roam the desert in flocks while others concentrate in quite large numbers in recently developed areas of cultivation.

Identification problems may be experienced in this region with the two desert larks *Ammomanes* and Dunn's Lark (*Eremalauda dunni*), the two short-toed larks *Calandrella* and possibly the skylarks *Alauda arvensis* and *A. gulgula*.

The two desert larks are usually found in different habitats: DESERT LARK (*A. deserti*) in hills and rocky areas, BAR-TAILED DESERT LARK (*A. cincturus*) in flatter, partially vegetated sandy or gravel desert. *A. deserti* has a longer, stouter, usually yellowish bill and a rather thrush-like appearance; the smaller *cincturus* has a more rounded head, a smaller, stubbier, grey bill and a noticeable sharp dark band across the tail tip when it flies.

The other 'desert' lark is DUNN'S LARK; it may be found on open plains close to Bar-tailed. It has a larger, pale, finch-like bill with a down-curved cutting edge. Unlike the two *Ammomanes*, it is lightly marked on the greyish head and mantle with wavy gingery striations. Some examples are lightly streaked on the breast and sides of the neck although there appears to be some individual variation. The greyness of the mantle may vary too, for some birds in breeding areas look uniform sandy-brown. The wings look bright ginger and in birds seen in the Eastern Province between September and February this contrasts quite well with the greyish mantle. The tail should also distinguish this little known species from the two *Ammomanes*: it is essentially dark, often looking blackish in the field; the central feathers are in fact brown and the outermost feathers have a paler edge. The calls are poorly documented in the literature. Wintering flocks have been heard uttering a brief trilling alarm, like the chirrup of Short-toed Lark but shorter and less dry, 'trrp-trrp'; also in alarm 'chip-chip-tweee', the last note almost a whistle.

The two *Calandrella* larks are generally present at different times, the Short-toed Lark (*C. brachydactyla*) in spring and autumn, the Lesser Short-toed Lark (*C. rufescens*) mainly in the winter. They have different calls, best learnt in the field, and while there are subtle differences in wing length and wing markings, the best character is probably the breast markings and the neck patch. Lesser Short-toed has a fairly noticeable zone of breast striations; most Short-toed do not, although the latter is variable and does not always have the 'characteristic' little dark patch on the side of the neck. The folded wing shape is diagnostic if it can be seen in the field: in Short-toed the tertials reach almost to the tips of the primaries while in Lesser Short-toed they fall well short. The Lesser Short-toed's call is a sharp, hard little rattle, while the Short-toed has a 'chirrup' that may recall the dry note of a House Martin.

According to most of the standard field guides, vagrant Small Skylarks should be almost indistinguishable from Skylark, but recent experience in the Eastern Province has shown that the bird has some very distinctive characteristics: in general proportions it resembles a miniature (two-thirds size) Crested Lark, rather than a Skylark, and with its short tail it suggests a Woodlark in some ways, though the buffish-white outer tail feathers distinguish it from that species; its call is particularly distinctive, a buzzy, almost spluttering 'shl-l-l-eerrp', quite unlike any other Eastern Province lark.

Eremopterix nigriceps · BLACK-CROWNED FINCH LARK — RB MB

A widespread breeding species in open, lightly vegetated, sandy desert. There would appear to be two distinct populations in the Province, one migratory and one resident. South of about 25°N the birds in eastern Arabia remain around the breeding localities throughout the year and have an earlier breeding season than those to the north. At Haradh (26° 35′N 50°E) it is a not uncommon resident, often encountered in small flocks and breeding in March (JHM, JP). In Oman it breeds from February to April, the resident breeding population being apparently swollen by a winter influx (Gallagher & Woodcock 1980).

North of about 25°N in the Eastern Province of Saudi Arabia it is very scarce in winter; odd birds or small groups have been noted in coastal areas from January through March but it is generally absent. In late April there is a large influx, although numbers appear to vary from year to year, and song flights begin as soon as the males are on territory. The first clutches are laid by the end of April. In May assemblies of up to about 400, but probably more, have been noted near the coast. These large atypical flocks are thought most likely to have been migrants, perhaps bound for Iran, since many birds were already breeding nearby. Males have been seen performing song flights as late as June at Abu 'Ali, several weeks after breeding had finished near Dhahran. There appears to be no evidence for more than a single brood in the region (JHM, JP). The nest is placed on the ground in a small hollow, usually at the side of a clod of soil, a grass tuft or a small plant, and is surrounded by a glacis of small pebbles. The 'cup' is relatively deep and is neatly lined with fine grasses or other vegetable matter, occasionally hair and natural wool fibres. The 2–3 eggs have a dirty white ground, irregularly spotted with varying tones of liver brown. Ashy shell marks are sometimes present (RJC). Most adults leave the breeding areas as soon as the young fledge. It is then more gregarious and during the hottest months flocks tend to congregate around the edges of muddy pools. From mid-June onwards there is a reduction in the number of birds present and departure of the northernmost migrant populations is generally complete by late September.

Eremalauda dunni · DUNN'S LARK — RB WV

The breeding distribution of this species in the Eastern Province needs to be clarified. It was found breeding in the desert near 'Ain Dar from 1975 to 1977 (GKB) but subsequent searches there have proved unsuccessful. A nest found on 16 April 1976 was in a tuft of grass, the entrance facing east. The 'cup' was deep and sparsely lined with fine dried grasses and some feathers. It then contained 3 eggs, and, when next visited on 19 April, 5 eggs. They were whitish, spotted with brown intermingled

Black-crowned Finch Lark (GKB)

with ashy purple, which tended to form a denser band at the broad end. On 30 April 1976, the nest contained young, 3–4 days old (GKB). In 1984 it was found in April and May breeding widely in the south of the Province, from Haradh to 'Udhailiyah, and fledglings were seen on 24 May (JP). At Judah also, it was found breeding, with juveniles seen on 20 July (JP). Small parties are regularly seen on the steppes between Nariya and Qaisumah from September to February, but searches there in March, April and May have so far been unsuccessful. These flocks may be nomadic wintering flocks from Jordan or from central Arabia where it is said to be common (Jennings 1980). Individuals have been seen from late July through September, albeit irregularly, at Abqaiq and Dhahran airport.

Identification: see p. 156.

Ammomanes cincturus RB

BAR-TAILED DESERT LARK

Where suitable habitat exists, this lark has a widespread breeding distribution in the Eastern Province. It frequents flat, stony desert and seems to avoid the broken rocky places generally associated with the Desert Lark. It has been recorded breeding from March (JP) in scattered localities to the west of Nariya in the north, sparingly around 'Ain Dar to the west of Abqaiq and in the vicinity of Haradh to the south. It probably breeds on the Summan plateau, and to the west of Hofuf, but confirmation is required. The nest is placed in a hollow under a small tuft of grass or an overhanging piece of stone, and is usually supported by a pebble glacis. The 'cup' is thinly lined with fine grasses and other vegetable material, sometimes with the addition of hairs or natural wool fibres. Two to three eggs are laid; they are dull white, sparsely marked with grey and lilac freckles which tend to be denser at the large end (RJC).

Identification: see p. 156.

Ammomanes deserti · DESERT LARK RB

Although widespread, in some areas is very thinly distributed and easily overlooked. During the breeding season appears to be confined to stony desert, especially around rocky outcrops and scree slopes. It is generally absent from the sandy plains covering much of the Province. The nest is usually placed in a hollow below a projecting piece of stone and does not always have a pebble glacis. It is thinly lined with vegetable material and sometimes animal hair or natural wool. The eggs are 2–4 in number, usually 3, and tend to be similar in appearance to those of the Bar-tailed Desert Lark, although they show greater variation and are slightly larger (RJC). Odd birds are recorded away from breeding places from July through March and may form small nomadic parties. It visits the stubble fields on the Haradh cultivation as well as the gravel desert flanking the enclosed farm area.

Identification: see p. 156.

Alaemon alaudipes · HOOPOE LARK RB

A widespread species on sandy desert plains where there is some light and scattered vegetation. Although thinly distributed it seems to occur throughout the region from the gravel plains of the Dibdibah, across the sandy Jafurah, to the empty wastes around Yabrin and Jawb. It appears to be absent only from extensive areas of *sabkha* and some of the larger stretches of high dunes. Unlike the *Ammomanes* larks it also extends to arid places quite close to the sea. The song flights are a feature of the desert wilderness from late January. The nest is usually quite well hidden under a projecting stone, a small salt bush, or some other vegetation; but it may be in an open situation, or off the ground in a thick bush. For a lark's nest, it is well constructed, of grasses and dried bents, lined with finer grasses, hair and wool. Two to three eggs are laid. They are

Bar-tailed Desert Lark (GKB)

Desert Lark (ALL)

Below:
Hoopoe Lark (ALL)

white, greenish white or very pale stone coloured, often showing large greyish shell markings, blotched and spotted with reddish brown (RJC). Eggs have only been seen in March and young still in the nest in mid-April (JP).

Ramphocoris clotbey · THICK-BILLED LARK WV

Regular only at Haradh where up to 80 have been seen on the farmlands between September and April. Only twice has it been seen elsewhere: a party of six was seen near Harmaliyah, about 50 km north of Haradh, on 21 November 1975 and one about 25 km north of Hofuf on 20 August 1976 (GKB).

Melanocorypha calandra VAGRANT
CALANDRA LARK

Single individuals at Dammam on 19 December 1975 and at Abqaiq on 19 November 1977 (GKB).

Melanocorypha bimaculata PM
BIMACULATED LARK

Possibly regular only in spring; during February and March it has been noted from Qaisumah in the north to Haradh in the south. Usually it is seen in small flocks, though up to about 100 have been noted at Haradh (JP) and in March 1982, on the steppes west of Nariya after heavy rain, a concentration of about 5,000 was seen, most of which had passed on by the following morning (JHM, JP). In autumn it is less often seen but it has been noted at Abqaiq and the Shedgum area from late October to mid-December while at the extensive Haradh cultivation up to 60 have been seen in December. At Haradh the freshly sown fields support a multitude of larks in winter but the locality is difficult of access and this species could possibly have been overlooked. It seems likely that some birds may spend the winter in the Province but this has yet to be established.

Bimaculated Lark (GKB)

Crested Lark (ALL)

Calandrella brachydactyla · SHORT-TOED LARK PM

A regular migrant but seldom very numerous except perhaps at Haradh where numbers are often difficult to assess. The peak passage is during March, September and October. Generally it is more numerous and widespread in spring. There was a spectacular passage over the Dibdibah on 18 March 1983, when an estimated 4,000 were heading northwards; and seven days later 800–1,000 were seen there (JP, DR). Odd birds occur infrequently and inexplicably in June, July and rarely August although there is no suspicion that it breeds in the Eastern Province. In autumn it is usually found in small numbers although recently far larger numbers have been noted at Haradh where it had previously been overlooked. By mid-October numbers have diminished and Lesser Short-toed Lark becomes numerous.

Identification: see p. 157.

Calandrella rufescens WV RB
LESSER SHORT-TOED LARK

Small numbers breed on vegetated *sabkha* near the sea at Abu 'Ali, Ras az-Zawr, Manifa and also on the Dibdibah. It may also breed on similar ground just west of Abqaiq and north of Hofuf. Song flights have been noted at Abu 'Ali, Haradh and Abqaiq from March through May and recently fledged young have been seen as late as early August. For nesting, it lines a natural depression or shallow scrape with fine vegetable matter, hairs and wool, etc, frequently in the shelter of a small plant, but also in quite open situations. Usually 3 eggs are laid. They are whitish or pale greenish grey, heavily spotted with pale brown and grey shell markings (RJC). It wanders away from the breeding areas in late summer and large numbers arrive during October from elsewhere. From October through to early March it occurs across the northern steppes, on the stony Shedgum plateau, at Abqaiq and near inundated areas north of Hofuf. By far the largest concentrations occur on the Haradh cultivation where it has been conservatively estimated that 5,000 overwinter. Most of the wintering flocks have departed by late February and early March, so competition with the migrant Short-toed Lark is minimal.

Identification: see p. 157.

Opposite above: *Short-toed Lark (GKB)*
Opposite below: *Skylark (GKB)*

Galerida cristata · CRESTED LARK RB

A common and widespread resident on lightly vegetated semi-desert, waste ground, cultivations and roadsides especially in the coastal zone. Away from the coastal vegetation it is widely distributed but decidedly local, being absent from large tracts of *sabkha* and sand dunes. It is a common resident at Haradh; and it was present daily around the camp at Jawb, about 300 km south of Haradh, from July through October (GJR). The nest is built on the ground, in a depression, usually in close proximity to a clump of grass or other vegetation. The cup is deep and well formed of fine grasses, lined with hair, wool and occasionally a few feathers. Three to four eggs are laid, dirty white with grey shell markings, heavily spotted with liver brown (RJC). Laying begins in March, and fledged juveniles are in evidence from mid-April onwards. Larger assemblies from June through September are composed mainly of juveniles and there is no evidence of immigration.

Alauda arvensis · SKYLARK WV

Although of annual occurrence it is usually rather scarce. It occurs throughout the better vegetated parts of the coastal zone from November through March, frequently extending south to Salwah and west to Abqaiq, Hofuf and Hanidh, although flocks seldom exceed 50.

Identification: see p. 157.

Alauda gulgula · SMALL SKYLARK VAGRANT

A party of at least 5 was present at Dhahran from 17 October 1984; up to 4 birds remaining until 14 March 1985 (GKB, JHM, JP, JAH, TSH).

Identification: see p. 157.

Eremophila bilopha RB
TEMMINCK'S HORNED LARK

Occurs mainly in the north of the Province. It breeds on the stony, partially vegetated plains of the Dibdibah north of the TAP-line road, and Qaisumah. In 1983 it was apparently breeding in the Jabal Shadgam area north of 'Uray'irah, where 3 pairs were seen (IR); and it was present in the Haradh area from April to October 1984 (JP). The nest is placed at the side of a tuft of grass or a prominent stone, and is nearly always surrounded by a glacis of small pebbles. The 'cup' is fairly deep and lined with fragments of dried vegetation, hairs and wool. Two eggs are normally laid; they are white or very pale pink, finely speckled with yellowish brown and lilac, often forming a zone or cap at the larger end (RJC). A nest was seen north of Wadi al-Batin in March (RR), and juveniles were seen in March 1983 on the Dibdibah. It becomes gregarious after the breeding season and flocks around the al-Musannah camp increased during May through September until a maximum of about 150 were present in autumn (GJR).

Family HIRUNDINIDAE

Seven species of swallows are represented here; one breeds, one is a vagrant and the remainder are migrants.

The only identification problems in this family are likely to concern the two crag martins *Ptyonoprogne*. In the Eastern Province the resident PALE ROCK MARTIN (*P. fuligula*) is a greyish-fawn bird, less sandy coloured than the North African populations and appreciably paler than the migrant CRAG MARTIN (*P. rupestris*). The Crag Martin looks dark brown above with deeper buff underparts and throat. Both species, when seen from below, have the wing-coverts darker than the flight feathers to some degree; however, the underwing-coverts of the Crag Martin are much darker than those of any Pale Rock Martin, whose underwing looks almost uniform with little contrast between the wing-coverts and the rest of the wing.

Riparia paludicola VAGRANT
BROWN-THROATED SAND MARTIN

One at Abqaiq lagoons, 14 May 1982 (GKB).

Riparia riparia · SAND MARTIN PM

An abundant migrant from March through May and from late August through October. Numbers are often difficult to assess satisfactorily but there have been consistent peaks in passage during the middle weeks of March and the latter half of September.

It has been noted annually in June and July in the coastal zone but is always scarce. Sightings decline sharply in November, and although it has been seen from December through February it is usually absent then.

Ptyonoprogne fuligula · PALE ROCK MARTIN RB

Breeds locally on rocky *jabals* and escarpments in the desert and is present throughout the year. Never very numerous, up to about 25 pairs have been noted around one rocky outcrop although its numbers are possibly restricted by suitable nesting areas. Prefers to nest on the inner face of an overhanging rock formation, frequently above the mouth of a cave, or in a crack in a cliff face. The nest is built of mud pellets, cemented to the rock in the shape of a half cup. An existing nest is frequently repaired and reused in successive years. It is lined with small pieces of vegetable matter, hairs, natural wool and a few feathers. Three to four eggs are laid towards the end of March. They are very thin shelled, white, with a few spots of reddish brown (RJC). It can be seen hawking silently around the nesting cliffs throughout the year but from October through March small numbers feed over the lagoons at Abqaiq, al-Qarn and elsewhere. It is usually absent from the coastal zone.

Identification: see opposite page.

Ptyonoprogne rupestris · CRAG MARTIN (PM)

Although it has not been recorded annually, it is probably regular in small numbers during March and April, when it is encountered mainly in coastal areas; it has been less frequently noted inland, although confusion with the last species may account for this. There appears to have been a substantial increase in its occurrence in recent years: at Jabal 'Ain Dar 5 were seen on 9 April 1982 and 8 on 13 April 1984 (GKB); on the Shedgum escarpment, north of Hofuf, there were 6 on 12 April 1984 (CVP), 8 the following day, resting on a rock face in a *shamal* (GKB), and 2 still present on 4 May.

Identification: see opposite page.

Hirundo rustica · SWALLOW PM

An abundant migrant throughout the Province. The highest numbers are consistently noted during March through May and from August to early November. Numbers drop sharply during November and it is scarce, although seen annually, from December through February. In some years numbers increase during February although it is usually outnumbered at this time by Red-rumped Swallow. During June and July it is again scarce but recorded annually.

A nest said to belong to this species has been found once in Bahrain and juveniles have been seen being fed there in early April and July (Gallagher & Rogers 1978). A bird ringed as a nestling in Czechoslovakia at 50°N 18°E on 11 June 1976 was found dead at Dammam on 16 April 1977 (BTO).

Hirundo daurica · RED-RUMPED SWALLOW PM

Common annually in February and March; numbers decline in the latter half of March and it becomes very scarce during April and May. Two were at Abqaiq on 29 June 1984 (DJBro, GKB). It is usually absent in autumn but there are a few records in September and October, including one at Jawb on the northern fringe of the Rub' al-Khali on 23 October (GJR). One on 13 December 1975 was exceptional (GKB).

Delichon urbica · HOUSE MARTIN PM

It is often common from late January through March with a noticeable peak in February and early March. Birds are occasionally noted in April, less often in May, June, and September through November, with only single sightings for July, August and December. Occurrences after the rather brief spring passage often coincide with dust storms or overcast weather, suggesting a larger, higher and unseen migration than is evident from the ground.

Family MOTACILLIDAE

Seven species of pipits *Anthus* and four wagtails *Motacilla* occur in the region. All except Richard's and Olive-backed Pipit are regular visitors.

While the adult wagtails are readily identified, many observers have problems with the brown and white, rather featureless pipits. The species are usually commonest at different times, often frequent different areas, even on passage, and have quite different calls.

Juvenile CITRINE WAGTAILS, until they acquire a yellow-faced appearance in late October, resemble the common White Wagtails but they lack the black 'necklace', have a broad buffish-white stripe over the eye, greyish flanks and two bold white wing bars.

Most text books are concerned with similarity to the closely related Yellow Wagtail but that species is always olive or olive-brown in tone rather than grey, has whiter flanks and usually much less obvious wing bars. Assuming that the observer is familiar with the shrill 'tsweeep' note of Yellow Wagtail, the voice is a good distinction. The usual call of the Citrine is lower pitched than this, drier, reedier and sometimes almost buzzing in quality. Once known, the birds can be identified by call alone, as can most of the closely allied pipits.

TAWNY PIPITS in their first autumn are rather like RICHARD'S PIPITS but moult by October and then resemble the pale adults. They are always more wagtail-like, less bulky with a more horizontal stance and have a less robust bill. Tawny's call is more like the 'tsweeep' of Yellow Wagtail; the call of Richard's is harsher, louder and more sparrow-like.

The two pale-legged *Anthus* species, MEADOW PIPIT and TREE PIPIT, are not usually seen at the same time of the year in eastern Arabia. Meadow Pipits search out open ground where there is some grass, while Tree Pipits are often associated with the presence of some trees. This is not necessarily true of migrants. The Tree Pipit looks more elongated, more olive above and buffer below, especially on the breast and flanks, and has a more pronounced buff moustachial stripe; it has a distinctive, buzzing 'teez' call quite different from the thin 'pip-pip-tit-tit-tit' calls of Meadow.

The spring RED-THROATED PIPITS are easily identified but autumn and winter birds that lack the rufous throat and breast might be overlooked. In winter it is a darker and more heavily, sometimes very heavily, streaked bird especially on the rump, than either Meadow or Tree Pipit. Red-throated Pipit has a quite distinctive call, and when it is known birds can be readily identified by the voice alone; this is a thin 'teee', slightly descending in pitch and lacking the buzzing quality of the Tree Pipit's note. The wintering WATER PIPITS are darker than Meadow and Tree and perhaps more like Red-throated at first glance. It is the only species dealt with here that has dark legs. Even in winter plumage it is almost unmarked below; the greyish head is paler than the dark brown upper parts and most birds exhibit a noticeable supercilium. The call is quite like a Meadow Pipit's but harsher, lower pitched and not usually repeated quickly. Mention might also be made of the OLIVE-BACKED PIPIT (*A. hodgsoni*), an eastern Palearctic species that has occurred as a vagrant on at least one occasion. It is superficially like a Tree Pipit but darker above and whiter below with less buff tones. The closed wing shows two distinct whitish bars and the underparts are quite boldly striated with black across the breast and along the flanks. One of the more striking characters is a conspicuous supercilium that broadens behind the eye and is lacking or much less noticeable in other pipits. The call is a high pitched 'twee' or 'tsweep', slightly descending in pitch; it lacks the harsh quality of Tree Pipit and the thin sound of Red-throated.

Tawny Pipit (ALL)

Anthus novaeseelandiae VAGRANT
RICHARD'S PIPIT

Two at Dhahran, from 14 to 18 December 1982 and thereafter at least one until 3 March 1983 (GKB, JP, DR). One at Haradh on 19 October 1984 (JHM, JP). One at Qatif on 20 December 1984 (GKB). One at Dhahran 12 November 1984 (JHM, JP).

Anthus campestris · TAWNY PIPIT PM WV

A regular migrant occurring throughout the region from February to early May and from September through December. It is usually scarcer in the autumn period, numbers increasing in late November and December with a few remaining during January and February; the main arrival in spring is during March.

Identification: see above.

Red-throated Pipit (GKB)

Anthus hodgsoni · OLIVE-BACKED PIPIT VAGRANT

One at Dhahran spray fields on 17 October 1984 (JHM, JP) and one (perhaps the same bird) on 1 November 1984 (GKB).

Identification: see opposite page.

Anthus trivialis · TREE PIPIT PM

Scarce but regular from March to early May with a small peak detectable in April. There is a small autumn passage from September through November with a peak in late September and early October. Most are seen in isolated 'green' areas of the coastal zone and numbers are usually about equal on each passage. From November to January it has been recorded irregularly at Dammam, and more regularly at Dhahran where small numbers were noted wintering in the period 1975–1977 and in 1980 and 1981.

Identification: see opposite page.

Anthus pratensis · MEADOW PIPIT WV

Until 1981 occurred regularly at Dhahran on grassy fields sustained by controlled flooding from nearby sewerage effluent evaporation ponds. Up to 30 birds fed and roosted there between October and early March with fewer sometimes into April. A few individuals have been seen during this period at Hofuf and Abqaiq but occurrences away from the coastal zone are irregular.

Identification: see opposite page.

Anthus cervinus · RED-THROATED PIPIT PM WV

A common spring migrant occurring from March through May with a peak in numbers during April. It is less numerous during autumn, September through November, although towards the end of this period in 1980 it was common at Haradh. Small numbers sometimes remain throughout the winter near inundated areas north of Hofuf and at Abqaiq. It is always most numerous near water and on irrigated crops or marshy places.

Identification: see opposite page.

Anthus spinoletta · WATER PIPIT WV

The first arrivals are noted in late October but the main arrival is in early November. It is common until late March and only a few stragglers are seen in

April. It chiefly frequents the coastal zone, inland to Abqaiq, Hofuf and as-Sarrar. It is very scarce at Haradh in the south.

Identification: see p. 166.

Motacilla flava · YELLOW WAGTAIL **PM**

A common, often abundant, migrant throughout the region, but chiefly localized near pools and wet places. It is conspicuous in suitable places from March through May; and possibly more numerous from August through October. It becomes scarce during November and is generally absent from December through February although it has been noted up to mid-December, especially on some offshore islands (RJC). In autumn when numbers are swollen by the presence of many juveniles, birds probably remain for longer periods than in spring. During the autumn passage large roosts are established in some reed beds. Communal roosting is less apparent in spring. In spring fresh plumaged and distinctive males of the races *feldegg*, *beema*, *lutea* and *thunbergi* arrive, with some overlap, in that

Water Pipit (ALL)

Yellow Wagtail (ALL) *Immature female with plumage indications of the race* thunbergi.

order. It is very scarce again and usually absent in June and July. Migrants were noted almost daily during September and October 1980 at Jawb on the northern fringe of the Rub' al-Khali (GJR).

Motacilla citreola · CITRINE WAGTAIL WV

A local though apparently regular winter visitor in small numbers. It has been observed mainly at the Abqaiq lagoons, but also at Qatif, Dammam, Dhahran and al-'Uyun.

It was first noted at Dammam marsh, with records of single birds on five separate occasions between February 1975 and December 1976 (GKB). It was next detected in October 1981 at Abqaiq, when up to five birds were present until early December (GB), and since then, largely due to observer familiarity with its field characters, it has been recorded annually. The earliest arrival on record is of five immatures on 24 August 1984 at Abqaiq, and a late August arrival may prove to be usual, birds having been overlooked in the past. The main presence is from October to December,

Yellow Wagtail male showing characteristics of flavissima *and* lutea. *(GKB)*

Citrine Wagtail (GKB)

White Wagtail (GKB)

and numbers then seem to drop though sightings, usually of single birds, have been made up to late March. The Abqaiq lagoons have attracted the largest numbers, with up to five birds present in each of the four years from 1981 to 1984.

Identification: see p. 165.

Motacilla cinerea · GREY WAGTAIL PM

A scarce but annual migrant from February through April, occasionally in May; with small numbers reappearing fairly regularly from August through October. One at Dhahran on 9 December 1981 was probably a late migrant, although a bird wintered at Hofuf in 1923–4 (Ticehurst & Cheesman 1925). It is usually seen singly near water.

Motacilla alba · WHITE WAGTAIL WV PM

An abundant winter visitor throughout the Province. The main arrival is during October with the spring departure in April; birds are only very occasionally met with in May and September. It is commonest around settlements, near pools and sewage works, and in cultivation and irrigated gardens. Many hundreds roost on car parks and other open spaces in the Aramco compound at Dhahran during April (RJC). This suggests that many of these birds may be on passage over the coastal zone at that time and are possibly attracted by reflections on the ground that can look like water from above. On the same theme, counts at Abqaiq lagoons of 700 in March 1976 and 600 in February 1977 were a huge increase on wintering numbers, and were obviously freshly arrived migrants, many apparently of the central USSR race *dukhunensis* (GKB). Onward passage in autumn is also suggested by the small numbers present in the open desert at Jawb (22°N 50°E) through September and October 1980 (GJR). Observations at Jawb were terminated on 1 November and it is not known whether or not these birds passed on or wintered at the site.

Family PYCNONOTIDAE

Pycnonotus leucogenys RB
WHITE-CHEEKED BULBUL

A common resident in the coastal zone. It is especially conspicuous in the Aramco compounds at Ras Tanura, Dhahran and Abqaiq, and in the oases of Qatif and Hofuf. It favours neglected palm groves, tamarisk scrub and well established gardens, where it often becomes very tame. Breeding begins in February. Most pairs are double or even treble brooded (RJC). The nest is usually placed in a fork, frequently of a lateral branch, between 2 and 5 metres high. It is scantily constructed, of coarse grasses and fine twiglets; frequently embodying a discarded piece of paper, and lined with finer materials, such as hair, wool and vegetable down. 2–4 eggs are laid. When fresh, they appear to be pinkish or purplish, heavily blotched with deep reddish brown and lilac; but the colour quickly fades and museum specimens have a white ground colour (RJC).

White-cheeked Bulbul (ALL)

Grey Hypocolius (ALL)
An elusive species endemic to the Gulf area, much given to skulking in overgrown palm groves.

Pycnonotus xanthopygos VAGRANT
YELLOW-VENTED BULBUL

Up to five at Haradh during February 1980 (JCD).

Family BOMBYCILLIDAE

Hypocolius ampelinus · GREY HYPOCOLIUS WV

A regular but local winter visitor from November through April.

It is unobtrusive and easily overlooked, frequenting thick palm scrub in oases and cultivated areas, often near settlements. It has been noted at Mulayjah, Nata and Hanidh in the north-west and also at Safwa, Qatif, Salasil, al-'Uyun, and Haradh. The highest numbers recorded were in the 1982–83 winter, when 85–120 were seen at Salasil (GKB, JP, LR); in December 1983 40 were observed at al-'Uyun, north of Hofuf (JP). In April odd males have been seen in scrub with migrants at Haradh and south of al-Kharj, away from the usual palms, suggesting that some are on the move during that month.

Family TURDIDAE

A large family, represented here by thirty-three species in ten genera. Only two species breed in the Eastern Province, six are currently thought to be vagrants and the remainder are more or less regular visitors. In addition to this assemblage, a further vagrant, Hume's Wheatear (*Oenanthe alboniger*), has been noted once in Qatar; and twice, in October and January, on Bahrain (Bundy & Warr 1980).

With the exception of the two nightingales *Luscinia luscinia* and *L. megarhynchos* and the wheatears *Oenanthe*, few identification problems are likely to arise. The first pair are dealt with adequately in field guides but the wheatears, especially the females, are curiously neglected in most of the available books.

Eleven wheatear species have been recorded in the region. The males are distinctive as a rule; only in the Isabelline are the sexes alike although the eastern races of the Mourning Wheatear, unlike those in North Africa, do not exhibit sexual dimorphism. The following summary assumes that the observer is familiar with at least one species, the Northern Wheatear, which breeds across and beyond the entire Palearctic region from Greenland eastwards through Siberia and into Alaska. The entire population from this vast range winters in Africa south of the Sahara.

The males of the closely related, and possibly conspecific, PIED WHEATEAR and BLACK-EARED WHEATEAR are dimorphic, especially the latter. Some male Pied Wheatears have white throats; this rather rare morph has been called '*vittata*' and some examples occur in eastern Arabia each spring. The females of these two species are difficult to separate from each other (some may not be identifiable at all in the field) and from female Northern Wheatear. Female Pied Wheatears are dull, earthy brown above with black wings; the strikingly white rump and black tail pattern are as in the males. They usually show a distinct pale supercilium and a dusky grey throat. The underparts are whitish, with a buff wash often discernible across the breast. They usually look more black and white in the field than Black-eared Wheatears with less contrast between the black wings and dull brown upper parts. Most of the female Black-eared Wheatears occurring in eastern Arabia have a 'cleaner' appearance than Pied Wheatears, with a whiter throat and paler upper parts, the upper parts approaching the colour of Northern or even having a sandy tone.

In addition, Pied Wheatears in autumn, especially immatures, show pale fringes to the wing-coverts and mantle; these scale-like edgings contrast well with the grey-brown upper parts and are lacking in female Black-eared. The female NORTHERN WHEATEAR is familiar to most European observers and the more familiar one becomes with the commoner species the easier the task in recognizing the rarer birds. It is brown above and warm buffish below; most have an obscure mask and darker ear coverts which contrast with a pale supercilium; the wings are sooty-brown (not black) and the tail pattern is like the male's. ISABELLINE WHEATEARS are large, pale and sandy coloured, rather like a pale female Northern Wheatear but with paler, less contrasting wings, a whiter underwing and much more black on the tail. The black area on the tail of Isabelline Wheatear extends about two-thirds the length of the tail while in Pied, Black-eared and Northern, for example, there is only a narrow terminal band of black and black central feathers.

One other species with a basically brown and white female and 'typical' wheatear tail and rump pattern is FINSCH'S WHEATEAR. This species is uncommon in eastern Saudi Arabia and a preponderance of males has been recorded; females are almost certainly being overlooked. The female is rather nondescript with brownish-grey upper parts, probably paler than female Pied Wheatears, with greyer and much less contrasting wings than that species. The throat is usually grey with faint whitish feather edgings and the underparts are white, lacking the buff gorget of female Pied Wheatear.

In early spring each year since observations were begun in 1978 there has been a small influx of mysterious grey and white wheatears. They are pale grey above and white below with darker wings and a pale gingery patch on the undertail coverts. The blackish wings show pale inner webs along the primaries when the bird is in flight and this, together with the pale rufous vent, suggest that they are MOURNING WHEATEARS. They are quite unlike the typical pied wintering birds and may be birds in their first year. There may, however, be more variation in the eastern populations of Mourning Wheatear than we are yet aware of and *some* sexual dimorphism. It has also been suggested that

Mourning and Finsch's Wheatears may be conspecific and that the grey and white birds occurring in this region might be Finsch's or even hybrids.

Female and immature DESERT WHEATEARS are like small and dainty Isabelline Wheatears but have the whole tail black and often the small rump patch is buff rather than pure white. It has been suggested (*British Birds* 1981, 74: 443) that Isabelline Wheatears might be identified by their constant tail wagging but this is very evident in Desert Wheatears too.

Cercotrichas galactotes · RUFOUS BUSH CHAT MB

It arrives from mid-March and is locally common until late August. Most have left by the end of September. It is found in areas of tamarisk scrub, shady gardens and edges of cultivation, chiefly in the coastal zone but also at Abqaiq, Hofuf and Haradh, as well as at other villages in the interior. It is scarce away from the scattered breeding oases and there is little evidence of any passage. One at Jawb, 300 km south of Haradh, on 1 August was presumably an early migrant (GJR). Breeding begins in April and continues into May. The nest is usually placed against the bole of a tree, or on a lateral branch in thick tamarisk scrub. It is solidly constructed of tamarisk twiglets or dried grasses and lined with finer materials, often including a few hairs or feathers. 4 eggs are usually laid. They are white, with small flecks and spots of dark grey. In appearance, they closely resemble eggs commonly laid by the House Sparrow (RJC).

Cercotrichas podobe · BLACK BUSH CHAT VAGRANT

One, Haradh 10 April 1987 (MAE).

Erithacus rubecula · ROBIN (WV)

A rare and irregular visitor, though secretive, and perhaps more regular than the records indicate. There are now about 15 records, all except one in the period from November to March, and most of these in November and December. Eight of the sightings have been at Dhahran, but it has also been seen at Abqaiq and Qatif, nearly always singly, except for 4+ at Dhahran during December 1981 (GB). But for one at Jubail on 24 August 1983, which is outside the normal pattern of occurrences, the earliest arrival date was 11 November (at Abqaiq, in 1983).

Luscinia luscinia · THRUSH NIGHTINGALE (PM)

A rare passage migrant, perhaps regular, though doubtless overlooked due to its skulking behaviour. It was first seen in September 1981, and has now been recorded on about 13 occasions (involving 20 individuals).

The five spring records have all fallen in the period 25 April to 4 May, with 5 present on 3 May 1983 at Jubail (AD). Similarly, the eight autumn occurrences have been confined to a remarkably restricted period, from 11 to 26 September. It has been observed at Haradh, Abqaiq, Dhahran, Judah and Jubail.

Luscinia megarhynchos · NIGHTINGALE PM

Always scarce but has been recorded annually from March to early May. During the autumn period it has only been noted rarely to date, from September

Bluethroat (GKB)

Stonechat (female) (ALL)

Stonechat (male) (ALL)

to early October (JHM, JP), including one at Jawb in the southern desert (GJR). It is apparently common in the Dhofar region of southern Oman in autumn (Gallagher & Woodcock 1980) and most presumably overfly northern and eastern Arabia.

Luscinia svecica · BLUETHROAT WV PM?

Although rather local, it occurs throughout the region in suitable places from late August through April. Most have left by late March and the birds encountered in late April, early May and late August are probably on passage. It frequents overgrown gardens, reed beds and scrubby places preferably near water. Onward passage is indicated by two autumn occurrences at the Jawb camp (22°N 50°E): a juvenile on 14 September and an adult on 21 October 1980 (GJR).

Irania gutturalis · WHITE-THROATED ROBIN PM

A scarce but probably regular spring migrant from March to early May. In autumn it has only been noted twice: at Haradh in early August and at Dhahran in September.

Phoenicurus erythronotus VAGRANT
EVERSMANN'S REDSTART

Up to five at Ras Tanura in December and January 1970–1 (LJ). One at Haradh, 31 January 1980 (GB). One at Khurais, 14 November 1980 (PJI). One at Dhahran from 21 January to 28 February 1982 (GB, JHM, JP).

Phoenicurus ochruros · BLACK REDSTART WV

A scarce but widely distributed visitor from late October through March. It is seldom seen away from vegetated places and frequents gardens, oases, cultivation and the vicinity of scrub near water. Females are relatively scarce and all males are of the distinctive race *phoenicuroides*.

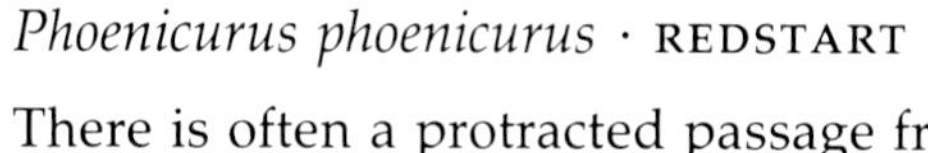

Phoenicurus phoenicurus · REDSTART PM

There is often a protracted passage from March to June with a consistent small peak in late April and early May. It is less regular and generally scarce from September through November and in some years only a few are seen. However, at Jawb on the northern fringe of the Rub' al-Khali, there were four in September and October 1980 (GJR). Some males in spring have conspicuous white wing patches and are thus of the eastern race *samamisicus*.

Above: *Isabelline Wheatear (GKB)*

Cercomela melanura · BLACKSTART VAGRANT

Two, al-'Aba oasis 23 April 1982 (JCB).

Saxicola rubetra · WHINCHAT PM

It is a regular but scarce spring migrant during April and May. One at Abqaiq on 29 June 1984 was unusual. It is even scarcer in the autumn in September and October. Two were noted in September and October at Jawb in the northern Rub' al-Khali (GJR).

Saxicola torquata · STONECHAT WV PM

A widespread, although never numerous, winter visitor from late August through February. The wintering birds, probably of the *maura/stejnegeri* populations, arrive mainly in October. Migrants become common during March when there is an arrival of strikingly different birds, apparently of the *armenica/variegata* populations that breed south and west of the Caspian Sea.

Oenanthe isabellina PM WV
ISABELLINE WHEATEAR

Chiefly a migrant although there is a regular scattering of birds throughout the winter from November through February, often in sparsely vegetated, open, sandy desert. Spring migrants are in evidence from late January through April and there is a consistent peak from late February through March. A few are seen almost annually in early May but June and July records are very few. The return passage starts in August and continues through November; the highest numbers usually occur during September. In 1980 onward passage was in

Left: *Pied Wheatear (GKB)*

evidence at Jawb in the northern Rub' al-Khali throughout August and until 1 November, with a peak there in October (GJR).

Identification: see p. 172.

Oenanthe oenanthe · NORTHERN WHEATEAR PM

A regular migrant, appearing from March through May and sometimes into early June, then again, but less numerously, from August through November. One was at Abqaiq on 29 June 1984 (DJBro, GKB). The spring peak is consistently in April, after the main passage of Pied Wheatear.

Identification: see p. 172.

Oenanthe pleschanka · PIED WHEATEAR PM

A common migrant from late February to early April. Numbers decline during April and although individuals have been noted as late as 30 May, it is usually absent from May through August. There is a variable autumn passage: birds occur from September to early November, exceptionally later, but never in the numbers that are present in spring. The autumn peak is consistently in October. A small passage was also apparent at Jawb on the northern fringe of the Rub' al-Khali in 1980, with a peak in numbers in late September (GJR).

Identification: see p. 172.

Oenanthe hispanica PM
BLACK-EARED WHEATEAR

A regular migrant, but always scarce, during March and early April. It is always much less numerous than the last two species. It is rare in autumn: there are a few records in September and exceptionally until early December. There were two at Jawb on 19 September 1980 (GJR).

Identification: see p. 172.

Oenanthe deserti · DESERT WHEATEAR WV PM

Common and widespread from September through March. The main arrival is during October with a sharp decline in numbers during March. After becoming very scarce in early April, it occurs again in late April and early May, albeit in very small numbers, suggesting that some are on passage from wintering grounds further south. There is some evidence of onward passage at Jawb in the northern Rub' al-Khali where an individual arrived (and departed) on 21 September and two occurred on 7 October 1980 (GJR). One on a ship some 50 km to the north-east of Ras Tanura on 17 March is also of interest (DMS).

Black-eared Wheatear (GKB)

Identification: see p. 173.

Oenanthe finschii · FINSCH'S WHEATEAR (WV)

Possibly an annual winter visitor in small numbers. It has been noted only since 1977, reflecting the better observer coverage in recent years. Although it has been noted as far south as Haradh and west to Khurais, it seems to be most regular and possibly more numerous in the northern half of the Province. It has occurred from early November through March.

Identification: see p. 172.

Oenanthe picata VAGRANT
EASTERN PIED WHEATEAR

One Jabal Umm Ar Ru'us 27 November 1986 (JP *et al*).

Oenanthe xanthoprymna WV
RED-TAILED WHEATEAR

A rather scarce winter visitor, that occurs throughout the Province from September to April, especially in the vicinity of *jabals* and rocky outcrops.

Oenanthe lugens · MOURNING WHEATEAR WV

A widespread visitor in substantial numbers from October through March. It occurs in open desert, especially near rocky outcrops; near villages and uncultivated areas but very seldom in the coastal zone. Birds collected near Hofuf by Meinertzhagen were of the race *persica*, which, unlike *halophila* of North Africa, does not exhibit sexual dimorphism. The wintering population is of black and white 'male' types but, as noted on p. 172, there is a small but regular influx during February and March of unfamiliar grey and white birds.

Identification: see p. 172.

Desert Wheatear (male) (ALL)

Desert Wheatear (female) (ALL)

Oenanthe monacha VAGRANT WV?
HOODED WHEATEAR

A male at Jabal Ghuraymil on 2 December 1976 (GKB) and two females on a *jabal* about 20 km south-west of Abqaiq on 10 and 18 February and 11 March 1977 (GKB, DMH, PJI). A male in hills some 35 km north of Hofuf on 15 November 1979 and a female on a *jabal* about 20 km north of 'Uray'irah on 28 January 1982 (GB). A male near 'Uray'irah on 2 December 1983 (JB, JP). A male at Judah on 6 April 1984 and single females on 20 and 27 June 1986 (JP).

Oenanthe leucopyga RB
WHITE-CROWNED BLACK WHEATEAR

Locally common, usually in the proximity of escarpments and *jabals*. Favours scree slopes and gullies containing rock debris. Most pairs are found between 'Uray'irah and Nata' with a few along the escarpment of the Shedgum plateau north of Hofuf. It is very rarely seen away from its breeding haunts. The nest is built of dried bents and grasses and the

Mourning Wheatear (GKB)

Hooded Wheatear (GKB)

White-crowned Black Wheatear (male) (ALL)

cup is lined with finer materials such as wool, hair, or a few feathers. It is usually placed out of reach in a deep crack amongst the rocks, or in a crevice at the mouth of a small cave. The eggs are very pale blue with fine reddish spots, usually forming a wreath about the broad end. There is no specific information on clutch size from the Eastern Province, but it is likely to consist of 4 or 5 eggs (RJC).

Monticola saxatilis · ROCK THRUSH — PM

A regular spring migrant from late February through to mid-May with the majority occurring in March. In autumn most birds presumably overfly the Province. It has been observed once at Abqaiq in late September and at Haradh it has been reported as common during September and early October. There are very few records from the coastal zone.

Monticola solitarius — PM (WV)
BLUE ROCK THRUSH

Chiefly a rather scarce migrant, most occurring in March and September. In March it occurs with some regularity, although only once near the coast, but numbers are probably less than half of those in autumn. Migrants, having presumably overflown the coast, occur with some regularity at Haradh in September where it is almost common. During the 1980 autumn watch at Jawb, 300 km further south, up to two were present between 15 and 29 September (GJR). It is also a scarce winter visitor, sometimes being noted from September through April on rocky outcrops in the desert away from the coastal zone.

White-crowned Black Wheatear (juvenile) (ALL)

Turdus torquatus · RING OUZEL — WV

A few individuals of both sexes remained at Dhahran during December and January 1970–1 after an influx of *Turdus* species (LJ). One at Dhahran during January 1972 (LJ). One at Abu 'Ali, 22 January 1977 (DMH). A male near Dammam, 8 February 1980 (RR). A male at Shedgum pools, 17 December 1982, was considered to be of the eastern race *amicorum* (GKB, JP, DR).

Turdus merula · BLACKBIRD — WV

Most records refer to first year males. At Dhahran, two during January and February 1974 (KJF, JAW); one, 4 February 1975 (GKB); up to two, 9 and 15 April 1975 (MSH); one, 2 March 1979 (DJBra); a female, 3 to 5 January 1980 (GB); one, 14 December 1982 (GKB). One at Abqaiq, 21 December 1979 (GB). At Dhahran: one present from 8 January to 21 February 1984 (JAH, TSH, CVP); one on 15 November 1984 (GKB).

Turdus ruficollis — (WV)
BLACK-THROATED THRUSH

Usually a scarce winter visitor from November to early March, but numbers vary from year to year and in some winters it is not recorded at all. In years when numbers are good, such as 1982–3, birds have been noted at oases and cultivated areas from the coast to Haradh and Hanidh. Single birds at Dhahran in April and May were possibly migrants.

Turdus pilaris · FIELDFARE — WV

Up to two at Dhahran, 23 November to 19 December 1973 (KJF, JAW). One at Dhahran on 23 January and two there on 5 March 1976 (GKB). At Abqaiq three on 14 November 1975, and two there the following day; two on 8 February 1976, and one on 2 February 1977 (GKB). One at Haradh, 31 January 1980 (GB).

Blue Rock Thrush (ALL)

Rock Thrush (ALL)

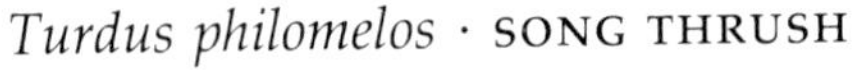

Turdus philomelos · SONG THRUSH WV

Locally fairly common in the vegetated areas of the coastal zone, occurring in varying numbers from November through March with only a few remaining into April. It is usually very scarce away from the coastal areas but if an influx occurs it is more widely distributed, although never in more than moderate numbers.

Turdus iliacus · REDWING (WV)

Single birds at Dhahran from 23 December 1973 to 23 January 1974; one on 13 February and two on 17 February 1974 (KJF, JAW). Individuals at the same locality from 8 to 19 December 1974 and on 4 and 15 February 1975; three on 16 and 23 January 1976 and two on 5 March 1976 (GKB). Two at Abqaiq on 25 November 1975; two at Abqaiq on 17 February 1976; and a party of 5 flying south over Abqaiq town on 30 November 1977 (GKB).

Turdus viscivorus · MISTLE THRUSH VAGRANT

One at Dhahran, 2 to 30 December 1982 (JB, JP). One at Abqaiq, 7 January 1983 (BW). There is also an unconfirmed report of a bird at Dhahran during an influx of *Turdus* species in 1970–1.

Family SYLVIIDAE

A large Old World family of insectivorous, mainly migratory birds dependent upon a wide variety of vegetation. Moreau (1972), dealing with the Africa-bound Palearctic migrants, listed 21 species belonging to this family which breed in the central portion of the Eurasian continent (45° to 90°E) and winter in tropical Africa; these are migrants which would presumably overfly Arabia en route. However, thirty-one species of six genera are included here. Only three breed in the Province, eleven are basically vagrants and the remaining seventeen are

Black-throated Thrush (GKB)

more or less regular migrants.

Identification problems for field observers and, in some species, even with birds in the hand, can be formidable in this family. Field identification of warblers requires patience, good uninterrupted views (itself often a problem) and perhaps some luck; very often a bird is skulking in thick cover and reveals itself only very briefly. Problems, especially for western based observers new to the Middle East, are often compounded by the appearance of birds from eastern populations not immediately recognizable in field guides. The following summary only attempts to highlight certain problems and the features which should be especially looked for.

The only regular *Locustella* warbler in the Province is Savi's Warbler and the migrants in eastern Arabia are usually *fusca*. This race from western Siberia and Transcaspia is decidedly duller above, olive or greyish-brown rather than rufous like the European populations. It tends to be whiter below with less buff along the flanks.

It can show some faint grey striations on the breast, but these are never as marked as in River Warbler. It seems likely now that some of the migrants trapped in Kuwait in the 1960s were Savi's Warblers and not River Warblers as was once supposed (Bundy & Warr 1980).

The *Acrocephalus* warblers are all brown above and whitish below and are often very difficult to see well. Perhaps the only satisfactory method for sorting out migrants in this genus is to trap them. We are mainly concerned here with spring adults, and some such migrants announce their presence and aid their identification by uttering phrases of song. Living in dense reed beds these birds would often be overlooked were it not for the songs, but normally all that is seen is a brown bird with a rounded tail diving into reeds. Great Reed Warblers are quite regular and, for this genus, almost conspicuous migrants. They have a heavy bill and a well marked pale supercilium that extends back past the eye. The Clamorous Reed Warbler has recently occurred in the region with singing males taking up reed bed territories at a number of localities. It can be identified by song, assuming that the observer is familiar with the repetitive chirpings and churrings of the better known Reed Warbler and Great Reed Warbler. The Clamorous Reed Warbler is about the size of the Great Reed Warbler and some familiarity with the latter might be desirable when attempting to make a positive identification. The Clamorous Reed Warbler has a longer looking bill and shorter, more rounded wings which do not extend past the tail coverts and so give a longer tailed impression. It also lacks the bold supercilium of the Great Reed Warbler; and the race of the Clamorous Reed Warbler likely to occur in eastern Arabia, *brunnescens*, is less rufous and more inclined to earthy or olive-brown tones.

In spring, Reed Warblers are probably commoner than records suggest. The Marsh Warbler is a later migrant and, in spring, looks as olive as the *Hippolais* warblers; though it tends to have browner tones. The Reed Warbler normally has a rusty-coloured rump. Marsh Warblers usually show a pale, thin stripe from bill to eye, often lacking in Reed Warblers but present in Blyth's Reed Warbler. It is doubtful whether the Marsh Warbler can be satisfactorily separated in the field from Blyth's Reed Warbler, although the Marsh Warbler has longer wings, a shorter bill on average and, most notable perhaps, paler, pink to straw-coloured legs. Autumn birds, especially the fresh plumaged immatures, are not safely identifiable in the field.

The race *mimica* of MOUSTACHED WARBLER which breeds in the Eastern Province is more like the Sedge Warbler than are European birds. It has a dusky crown, not as black as in western birds, and the well defined, square ended supercilium contributes to a facial expression that differs somewhat from the longer headed Sedge Warbler. The upper parts are olive rather than the rufous brown of the western birds, and the flanks are pale sandy-buff rather than rusty. It tends to be a dumpier, shorter-winged bird than the Sedge Warbler with a nervous habit of cocking the tail when disturbed, rather like some *Sylvia* warblers.

The *Hippolais* warblers are similar to *Acrocephalus* in outline although they have square, rather than rounded, tails. The largest species, OLIVE-TREE WARBLER, is almost the size of a Great Reed Warbler; it is greyish above and white below with darker wings. It may need to be separated from the superficially similar female and immature BARRED WARBLER, but it has a longer, heavier looking bill, a partial supercilium, usually longitudinal pale edgings along the closed wings and lacks the pale wing bars formed by the edges to the median and greater coverts which often show up well on Barred Warbler. The slightly smaller UPCHER'S WARBLER is superficially similar but should be easily identified being the only member of this genus which has a tail noticeably darker than the upper parts. The blackish looking tail is made more obvious by the bird's habit of continually elevating, lowering, fanning and waving it in a manner reminiscent of a shrike (*Lanius*).

The two smaller *Hippolais* species are even more difficult to identify although one, BOOTED WARBLER, is only a vagrant in the Eastern Province. The OLIVACEOUS WARBLER breeds locally in this region and is, on average, larger than the Booted Warbler with a noticeably longer bill and a 'bare-faced' expression. One race of the Booted Warbler, *rama*, breeding in southern Asia and as close to the Province as Iran, overlaps with Olivaceous Warbler in some measurements (Williamson 1976a). The Booted Warbler, however, has a rounder head with a less sloping, 'low' forehead than the Olivaceous Warbler. It has a shorter bill and this is probably the best character, assuming that the Olivaceous Warbler is well known to the observer. The low forehead, with the peak of the crown behind the eye of Olivaceous Warblers, tends to exaggerate the length of the bill. The Booted Warbler also has a dark line along the lores and just behind the eye and a pale supercilium which extends about as far behind the eye as it does in front. In Olivaceous Warblers there is a pale, ill defined area on the lores and hardly any supercilium extending behind the eye.

The *Sylvia* warblers are relatively easy to identify when they are seen well but one regular migrant to this region is often misleadingly illustrated in field guides. This is MENETRIES' WARBLER which is very similar to, perhaps even conspecific with, the Sardinian Warbler (*S. melanocephala*) of the Mediterranean region. The best character in birds of all ages is the pale, straw-coloured orbital ring. Males are seldom as pink below as depicted in field guides: of the males seen in the Eastern Province from 1979 through 1981 about 80% were creamy-white, buffish or pinkish-buff on the underparts; the remainder were pinkish-brown with the pink sometimes, but not invariably, extending to the throat. Females are rather nondescript but have the graduated black, white edged tail and greyish-brown upper parts of the Sardinian Warbler. They lack, however, the grey tones on the head of the Sardinian Warbler and are paler, and cleaner looking with the upper side sometimes approaching a sandy tone. They share the tail cocking habit and other mannerisms. There are races of the Sardinian Warbler, *momus* and *norrisae*, that resemble the Menetries' described above but they always have a red orbital ring.

The *Phylloscopus* warblers are a large assemblage of Palearctic species, with eight included here. Great caution is required with field identification. One of the relatively easy ones is the WOOD WARBLER with its bright yellow throat and pure white underparts. However, such is the high degree of variation in the migrant Willow Warblers occurring in this region that all but one record of Wood Warbler has been dropped, since it is now thought that some errors may have been made in the past.

WILLOW WARBLERS and CHIFFCHAFFS do not usually occur together in eastern Arabia and it is intended here only to draw attention to the wide variation in the migrant Willow Warblers. This species is remarkable in having an enormous distribution almost right across the Palearctic, breeding as far east as 145°E in eastern Siberia, with the whole population wintering in Africa south of the Sahara. Birds crossing Arabia might be from any part of the huge Asian half of that range, so some variability in plumage is to be expected. Perhaps the most common type is olive above and whitish below with a yellowish wash across the breast; it has a well marked supercilium and often a yellow area at the bend of the closed wing. Another type has no green or olive tones at all: it is dull brown above and off-white below, with sometimes the only trace of yellow being the mark at the bend of the wing. A yellow form is very different from the brown and white birds: it is much brighter green above and often the whole underparts are varying shades of yellow, sometimes with some light grey striations across the breast; it too has a fairly long and conspicuous supercilium. These three types are normally assigned to separate races, but the geographical variations seem clinal rather than regionally disjunct (see the discussion in Williamson 1976b).

Birds from western Europe are of the nominate race, *trochilus*, those from eastern Siberia are *yakutensis*, and those between, from eastern Scandinavia and Russia east to the Yenesi river basin, are *acredula*. The nominate form occurs in the south-west of this vast range and the brown and white types in the north and north-east, with all types of gradation between, so that it is impossible to define races with any degree of precision. All Willow Warblers have paler legs and longer wings than Chiffchaffs.

Prinia gracilis · GRACEFUL WARBLER RB

This species is a common resident, although rather local since it is confined in this region to reed beds and tamarisk scrub adjacent to water. It is found almost throughout the coastal zone where suitable areas still exist. Away from the coast it is abundant at the al-Hasa oases around Hofuf and al-'Uyun but it has not yet established itself in the Abqaiq area. The nest is placed in a clump of juncus, or low in a tamarisk, especially where there is a secondary growth of phragmites. It is a small, purse shaped structure, domed and with a well defined entrance at the side. It is built of dried phragmites flowers, fine grasses and spiders' webs; sometimes unlined, but at other times with a lining of vegetable down. Laying begins at the end of March and at least some pairs are double brooded. 3–5 eggs are laid. They are pinkish, closely flecked with orange-red pigment which often forms a zone about the larger end (RJC). It is rare away from its regular breeding areas, and occasional singing birds at Imhoff in late autumn have most likely been due to post juvenile dispersal from the nearby coastal marshes.

Locustella naevia VAGRANT
GRASSHOPPER WARBLER

One was obtained at al-'Uqayr, 29 March 1921 (Ticehurst & Cheesman 1925). One at al-Khobar, 23 March 1974 (GKB). Single birds at Abqaiq on 17 November 1977 (GKB), 1 May 1981 (GB, RH), 23 April 1982 (JHM, JP, DR) and 13 August 1982 (JHM, JP). One at Dhahran on 21 March 1984 (JAH, TSH) and another on 18 September 1984 (GKB, JHM).

Locustella fluviatilis · RIVER WARBLER VAGRANT

One, al-'Aba oasis 1 April 1983 (JCB).

Locustella luscinioides · SAVI'S WARBLER PM

A scarce but probably regular migrant, it is most likely overlooked like other skulking *Locustella*

Savi's Warbler (GKB)

warblers. In recent years it has occurred sparingly in March and April, and in September and October; in 1980 there was a small influx during late May. At a huge reed bed near al-'Uyun, one was heard singing in mid-June 1976; and at the same locality in late May 1982 one bird was seen carrying food in the bill and three other adults were seen (GKB). One bird has been seen at Dammam marsh in early December (GKB). The more recent, critically observed examples have been considered to be the race *fusca*.

Identification: see p. 181.

Acrocephalus melanopogon RB
MOUSTACHED WARBLER

It has been proved to breed only in the Hofuf drainage and irrigation system. On 18 April 1980, a nest containing 2 eggs was found near al-'Uyun. It was in a clump of juncus growing in shallow water amongst young phragmites. The nest was well concealed and built of coarse grasses that were woven around the juncus stems, and lined with finer grasses. A third egg was laid on 19 April and the bird then began to incubate. No further eggs were laid; they were off-white suffused with dull greyish olive markings (RJC). Although large areas of reeds subsequently died when the flow of water was rerouted, the species was found to be well established in several reed beds north of al-'Uyun in 1981. Singing males have been located at Abqaiq, at the former Dammam marsh, at Qatif and also at al-'Aba oasis, but breeding at these localities has not been established. One bird seen on board a ship at Ras Tanura, 11 November 1979 (DMS), suggests that some immigration may occur.

Identification: see p. 182.

Marsh Warbler (GKB)

Acrocephalus schoenobaenus · SEDGE WARBLER PM

A regular but usually scarce migrant noted from March to early June, mostly in May. The March records may however refer to the local race *mimica* of Moustached Warbler. The only autumn records are of single birds at Abqaiq on 17 and 28 September 1982 (GKB).

Identification: see p. 182.

Acrocephalus palustris · MARSH WARBLER PM

Although specifically recorded only from 1980 when one was trapped in May at Abqaiq, olive backed *Acrocephalus* become almost common during this month. In 1981 birds were detected and identified with certainty from mid-April to late May; more were trapped (JHM) and it was once again locally 'common'. There was an exceptional fall of migrants on 11 May 1984 at Abqaiq, when 29 were counted, and many more doubtless present (GKB, JP). It is also a regular migrant in Bahrain at this time (TJH). There are no autumn records.

Identification: see p. 181.

Acrocephalus scirpaceus · REED WARBLER PM MB?

It is scarce but also probably overlooked as it occurs typically in thick reed beds. It has been seen in the coastal zone, at Abqaiq and throughout the Hofuf drainage system. Migrants have been disturbed from long grasses and scrub adjacent to the artificially maintained water meadows and lagoons that formerly existed near Dhahran. Migrants arrive from late February and probably reach a peak during March, a full month before the Marsh Warbler. Small numbers sometimes remain in suitable reed beds and singing males have been located at Abqaiq from April to early July. It could well have made undetected breeding attempts. In autumn it has occurred in September and October; even allowing for the ease with which *Acrocephalus* warblers can be overlooked, it would appear to be much scarcer than in spring.

Identification: see p. 181.

Acrocephalus stentoreus PM? MB?
CLAMOROUS REED WARBLER

Possibly a new colonist, it breeds in Iran and probably in coastal mangroves in the UAE (Bundy & Warr 1980). In 1980 a singing male was present at Abqaiq from 9 to 23 May; it was tape recorded, trapped and considered to be the race *brunnescens* (GB, JHM). One was again present in the same reed bed in late March and early April 1981, after which the site was drained (JHM, JP). Single birds were singing in reed beds near al-'Uyun on 24 April 1981 and 10 km south of Dhahran on 17 March 1982 (GB, JP). One at al-'Uyun on 28 May 1982 was seen carrying food. In more recent years singing males have advertised their presence throughout the breeding season at a number of suitable localities extending from Hofuf to Dhahran, but determined searches have failed to disclose a nest (RJC). Large *Acrocephalus* warblers, possibly this species, have been noted occasionally in the coastal zone in November, December and January.

Identification: see p. 181.

Acrocephalus arundinaceus PM
GREAT REED WARBLER

Small numbers of migrants are regular from March through May and from August through October. Birds not infrequently occur in areas of low trees and scrub away from water. There are probably more records for spring than autumn.

Identification: see p. 181.

Hippolais pallida · OLIVACEOUS WARBLER MB

The main arrival at breeding localities occurs during April, and most depart in September. Small numbers have also been detected wintering in some years; they are much less conspicuous then, but can sometimes be located by a quietly uttered sub-song. Breeding birds favour mature introduced tamarisks and mesquite, especially tamarisks overhanging water. In 1980, in the proximity of the Imhoff sewerage effluent evaporation ponds at Dhahran there was a minimum of 52 pairs (RJC); due to drainage and clearance of some trees, numbers were reduced to about 15 pairs from 1981–3; and although the locality has become increasingly arid, there were still about 10 pairs present in 1984.

At Abqaiq there were ten pairs in 3 km^2 in 1979–80 but only five after the partial clearance of scrub in 1981. It probably also breeds in small numbers at Hofuf and Haradh but confirmation is still required for these localities. Breeding begins towards the end of April. The nest may be situated at any height from 1 to 8 metres, usually at the extremity of a lateral or suspended between slender uprights. Typically, the nest is compact and thick walled, built of tamarisk, grasses, fine creepers and spiders' webs and lined with finer materials including vegetable down, hair and sometimes a few feathers.

The eggs are usually 3 or 4 in number, occasionally 2 and very rarely 5. When fresh, they are pale pinkish-grey with leaden shell markings and a few small spots or streaks of dark, almost black, pigment; but in museum specimens the pinkish hue and leaden shell markings quickly fade (RJC). Away from the breeding places it is very scarce. Birds in thorn scrub at Haradh in March, April and September are thought to have been migrants, and one at Jawb, 300 km further south, on 21 July 1980 certainly was (GJR).

Identification: see p. 182.

Hippolais caligata · BOOTED WARBLER VAGRANT

Three at Abqaiq, 23 September 1977 (GKB). Individuals at Dhahran, 24 August 1979 and at Abqaiq, 5 September 1979 (GB). One at Haradh, 27 March 1981 (GB, RH). Possibly two at Abqaiq, 3 September 1982 (GKB). One at Dhahran, 25 September 1982 (GKB). One at Abqaiq on 26 August 1983 (JP). One at Dhahran on 30 August 1984 (JHM). One at Abqaiq on 19 October 1984 (GKB).

Identification: see p. 182.

Hippolais languida · UPCHER'S WARBLER PM

A regular migrant to all areas but never numerous, occurring during April, May, August and September. The records are currently about equal for the two passage seasons. It has been recorded twice in June.

Identification: see p. 182.

Hippolais olivetorum VAGRANT
OLIVE-TREE WARBLER

One at al-Musannah camp in the north on 19 September 1978 (RR). Another at the same locality, 18 September 1979 (GJR). One at Abqaiq, 18 April and 2 May 1980 (GB, JHM). One at Abqaiq on 7 May 1982 (GKB).

Identification: see p. 182.

Hippolais icterina · ICTERINE WARBLER VAGRANT

One at Dhahran on 10 April 1975 (GKB). One at Abqaiq for several days late March/early April 1982 (LR). One in bushes by the Shedgum escarpment, about 35 km north of Hofuf on 22 April 1982 (JHM, JP). One at Judah on 17 August 1984 (JP).

Sylvia mystacea · MENETRIES' WARBLER PM (WV)

A regular migrant in small numbers, mostly from late February through to early April but especially in March. In autumn it is probably regular from mid-September through October. Most autumn records have been away from the coastal zone, especially immatures at Haradh. It has been noted only once in November, at al-'Uqayr on the coast (Ticehurst & Cheesman 1925). A few may occasionally winter in the region: there was an adult male at Hanidh during January 1981 and probably one at Dhahran too (JHM, JP); also a male at Abqaiq on 17 December 1982, and at least one at Salasil on 7 January 1983 (GKB, JP, DR, LR).

Identification: see p. 182.

Sylvia nana · DESERT WARBLER WV

A common and widespread winter visitor in arid country where there is scrub or low scattered xerophytic vegetation. It occurs from September but most arrive during October and depart during March, being usually very scarce in early April. There is no evidence to suggest that any birds occur purely on passage.

Sylvia hortensis · ORPHEAN WARBLER PM

An annual migrant, rather scarce but quite widespread from late February to early April. Near the coast, it is much scarcer in autumn but has been almost common at Haradh in September. At Jawb, 300 km further south, two recorded in mid-September (GJR). Migrants are invariably dark eyed examples, possibly *crassirostris*. The race breeding in nearby Iran and southern Asia, *jerdoni*, is said to winter in India (Williamson 1976c).

Sylvia nisoria · BARRED WARBLER PM

A regular migrant from mid-April through May, birds being widespread in scrubby places and sometimes common. In autumn it is decidedly scarce everywhere except, curiously, at Haradh in the south where it is often common in the thorn scrub in the wadis and around the farm area during September and early October. There is often a small scattering of singletons in the coastal zone and at Abqaiq during September and exceptionally to November.

Sylvia curruca · LESSER WHITETHROAT WV PM

Small numbers of the pale race *minula* winter in many scattered localities wherever there is suitable cover. There is an arrival in September of darker migrants, presumably *blythi*, with a peak during September and numbers declining during October. The spring arrival of presumed *blythi* is more marked; these birds are common in March and sometimes April, and it has been noted exceptionally in late May. Well marked males seen at Dhahran and Abqaiq, in September 1979 and 1980 and in March 1981, were thought to be the race *althaea*.

Sylvia communis · COMMON WHITETHROAT PM

Common from mid-April through most of May and sometimes common also from August to early October; it is scarce but normally absent in March and November. Small peaks in numbers are usual in May and September.

Sylvia borin · GARDEN WARBLER PM

Small numbers are probably regular from late April through May. In autumn there is another scattering of records in September and October. Although it is scarcer in the coastal zone it has been almost common at Haradh.

Sylvia atricapilla · BLACKCAP PM

An annual migrant in small numbers, usually being seen in scrubby places like other warblers. It is always scarce but probably regular from late March to early May. Like Orphean and Barred Warblers, autumn birds are scarcer in the coastal zone and at Abqaiq, but at Haradh in the south it becomes almost common during September and October.

Phylloscopus nitidus · GREEN WARBLER VAGRANT

One at Dhahran on 28 November 1974 (GKB). One in a canyon about 35 km north of Hofuf town on 6 May 1982 (JHM, DR).

Phylloscopus borealis VAGRANT
ARCTIC WARBLER

One at Dhahran, 21 April 1975 (GKB). One at Dhahran airport, 6 September 1978 (GB).

Phylloscopus inornatus VAGRANT
YELLOW-BROWED WARBLER

One near Nabak, a desert drilling camp some 60 km south of Salwah, 6 November 1978 (RR); this example was probably *humei* from central Asia, a race that has occurred in Bahrain in November, December and February and which winters in Iran and Baluchistan. One at al-'Aba 11 February 1983 (JCB). One present at Jubail from 2 March to 18 April 1983 (AD). An adult was present at al-'Aba near Jubail on 9, 13 and 29 January 1987 (MH, MAE, TSH, ALL).

Phylloscopus fuscatus · DUSKY WARBLER VAGRANT

One at Dhahran on 16 February 1983 (GKB).

Phylloscopus bonelli VAGRANT
BONELLI'S WARBLER

One at al-'Aziziyah, about 20 km south of al-Khobar, 8 September 1981 (JP, DR). This example was well described and in autumn this species is more distinctive than most *Phylloscopus* warblers.

Phylloscopus sibilatrix VAGRANT
WOOD WARBLER

One at Dhahran, 6 November 1980 (JP). There are also several unconfirmed records.
Identification: see p. 182.

Above right: *Yellow-browed Warbler (ALL)*
Right: *Chiffchaff (ALL)*

Phylloscopus collybita · CHIFFCHAFF WV PM

It is present from late October through to early April. Small numbers of what are presumed to be the north European race *abietinus* (because of its different call and range) winter locally throughout the region where there are some trees and suitable scrub cover. However, from early December 1982 to March 1983, at least, some of the wintering birds were considered to be the south European nominate race *collybita*; and in October 1984 migrants were again encountered with the distinctive call of the nominate race (GKB, JHM, JP). Numbers from late February through March are very much higher and an influx of migrants is then obvious. Numbers drop very sharply in early April and there is little known overlap with Willow Warbler in the period of occurrence. A small late passage has been suspected in May, possibly of birds heading for the far north, but this needs to be confirmed. There is no evidence of any through passage in autumn.

Identification: see p. 182.

Phylloscopus trochilus · WILLOW WARBLER PM

A common, sometimes abundant, spring migrant; possibly from late March but mostly in the latter half of April and through most of May, and exceptionally in June. Numbers fluctuate annually but the peak in numbers is usually some time in May. It is scarce from August to early November. The migrants vary considerably in appearance; see p. 182.

Family MUSCICAPIDAE

This large family is represented in the Eastern Province by only three species. Records of *Ficedula* species in the past have been confused by the similarity of and taxonomic changes in the two 'collared' flycatchers. Voous (1977) has recently given specific rank to the Semi-collared Flycatcher (*F. semitorquata*) and the only record in the Gulf region for the similar Collared Flycatcher (*F. albicollis*) is of a single male on Bahrain in early April (TJH).

Muscicapa striata · SPOTTED FLYCATCHER PM

A common migrant in April and May but recorded infrequently in June and only twice in July. It is probably less numerous in autumn when it is in evidence from late August through October with a small peak in late September and early October. This peak was also noticed during the 1980 watch at Jawb in the far south (GJR): birds were first seen on 10 September, then none until 25th and thereafter it was present daily until 1 November. In northern coastal areas there have only been two records for November.

Ficedula parva · RED-BREASTED FLYCATCHER (WV)

A rare and irregular winter visitor or passage migrant. One was seen in late December 1970 in the garden of the US Consulate at Dhahran (RGW). A single bird was seen at Dhahran in November 1974 (GKB).

Two individuals remained at Dhahran from November 1979 to mid-March 1980, but not the following year (GB). Two birds were seen at Jawb (22°N 50°E) on 23 October 1980 (GJR). One at Abqaiq on 17 February 1984 (CVP, TSH, JAH). One at Dhahran on 30 October and 1 November 1983 (CVP, TSH, JAH). One was at Abqaiq from 24 September to 15 October 1982 (GKB, JP, DR).

Spotted Flycatcher (ALL)

Ficedula semitorquata PM
SEMI-COLLARED FLYCATCHER

A rather scarce migrant, but recorded annually from early March until about mid-April; the majority are males and most are seen in mid-March. There are no autumn records.

Family REMIZIDAE

Remiz pendulinus · PENDULINE TIT VAGRANT

Two, perhaps three, in reeds at Dammam marsh, 12 December 1981 (GB). A party of three at Abqaiq on 1 April 1983 (JP, DR, LR). Three at Abqaiq on 28 December 1984 (GKB, JP), and still present in January 1985. It is inconspicuous, easily overlooked (though with a distinctive call), and perhaps more regular than the few records indicate.

Family ORIOLIDAE

Oriolus oriolus · GOLDEN ORIOLE PM CB?

A scarce but regular migrant in small numbers from mid-April through May and occasionally later. It is less often seen from late August through October. A pair summered in a well vegetated area adjoining the sewerage effluent evaporation ponds at Dhahran in 1978, one of the few localities with large mature trees suitable for breeding. Although a bird was seen carrying nest material on several occasions breeding was not established. In 1984 a male was present in Dhahran from 30 April to at least 16 June (CVP, WHP).

Family LANIIDAE

There are six species of shrike included here; all are more or less regular migrants. There is also an unconfirmed record of one of the oriental shrikes, *Lanius schach* or *L. tephronotus*.

Identification problems should be minimal. The ISABELLINE SHRIKE is a rather variable species with two quite well marked races, *phoenicuroides* and nominate *isabellinus*, and many intergrades. These red-tailed shrikes have now been separated from the western Red-backed Shrike (Voous 1977) although there is apparently a region of overlap in central Asia where they meet and hybridize; some possible hybrids have been noted in eastern Saudi Arabia.

The Isabelline Shrike, unlike Red-backed, does not exhibit much sexual dimorphism. The rufous race, *phoenicuroides*, breeds in Iran and adjacent parts of southern Asia and is, in its purest form, quite easily distinguished from the sandy or sometimes greyish *isabellinus*. The small white patch at the base of the primaries is not always easy to see in the field; in fact on perched birds it is often concealed by the greater coverts, especially when the bird adopts a hunched posture. Immatures are commonly encountered in Arabia: they are usually rather plain sandy-brown and buffish-white birds, lacking a well defined eye stripe and with the tail a varying shade of gingery-brown; they commonly have *no* visible wing patch during their first winter.

The GREAT GREY and LESSER GREY SHRIKES have been well described in various western text books, but they still cause problems. In eastern Arabia a number of Great Greys arrive in autumn looking unlike the usual field guide pictures. They are paler, rather 'washed-out' looking birds, probably of the race *pallidirostris* from the arid country around the Caspian Sea. There is no need to describe these birds in detail here but merely to alert observers. The smaller eastern forms of Great Grey may very easily be mistaken for Lesser Grey and there are a number of winter records claimed for Lesser Grey although the species in fact winters in southern Africa. Such birds are almost certainly odd looking Great Greys.

Should there be any doubt, the two species are probably best distinguished by structural characters rather than by the much publicized plumage features that are not always to be seen. Size is of little real value in the field. The Lesser Grey often looks quite bulky and heavy headed; it tends to have a more upright stance and flies to its next perch in a low undulating flight. In contrast, Great Grey usually sits across its perch at an angle and its flight between vantage points is low, direct and straight. The Lesser Grey has a longer wing point. In keeping with such a long distance migrant the wings extend well past the tail coverts while the Great Grey's do not. This helps to give Lesser Grey a shorter tailed appearance; and in fact Great Grey does have a relatively longer and more graduated tail that normally shows more white. The bill in Lesser Grey is short and stubby looking while the Great Grey has a more protruding bill. This is a fairly obvious character once both birds have been seen in the field.

Lanius isabellinus · ISABELLINE SHRIKE PM WV

A common migrant especially from late February to early June and from August through November. The peak passage times are not well marked; and are also obscured by a scattering of birds (commonly, but not invariably, immatures) that remain throughout the winter. During the spring passage the paler and greyer nominate western race, *isabellinus*, outnumbers the rufous *phoenicuroides*. In August and September *phoenicuroides* is often the more numerous but many birds are indeterminate and perhaps of the Mongolian race *speculigerus*. At Jawb, on the northern fringe of the Rub' al-Khali, migrants were numerous in September 1980 and some *phoenicuroides* were identified (GJR).

Identification: see p. 189.

Isabelline Shrike (ALL)

Red-backed Shrike (GKB)

Lanius collurio · RED-BACKED SHRIKE PM

A common, occasionally abundant, passage migrant from mid-April to early June. The maximum numbers in the first half of May are usually later than the peak passage of the closely related Isabelline Shrike. It is scarcer but still regular in autumn from late August through October. Passage has been noted at distant Jawb: birds were present daily in September 1980 with up to five in a day (GJR). A male killed at Qatif on 6 May 1967 had been ringed in southern Czechoslovakia (48°N 17°E) on 18 June 1966 (JPM).

Lanius minor · LESSER GREY SHRIKE PM

A scarce but regular migrant from late April to early June. The autumn passage in August and September is less regular and in some years it is not seen at all. During one autumn period, birds were noted almost daily at Jawb in the Rub' al-Khali during August and early September (GJR). Most birds presumably overfly the coastal zone in autumn.

Identification: see p. 189.

Lanius excubitor · GREAT GREY SHRIKE RB WV PM

Present throughout the year at Haradh; one to three pairs are thought to have bred in 1979 and 1980 and nests were seen (JCD). There was no proof of breeding in 1981, but birds were nest building in April 1982.

The nest is placed in a thorn bush, a prickly shrub or a low tree. It is built of fine twiglets, roots and coarse grasses and lined with finer materials that sometimes include a little wool or hair. 4–6 eggs are laid. They are greyish or greenish white, with bold spots and blotches of greyish olive, frequently showing leaden shell markings (RJC).

Away from Haradh it tends to be rather scarce during the winter period from November through February. The passage in spring is not very marked but small numbers occur widely in March in places where none had wintered, occasionally in April and twice in May. In 1973 what was probably the same individual remained at Dhahran during June and July (KJF, JAW), and in 1975 and 1981 there were single birds at Dhahran in late June (MH, JHM). In autumn there are two small peaks in the numbers of migrants, probably of birds from different populations in southern Asia. The first small wave arrives

Above right:
Woodchat Shrike (ALL)

Great Grey Shrike (ALL)

Brown-necked Raven, first-year bird. (BS)

Indian House Crow (GKB)

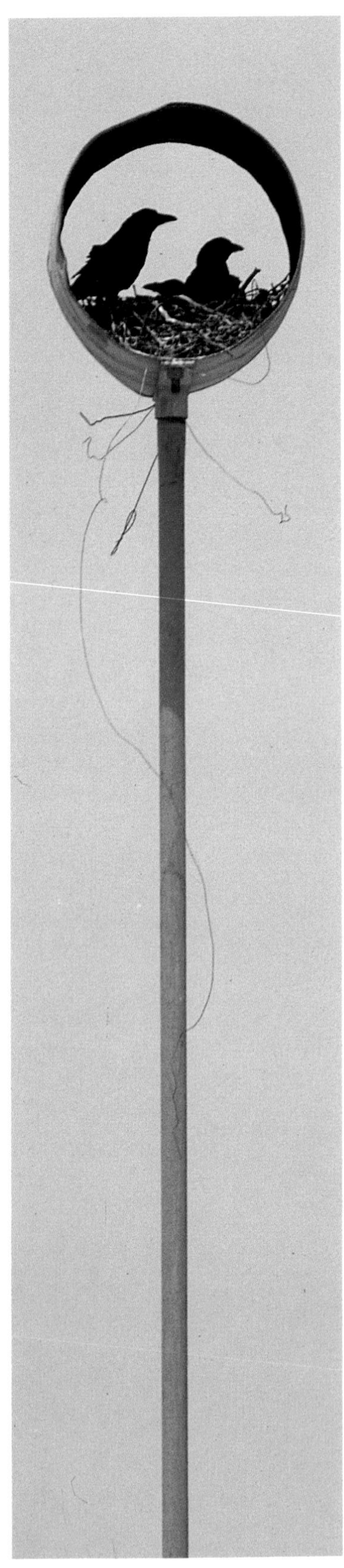

Brown-necked Raven's nest in well head marker. (BS)

in September when many examples are of one of the paler Asiatic races, possibly *pallidirostris*; a second small peak is sometimes apparent in November, after which a few widely scattered birds remain during the winter.

Identification: see p. 189.

Lanius senator · WOODCHAT SHRIKE PM

Usually common only during two rather brief periods: from late February to early April, and from late August through September. In spring, stragglers have been noted from late April to (exceptionally) early June.

Lanius nubicus · MASKED SHRIKE PM (WV)

A regular migrant in small numbers from mid-March to early May and from late August through September. One was at Abqaiq on 29 June 1984 (GKB).

Up to three birds were noted at the Jawb camp in the northern Rub' al-Khali in mid-September 1980 (GJR). It is scarce and irregular in October and November. At Dhahran single birds (occasionally two) have been recorded in several winters: in 1972–3 (LJ), 1973–4 (KJF, JAW), 1976–7 (GKB), 1980–1 (RH, JHM, JP) and 1983–4 (JP).

Family CORVIDAE

Corvus splendens · INDIAN HOUSE CROW RB

One at Dhahran airport, 30 September 1980 (JHM). Since about 1984 a single bird has frequented the Aramco compound at Dhahran and was still present in the autumn of 1988. Five adults and a nest with three well grown feathered young were seen on the Aramco compound at Ras Tanura on 5 May 1983 (JP, LR). Reports by local residents indicate that birds had been present for some years before this date. By 1986 it was breeding regularly and successfully. Over 30 were seen in one tree on 22 July 1986 (RJC). By April 1987 the Ras Tanura population had grown to over 40 birds and split into 3 colonies. Breeding begins towards the middle of March. The nest is placed high in a tree and is built of slender sticks and lined with roots, coarse grasses, animal wool and occasionally discarded pieces of fabric. 3–5 eggs are laid. They are bluish green, heavily blotched with olive brown (RJC).

Corvus ruficollis · BROWN-NECKED RAVEN RB

Occurs throughout the Eastern Province as a conspicuous, but rather thinly distributed resident. As a breeding species it has traditionally been associated with *jabal* outcrops and rocky escarpments; but in remote areas of the far south where rocks are lacking, breeds in low bushes. In relatively recent years has adapted to nesting on man-made structures, especially oil well markers and electricity pylons. The nest is bulky and built of slender sticks and copiously lined with sheeps' wool and pieces of discarded fabric. The first eggs are laid at the end of January, but some females do not lay eggs until March. 3–7 eggs are laid, usually 5 or 6. They are small for the size of the bird, light blue in ground colour with spots and small blotches of olive brown (RJC).

It is generally scarce in the coastal zone but birds forage near the shore locally and frequent rubbish dumps and roadside verges, especially after the breeding season, from May through December. In late May concentrations of up to 120 have been noted near Abqaiq.

Family STURNIDAE

Apart from the two wild starlings, two Indian species have been recorded, presumably escapes from captivity: Common Myna (*Acridotheres tristis*) and Bank Myna (*A. ginginianus*).

Sturnus vulgaris · STARLING WV

Abundant, often occurring in large flocks, from November through March. Scarce and usually absent at other times and not recorded in June. The highest numbers are usually seen in the coastal zone where it becomes very numerous in some years, especially about the palm groves and thinly cultivated land between Safwa and al-Khobar. It is generally much less numerous inland but small flocks are fairly regular at Abqaiq, Hofuf and Haradh. In May 1981 a pair in summer plumage were seen briefly around some recently deserted buildings at Dhahran, but are not known to have bred.

Sturnus roseus · ROSE-COLOURED STARLING PM

A rare migrant, with about 13 records to date. In the

autumn it has been observed from August to October, with a well marked peak in the second half of August. These are usually single birds (though up to four have occurred together), and so far all have been immatures except for one adult on 28 September 1984 (GKB). The only spring record is of an adult at Abqaiq on 1 May 1981 (GB, RH). Most of the records have been from the well watched Abqaiq lagoons, but it has also been seen at Dammam, Dhahran, Haradh and the al-'Uyun reed beds.

Acridotheres tristis · COMMON MYNA ESCAPE?

A party of 3 at Dhahran on 3 and 4 May 1984 (CVP, WHP). Two present at al-Khobar during the autumn of 1986 remained into the winter (JP, TC).

Acridotheres ginginianus · BANK MYNA ESCAPE?

One present in Dhahran from 3 to 6 May 1984, originally in the company of three Common Mynas (CVP, WHP).

NOTE: Mynas are frequently sold at local pet shops and markets, so these birds may have escaped from captivity.

Family PASSERIDAE

Passer domesticus · HOUSE SPARROW RB

The ubiquitous bird of the Eastern Province: common and widespread in all towns, villages and settlements, around artifacts, gardens, cultivations, palm groves, reed beds, scrub in semi-desert and, in several localities, on rocky outcrops in open desert (see p. 63). The wide range of niches occupied may well be due to a lack of competition in a region only recently developed and it has almost certainly increased very considerably during the last 50 years in eastern Arabia. The phenomenal increase in human activity along the Gulf coastal zone and in the oilfields of the interior has taken House Sparrows to areas where there were none until recent years. Ticehurst and Cheesman named in 1925 what was then probably an isolated race, *hufufae*: it is doubtfully distinct today. Quite large flocks occur locally around some cultivated areas and near communal roosts; flocks of up to about 500 have been noted at some reed beds in the coastal zone. As elsewhere, however, it tends to keep in social groups around the breeding places. Has a very extended breeding season and many pairs are double, perhaps treble brooded. Usually breeds socially, sometimes in large colonies. Nest construction varies with the site chosen. In trees and bushes the nest is bulky, an untidy ball of dried grasses, with an entrance towards the top, lined with finer grasses, feathers, vegetable down, etc. When nesting in fissures on *jabals*, nest construction is much more scanty and frequently lacks a dome. Also commonly places its nest in any convenient cavity in a building or man-made structure. The clutch usually consists of 3–5 eggs. They are greyish white, marked with small spots and flecks of dark grey or brown (RJC).

Passer hispaniolensis · SPANISH SPARROW WV

A regular visitor to some oases and farm areas in the northern half of the Province, notably at Mulayjah, Nata', as-Sarrar and Hanidh, but also occasionally to the palm groves around Qatif. It occurs from November to early April and the size of the wintering flocks varies. In 1979–80 small gatherings of about 30 were noted in the northern oases, but in early 1981, especially at Mulayjah, there were large flocks with one concentration of about 600 birds. Two wintering flocks were noted at Hofuf in February 1951 (Meinertzhagen 1954), and two birds that were obtained were assigned to the Asian race *transcaspicus*.

Petronia brachydactyla PM?
PALE ROCK SPARROW

It is uncertain whether this species is a regular migrant since it has not been recorded annually. In 1981 it was locally numerous during March and early April, especially at Haradh, an area not covered well during the critical first weeks of March in previous years. Flocks of up to 200 were present, and very probably three times that number. There was also a migrant flock of 300 on 15 March 1975 near Abqaiq (GKB) and 50+ near Judah on 6 April 1984 (JP), while smaller flocks were seen near al-Khobar and at the Hanidh cultivation. In the north, at al-Musannah it has been seen once in mid-May (GJR). It may be regular in autumn but flocks can be overlooked. It has been noted near the coast at al-Khobar in October (AB) and at Abqaiq in March and April (GKB). Onward passage is suggested by the occurrence of nine at Jawb in the northern Rub' al-Khali in mid-September (GJR).

Petronia xanthocollis VAGRANT
YELLOW-THROATED SPARROW

One at Abqaiq on 8 May 1981 (JHM, JP, DR). One at Dhahran on 21 April 1984 (GKB).

Family ESTRILIDIDAE

Four species have been recorded, three of very dubious origin since members in this family are commonly kept in captivity and are sold in local pet shops. The Indian Silverbill is principally an oriental species but extends west into south-eastern Iran, northern Oman and the United Arab Emirates (Voous 1977, Bundy & Warr 1980, Gallagher & Woodcock 1980) so its presence in Saudi Arabia could possibly denote colonization by genuinely wild stock. The other three species are Chestnut Munia (*Lonchura malacca*), an adult at Dhahran, 15 to 17 September 1979 (GB); White-headed Munia (*L. maja*), an adult at Dhahran, 21 April 1981 (JP) and one there on 19 September 1982 (GKB); and Scaly-breasted Munia (*L. punctulata*), one at Dhahran, 1 January 1982 (JP). These are considered to have been escapes.

Euodice malabarica ESCAPE? CB?
INDIAN SILVERBILL

First noted at Dhahran in 1974, when up to 15 were seen irregularly (often with House Sparrows) from April to December; they were considered to be escapes, since many were available for sale in nearby al-Khobar at that time (GKB, KJF). A pair and a party of four were seen around the Dammam sewage works on 23 May 1980 and were seemingly wild. At Dhahran up to four were again present between 19 September and 18 October 1981 with up to six reappearing during January 1982. In July and August 1984 up to 12 were found in an area of neglected cultivation on the outskirts of Dammam, and a few were seen also in Dhahran (GKB, JHM, JP). By 1988 small flocks of about 10 birds had established themselves at a number of locations within the Aramco residential compound at Dhahran, but breeding had not been recorded (RJC).

Family FRINGILLIDAE

Only seven species from this large family have been recorded in eastern Saudi Arabia and on present evidence all but one are probably no more than vagrants. One further species has been recorded in Bahrain: a flock of up to 25 Mongolian Trumpeter Finches (*Bucanetes mongolicus*) from December through February 1970–1 (Bundy & Warr 1980).

Fringilla coelebs · CHAFFINCH VAGRANT

Five, a male and four females, Dhahran 28 January 1971 (LJ). One female Hanidh 26 February 1982 (JHM, JP, DR). One female Dhahran 12 December 1986 (ALL, CR). A small flock at Jubail winter 1986/7 (MAE per ALL).

Fringilla montifringilla · BRAMBLING VAGRANT

One at Khurais, 14 November 1980 (PJI). A male 30 km east of Nariya, 1 to 2 December 1980 (Raby 1981). One at Dhahran on 19 November 1982 (CMS), two there on 14 December 1982 (TSH, JAH, CVP); and one there on three dates until 28 December (GKB). Three at Hanidh on 16 December 1982 (JP). Five at Abqaiq, 25 December 1982 (GKB).

Carduelis carduelis · GOLDFINCH VAGRANT

One at Dhahran on 26 April 1983 (JAH, TSH, CVP, WHP).

Carduelis spinus · SISKIN VAGRANT

A 'flock' at Dhahran, 13 November 1959 (Eddy 1962). Two at Dhahran, 23 November 1974 and seven at 'Udhailiyah camp, south-west of Hofuf, 18 November 1977 (GKB). One dead at Dhahran, 12 November 1981 (WR per JP). Six at Shedgum, 19 November 1981 (GB).

Carduelis cannabina · LINNET WV

Six at Dammam marsh on 1 February 1974 and up to four there until 15 March (KJF, JAW). Ten at 'Udhailiyah camp, 12 to 18 November 1977 (GKB). Four at Shedgum pools, 26 November 1982 (GKB, JP, DR).

Bucanetes githagineus · TRUMPETER FINCH RB

Local and thinly distributed in the Eastern Province, although it is common along the Tuwayq escarpment west of Riyadh. It breeds in the low, rocky outcrops west of Abqaiq, on the Shedgum escarpment north of Hofuf and on the south-facing escarpment between Judah and 'Uray'irah (GKB, JHM, JP, DR). Song flights have been observed in the period March/April. A female was seen on a nest on 30 March 1977 about 20 km south-west of Abqaiq (GKB). Small parties with juveniles have been seen in April at Shedgum and also near Judah, where a female was observed carrying nest material as late as May in 1984 (JHM, JP). The nest is built of grasses and positioned in a narrow crack amongst rocks. 4–5 eggs are laid. They are pale blue, sparsely marked with very dark reddish brown pigment. At Haradh it has been noted in October 1983, and May and September 1984 (JHM, JP). Elsewhere individuals or 'pairs' have been noted in January, February and November in the hills near Hanidh and as-Sarrar (JHM, RR).

Carpodacus erythrinus VAGRANT
COMMON ROSEFINCH

All records are of immatures. One at Abqaiq, 9 May 1976 (GKB). Singles at Dhahran on 13 October 1978, 25 August 1979 (GB) and 3 October 1980 (JHM, JP). Two at the Shedgum pools, 22 October 1981 (GB, JP). One at Dhahran, 16 September 1982 (GKB, JP, DR). One at Dhahran on 10 September 1984 (GKB). There have been further unconfirmed reports, notably in isolated camps where migrants are often more easily observed, but details of dates, etc, have not been forthcoming. This species is possibly more regular than the records currently suggest.

Family EMBERIZIDAE

Of the nine species represented here, only two, Cinereous and Ortolan Buntings, winter south of the Sahara. Cinereous has a very limited range in southern Asia but Ortolan, a common migrant in eastern Arabia, is widespread. Migrant buntings, especially in autumn, are often dull brown immatures rather than the bright males that take pride of place in field guide plates. However, the standard books cover the family reasonably well.

Emberiza leucocephalos · PINE BUNTING VAGRANT

A female or immature at Imhoff, 24 August 1979 (GB).

Emberiza cineracea · CINEREOUS BUNTING (PM)

A very scarce migrant, recorded sparingly from mid-March through April and once in mid-May (GKB, JHM, JP, GJR). There are only two autumn occurrences: up to four birds at Abqaiq between late August and mid-September (GKB).

Emberiza hortulana · ORTOLAN BUNTING PM

Occurs from late March through May, with a noticeable peak in mid-April when it becomes locally common. It is generally scarcer in autumn, from late August to October, although up to 40 have been noted at Haradh in September and early October. A 'small passage' was noted at Jawb, 300 km further south, from late September to late October (GJR).

Emberiza rustica · RUSTIC BUNTING VAGRANT

A male at Dhahran from 16 December 1981 to at least 18 January 1982 (GB, JHM, JP). One, possibly the same individual, at the Aramco Beach Road sewage pool compound on 26 January 1982 (JP).

Emberiza pusilla · LITTLE BUNTING VAGRANT

One at Dammam marsh, 3 December 1976 (GKB, AJS).

Emberiza aureola VAGRANT
YELLOW-BREASTED BUNTING

An immature, at al-Hunay 13 to 14 September 1979 (RR).

Emberiza schoeniclus · REED BUNTING VAGRANT

Two males and a probable female at Dammam marsh on 1 March 1974 (KJF, JAW). A female/immature at the same locality on 13 December 1975, and a female there on 5 March 1976 (GKB). A female at Abqaiq from 9 to 16 March 1979 (GB).

Emberiza melanocephala PM
BLACK-HEADED BUNTING

Probably regular only in early autumn when there is a wide scattering of birds, mainly immatures, from mid-August to about mid-September. It is most frequently seen in the northern half of the Province during this period; up to six have been present at the al-Musannah camp near the Kuwait border

(GJR). Birds have been noted as far south as Haradh and once at Jawb on the northern fringe of the Rub' al-Khali (GJR). Although scarce in the coastal zone, it has been seen on Jurayd island (KJF, JAW). There are only two spring records: an adult male at Haradh on 18 April 1980 (JCD) and a female at Dhahran on 22 April 1984 (GKB).

Miliaria calandra · CORN BUNTING WV

Probably a regular non-breeding visitor from November to March, though it has been noted in October and as early as 23 September (JAH, TSH). It occurs mostly in the coastal zone in arid, scrubby semi-desert but extends not infrequently to inland areas such as Abqaiq, the Shedgum plateau and Hanidh. It is usually seen in small flocks of up to ten or so birds but 'large numbers' were seen at Dammam marsh from January to March 1974 (KJF, JAW) and there were also unusual numbers in November and December 1984, with up to 28 at Dhahran and 46 at Abqaiq lagoons; numbers at Abqaiq later rose to a maximum of 180 in January 1985 (GKB, JHM, JP).

APPENDIX I

Systematic List of Species and their Status

For an explanation of the abbreviations indicating status see pages 74–5.

Family STRUTHIONIDAE

Struthio camelus — FB
OSTRICH

Family PODICIPEDIDAE

Tachybaptus ruficollis — RB
LITTLE GREBE

Podiceps cristatus — WV
GREAT CRESTED GREBE

Podiceps grisegena — VAGRANT
RED-NECKED GREBE

Podiceps nigricollis — WV
BLACK-NECKED GREBE

Family HYDROBATIDAE

Oceanites oceanicus — WV
WILSON'S PETREL

Family PHAETHONTIDAE

Phaethon aethereus — VAGRANT
RED-BILLED TROPICBIRD

Family PELECANIDAE

Pelecanus onocrotalus — (PM)
WHITE PELICAN

Family PHALACROCORACIDAE

Phalacrocorax carbo — WV
CORMORANT

Phalacrocorax nigrogularis — RB
SOCOTRA CORMORANT

Family ARDEIDAE

Botaurus stellaris — VAGRANT
BITTERN

Ixobrychus minutus — RB
LITTLE BITTERN

Nycticorax nycticorax — PM (WV)
NIGHT HERON

Ardeola ralloides — PM (WV)
SQUACCO HERON

Bubulcus ibis — PM (WV)
CATTLE EGRET

Egretta gularis — RB
WESTERN REEF HERON

Egretta garzetta — WV PM
LITTLE EGRET

Egretta alba — WV PM?
GREAT WHITE EGRET

Ardea cinerea — WV PM
GREY HERON

Ardea purpura — PM
PURPLE HERON

Family CICONIIDAE

Ciconia nigra — VAGRANT
BLACK STORK

Ciconia ciconia — PM
WHITE STORK

Family THRESKIORNITHIDAE

Threskiornis aethiopicus — VAGRANT
SACRED IBIS

Plegadis falcinellus — PM
GLOSSY IBIS

Platalea leucorodia — (WV)
SPOONBILL

Family PHOENICOPTERIDAE

Phoenicopterus ruber — WV
GREATER FLAMINGO

Family ANATIDAE

Anser anser — WV
GREYLAG GOOSE

Anser albifrons — VAGRANT
WHITE-FRONTED GOOSE

Tadorna ferruginea — RB WV
RUDDY SHELDUCK

Tadorna tadorna — WV
SHELDUCK

Nettapus coromandelianus COTTON TEAL	VAGRANT
Anas penelope WIGEON	WV
Anas strepera GADWALL	WV
Anas crecca TEAL	WV
Anas platyrhynchos MALLARD	WV
Anas acuta PINTAIL	WV
Anas querquedula GARGANEY	PM
Anas clypeata SHOVELER	WV
Marmaronetta angustirostris MARBLED TEAL	VAGRANT
Netta rufina RED-CRESTED POCHARD	VAGRANT
Aythya ferina POCHARD	WV
Aythya nyroca FERRUGINOUS DUCK	RB (PM)
Aythya fuligula TUFTED DUCK	WV
Mergus serrator RED-BREASTED MERGANSER	VAGRANT

Family ACCIPITRIDAE

Pernis apivorus HONEY BUZZARD	VAGRANT
Milvus migrans BLACK KITE	PM (WV)
Haliaeetus leucoryphus PALLAS'S FISH EAGLE	VAGRANT
Haliaeetus albicilla WHITE-TAILED EAGLE	VAGRANT
Neophron percnopterus EGYPTIAN VULTURE	RB
Gyps fulvus GRIFFON VULTURE	VAGRANT
Aegypius monachus BLACK VULTURE	VAGRANT
Circaetus gallicus SHORT-TOED EAGLE	PM
Circus aeruginosus MARSH HARRIER	WV PM
Circus cyaneus HEN HARRIER	(PM)
Circus macrourus PALLID HARRIER	PM WV
Circus pygargus MONTAGU'S HARRIER	PM
Accipiter gentilis GOSHAWK	(WV)
Accipiter nisus SPARROWHAWK	WV
Accipiter brevipes LEVANT SPARROWHAWK	VAGRANT
Buteo buteo BUZZARD	PM (WV)
Buteo rufinus LONG-LEGGED BUZZARD	MB WV
Aquila pomarina LESSER SPOTTED EAGLE	VAGRANT
Aquila clanga SPOTTED EAGLE	WV
Aquila nipalensis STEPPE EAGLE	WV PM
Aquila heliaca IMPERIAL EAGLE	WV
Aquila chrysaetos GOLDEN EAGLE	VAGRANT
Hieraaetus pennatus BOOTED EAGLE	VAGRANT
Hieraaetus fasciatus BONELLI'S EAGLE	VAGRANT

Family PANDIONIDAE

Pandion haliaetus OSPREY	RB

Family FALCONIDAE

Falco naumanni LESSER KESTREL	PM
Falco tinnunculus KESTREL	WV RB
Falco columbarius MERLIN	VAGRANT
Falco subbuteo HOBBY	PM
Falco concolor SOOTY FALCON	VAGRANT
Falco biarmicus LANNER	FB?
Falco cherrug SAKER	(WV)
Falco peregrinus PEREGRINE	WV
Falco pelegrinoides BARBARY FALCON	VAGRANT

Family PHASIANIDAE

Francolinus francolinus BLACK FRANCOLIN	FB?

Coturnix coturnix MB PM
QUAIL

Family RALLIDAE

Rallus aquaticus RB (WV?)
WATER RAIL

Porzana porzana PM (WV?)
SPOTTED CRAKE

Porzana parva PM
LITTLE CRAKE

Porzana pusilla PM
BAILLON'S CRAKE

Crex crex PM
CORNCRAKE

Gallinula chloropus RB
MOORHEN

Fulica atra RB WV
COOT

Family GRUIDAE

Grus grus VAGRANT
CRANE

Anthropoides virgo VAGRANT
DEMOISELLE CRANE

Family OTIDIDAE

Chlamydotis undulata MB? (WV)
HOUBARA BUSTARD

Family HAEMATOPODIDAE

Haematopus ostralegus WV
OYSTERCATCHER

Family RECURVIROSTRIDAE

Himantopus himantopus RB PM?
BLACK-WINGED STILT

Recurvirostra avosetta WV CB
AVOCET

Family DROMADIDAE

Dromas ardeola PM
CRAB PLOVER

Family BURHINIDAE

Burhinus oedicnemus (PM)
STONE CURLEW

Family GLAREOLIDAE

Cursorius cursor MB
CREAM-COLOURED COURSER

Glareola pratincola PM
COLLARED PRATINCOLE

Glareola nordmanni (PM)
BLACK-WINGED PRATINCOLE

Family CHARADRIIDAE

Charadrius dubius PM (WV)
LITTLE RINGED PLOVER

Charadrius hiaticula WV
RINGED PLOVER

Charadrius alexandrinus RB
KENTISH PLOVER

Charadrius mongolus WV PM
LESSER SAND PLOVER

Charadrius leschenaultii WV PM
GREATER SAND PLOVER

Charadrius asiaticus PM
CASPIAN PLOVER

Charadrius morinellus WV
DOTTEREL

Pluvialis dominica (WV)
LESSER GOLDEN PLOVER

Pluvialis apricaria VAGRANT
GOLDEN PLOVER

Pluvialis squatarola WV PM
GREY PLOVER

Hoplopterus spinosus VAGRANT
SPUR-WINGED PLOVER

Hoplopterus indicus (PM) (WV)
RED-WATTLED PLOVER

Chettusia gregaria VAGRANT
SOCIABLE PLOVER

Chettusia leucura PM (WV)
WHITE-TAILED PLOVER

Vanellus vanellus (WV)
LAPWING

Family SCOLOPACIDAE

Calidris tenuirostris VAGRANT
GREAT KNOT

Calidris alba WV PM
SANDERLING

Calidris minuta WV PM
LITTLE STINT

Calidris temminckii PM WV
TEMMINCK'S STINT

Calidris subminuta VAGRANT
LONG-TOED STINT

Calidris melanotos VAGRANT
PECTORAL SANDPIPER

Calidris ferruginea PM WV
CURLEW SANDPIPER

Calidris alpina WV
DUNLIN

Limicola falcinellus PM (WV)
BROAD-BILLED SANDPIPER

Tryngites subruficollis VAGRANT
BUFF-BREASTED SANDPIPER

Philomachus pugnax WV PM
RUFF

Lymnocryptes minimus (WV)
JACK SNIPE

Gallinago gallinago WV PM
COMMON SNIPE

Gallinago media VAGRANT
GREAT SNIPE

Gallinago stenura VAGRANT
PINTAIL SNIPE

Scolopax rusticola VAGRANT
WOODCOCK

Limosa limosa WV
BLACK-TAILED GODWIT

Limosa lapponica WV
BAR-TAILED GODWIT

Numenius phaeopus PM
WHIMBREL

Numenius arquata WV
CURLEW

Tringa erythropus PM WV
SPOTTED REDSHANK

Tringa totanus WV (PM?)
REDSHANK

Tringa stagnatilis PM (WV)
MARSH SANDPIPER

Tringa nebularia WV (PM)
GREENSHANK

Tringa ochropus PM WV
GREEN SANDPIPER

Tringa glareola PM WV
WOOD SANDPIPER

Xenus cinereus PM WV
TEREK SANDPIPER

Actitis hypoleucos PM (WV)
COMMON SANDPIPER

Arenaria interpres PM WV
TURNSTONE

Phalaropus lobatus PM
RED-NECKED PHALAROPE

Phalaropus fulicarius VAGRANT
GREY PHALAROPE

Family STERCORARIIDAE

Stercorarius pomarinus VAGRANT
POMARINE SKUA

Stercorarius parasiticus (PM)
ARCTIC SKUA

Family LARIDAE

Larus hemprichii VAGRANT
SOOTY GULL

Larus ichthyaetus WV PM?
GREAT BLACK-HEADED GULL

Larus melanocephalus VAGRANT
MEDITERRANEAN GULL

Larus minutus VAGRANT
LITTLE GULL

Larus ridibundus WV
BLACK-HEADED GULL

Larus cirrocephalus VAGRANT
GREY-HEADED GULL

Larus genei WV
SLENDER-BILLED GULL

Larus canus VAGRANT
COMMON GULL

Larus fuscus WV PM?
LESSER BLACK-BACKED GULL

Larus argentatus WV
HERRING GULL

Family STERNIDAE

Gelochelidon nilotica WV PM?
GULL-BILLED TERN

Sterna caspia WV
CASPIAN TERN

Sterna bergii MB
SWIFT TERN

Sterna bengalensis MB
LESSER CRESTED TERN

Sterna sandvicensis (WV)
SANDWICH TERN

Sterna hirundo (PM)
COMMON TERN

Sterna repressa MB
WHITE-CHEEKED TERN

Sterna anaethetus MB
BRIDLED TERN

Sterna albifrons MB
LITTLE TERN

Sterna saundersi MB PM
SAUNDERS' LITTLE TERN

Chlidonias hybridus WV
WHISKERED TERN

Chlidonias niger VAGRANT
BLACK TERN

Chlidonias leucopterus PM (WV)
WHITE-WINGED BLACK TERN

Family PTEROCLIDAE

Pterocles senegallus RB
SPOTTED SANDGROUSE

Pterocles orientalis VAGRANT
BLACK-BELLIED SANDGROUSE

Pterocles alchata VAGRANT
PIN-TAILED SANDGROUSE

Family COLUMBIDAE

Columba livia — RB
ROCK DOVE

Streptopelia decaocto — RB
COLLARED DOVE

Streptopelia turtur — MB PM
TURTLE DOVE

Streptopelia orientalis — VAGRANT
RUFOUS TURTLE DOVE

Streptopelia senegalensis — VAGRANT
PALM DOVE

Oena capensis — MB RB?
NAMAQUA DOVE

Family PSITTACIDAE

Psittacula krameri — WV RB?
ROSE-RINGED PARAKEET

Family CUCULIDAE

Clamator glandarius — VAGRANT
GREAT SPOTTED CUCKOO

Cuculus canorus — PM
CUCKOO

Family TYTONIDAE

Tyto alba — RB
BARN OWL

Family STRIGIDAE

Otus scops — PM
SCOPS OWL

Strix butleri — RB
HUME'S TAWNY OWL

Bubo (bubo) ascalaphus — RB
EAGLE OWL

Athene noctua — RB?
LITTLE OWL

Asio flammeus — WV
SHORT-EARED OWL

Family CAPRIMULGIDAE

Caprimulgus nubicus — VAGRANT
NUBIAN NIGHTJAR

Caprimulgus europaeus — PM
EUROPEAN NIGHTJAR

Caprimulgus aegyptius — VAGRANT
EGYPTIAN NIGHTJAR

Family APODIDAE

Apus apus — PM
NORTHERN SWIFT

Apus pallidus — MB PM?
PALLID SWIFT

Apus melba — (PM)
ALPINE SWIFT

Apus affinis — VAGRANT
LITTLE SWIFT

Family ALCEDINIDAE

Halcyon smyrnensis — VAGRANT
WHITE-BREASTED KINGFISHER

Alcedo atthis — WV
KINGFISHER

Ceryle rudis — (WV)
PIED KINGFISHER

Family MEROPIDAE

Merops orientalis — VAGRANT
LITTLE GREEN BEE-EATER

Merops superciliosus — PM
BLUE-CHEEKED BEE-EATER

Merops apiaster — PM
BEE-EATER

Family CORACIIDAE

Coracias garrulus — PM
ROLLER

Coracias benghalensis — VAGRANT
INDIAN ROLLER

Family UPUPIDAE

Upupa epops — PM (WV)
HOOPOE

Family PICIDAE

Jynx torquilla — PM
WRYNECK

Family ALAUDIDAE

Eremopterix nigriceps — RB MB
BLACK-CROWNED FINCH LARK

Eremalauda dunni — RB WV
DUNN'S LARK

Ammomanes cincturus — RB
BAR-TAILED DESERT LARK

Ammomanes deserti — RB
DESERT LARK

Alaemon alaudipes — RB
HOOPOE LARK

Ramphocoris clotbey — WV
THICK-BILLED LARK

Melanocorypha calandra — VAGRANT
CALANDRA LARK

Melanocorypha bimaculata — PM
BIMACULATED LARK

Calandrella brachydactyla — PM
SHORT-TOED LARK

Calandrella rufescens — WV RB
LESSER SHORT-TOED LARK

Galerida cristata RB
CRESTED LARK

Alauda arvensis WV
SKYLARK

Alauda gulgula VAGRANT
SMALL SKYLARK

Eremophila bilopha RB
TEMMINCK'S HORNED LARK

Family HIRUNDINIDAE

Riparia paludicola VAGRANT
BROWN-THROATED SAND MARTIN

Riparia riparia PM
SAND MARTIN

Ptyonoprogne fuligula RB
PALE ROCK MARTIN

Ptyonoprogne rupestris (PM)
CRAG MARTIN

Hirundo rustica PM
SWALLOW

Hirundo daurica PM
RED-RUMPED SWALLOW

Delichon urbica PM
HOUSE MARTIN

Family MOTACILLIDAE

Anthus novaeseelandiae VAGRANT
RICHARD'S PIPIT

Anthus campestris PM WV
TAWNY PIPIT

Anthus hodgsoni VAGRANT
OLIVE-BACKED PIPIT

Anthus trivialis PM
TREE PIPIT

Anthus pratensis WV
MEADOW PIPIT

Anthus cervinus PM WV
RED-THROATED PIPIT

Anthus spinoletta WV
WATER PIPIT

Motacilla flava PM
YELLOW WAGTAIL

Motacilla citreola WV
CITRINE WAGTAIL

Motacilla cinerea PM
GREY WAGTAIL

Motacilla alba WV PM
WHITE WAGTAIL

Family PYCNONOTIDAE

Pycnonotus leucogenys RB
WHITE-CHEEKED BULBUL

Pycnonotus xanthopygos VAGRANT
YELLOW-VENTED BULBUL

Family BOMBYCILLIDAE

Hypocolius ampelinus WV
GREY HYPOCOLIUS

Family TURDIDAE

Cercotrichas galactotes MB
RUFOUS BUSH CHAT

Cercotrichas podobe VAGRANT
BLACK BUSH CHAT

Erithacus rubecula (WV)
ROBIN

Luscinia luscinia (PM)
THRUSH NIGHTINGALE

Luscinia megarhynchos PM
NIGHTINGALE

Luscinia svecica WV PM?
BLUETHROAT

Irania gutturalis PM
WHITE-THROATED ROBIN

Phoenicurus erythronotus VAGRANT
EVERSMANN'S REDSTART

Phoenicurus ochruros WV
BLACK REDSTART

Phoenicurus phoenicurus PM
REDSTART

Cerconela melanura VAGRANT
BLACKSTART

Saxicola rubetra PM
WHINCHAT

Saxicola torquata WV PM
STONECHAT

Oenanthe isabellina PM WV
ISABELLINE WHEATEAR

Oenanthe oenanthe PM
NORTHERN WHEATEAR

Oenanthe pleschanka PM
PIED WHEATEAR

Oenanthe hispanica PM
BLACK-EARED WHEATEAR

Oenanthe deserti WV PM
DESERT WHEATEAR

Oenanthe finschii (WV)
FINSCH'S WHEATEAR

Oenanthe picata VAGRANT
EASTERN PIED WHEATEAR

Oenanthe xanthoprymne WV
RED-TAILED WHEATEAR

Oenanthe lugens WV
MOURNING WHEATEAR

Oenanthe monacha VAGRANT WV?
HOODED WHEATEAR

Oenanthe leucopyga RB
WHITE-CROWNED BLACK WHEATEAR

Monticola saxatilis PM
ROCK THRUSH

Monticola solitarius PM (WV)
BLUE ROCK THRUSH

Turdus torquatus WV
RING OUZEL

Turdus merula WV
BLACKBIRD

Turdus ruficollis (WV)
BLACK-THROATED THRUSH

Turdus pilaris WV
FIELDFARE

Turdus philomelos WV
SONG THRUSH

Turdus iliacus (WV)
REDWING

Turdus viscivorus VAGRANT
MISTLE THRUSH

Family SYLVIIDAE

Prinia gracilis RB
GRACEFUL WARBLER

Locustella naevia VAGRANT
GRASSHOPPER WARBLER

Locustella fluviatilis VAGRANT
RIVER WARBLER

Locustella luscinioides PM
SAVI'S WARBLER

Acrocephalus melanopogon RB
MOUSTACHED WARBLER

Acrocephalus schoenobaenus PM
SEDGE WARBLER

Acrocephalus palustris PM
MARSH WARBLER

Acrocephalus scirpaceus PM MB?
REED WARBLER

Acrocephalus stentoreus PM? MB?
CLAMOROUS REED WARBLER

Acrocephalus arundinaceus PM
GREAT REED WARBLER

Hippolais pallida MB
OLIVACEOUS WARBLER

Hippolais caligata VAGRANT
BOOTED WARBLER

Hippolais languida PM
UPCHER'S WARBLER

Hippolais olivetorum VAGRANT
OLIVE-TREE WARBLER

Hippolais icterina VAGRANT
ICTERINE WARBLER

Sylvia mystacea PM (WV)
MENETRIES' WARBLER

Sylvia nana WV
DESERT WARBLER

Sylvia hortensis PM
ORPHEAN WARBLER

Sylvia nisoria PM
BARRED WARBLER

Sylvia curruca WV PM
LESSER WHITETHROAT

Sylvia communis PM
COMMON WHITETHROAT

Sylvia borin PM
GARDEN WARBLER

Sylvia atricapilla PM
BLACKCAP

Phylloscopus nitidus VAGRANT
GREEN WARBLER

Phylloscopus borealis VAGRANT
ARCTIC WARBLER

Phylloscopus inornatus VAGRANT
YELLOW-BROWED WARBLER

Phylloscopus fuscatus VAGRANT
DUSKY WARBLER

Phylloscopus bonelli VAGRANT
BONELLI'S WARBLER

Phylloscopus sibilatrix VAGRANT
WOOD WARBLER

Phylloscopus collybita WV PM
CHIFFCHAFF

Phylloscopus trochilus PM
WILLOW WARBLER

Family MUSCICAPIDAE

Muscicapa striata PM
SPOTTED FLYCATCHER

Ficedula parva (WV)
RED-BREASTED FLYCATCHER

Ficedula semitorquata PM
SEMI-COLLARED FLYCATCHER

Family REMIZIDAE

Remiz pendulinus VAGRANT
PENDULINE TIT

Family ORIOLIDAE

Oriolus oriolus PM CB?
GOLDEN ORIOLE

Family LANIIDAE

Lanius isabellinus PM WV
ISABELLINE SHRIKE

Lanius collurio PM
RED-BACKED SHRIKE

Lanius minor PM
LESSER GREY SHRIKE

Lanius excubitor RB WV PM
GREAT GREY SHRIKE

Lanius senator PM
WOODCHAT SHRIKE

Lanius nubicus PM (WV)
MASKED SHRIKE

Family CORVIDAE

Corvus splendens RB
INDIAN HOUSE CROW

Corvus ruficollis RB
BROWN-NECKED RAVEN

Family STURNIDAE

Sturnus vulgaris WV
STARLING

Sturnus roseus PM
ROSE-COLOURED STARLING

Acridotheres tristis ESCAPE?
COMMON MYNA

Acridotheres ginginianus ESCAPE?
BANK MYNA

Family PASSERIDAE

Passer domesticus RB
HOUSE SPARROW

Passer hispaniolensis WV
SPANISH SPARROW

Petronia brachydactyla PM?
PALE ROCK SPARROW

Petronia xanthocollis VAGRANT
YELLOW-THROATED SPARROW

Family ESTRILDIDAE

Euodice malabarica ESCAPE? CB?
INDIAN SILVERBILL

Family FRINGILLIDAE

Fringilla coelebs VAGRANT
CHAFFINCH

Fringilla montifringilla VAGRANT
BRAMBLING

Carduelis carduelis VAGRANT
GOLDFINCH

Carduelis spinus VAGRANT
SISKIN

Carduelis cannabina WV
LINNET

Bucanetes githagineus RB
TRUMPETER FINCH

Carpodacus erythrinus VAGRANT
COMMON ROSEFINCH

Family EMBERIZIDAE

Emberiza leucocephalos VAGRANT
PINE BUNTING

Emberiza cineracea (PM)
CINEREOUS BUNTING

Emberiza hortulana PM
ORTOLAN BUNTING

Emberiza rustica VAGRANT
RUSTIC BUNTING

Emberiza pusilla VAGRANT
LITTLE BUNTING

Emberiza aureola VAGRANT
YELLOW-BREASTED BUNTING

Emberiza schoeniclus VAGRANT
REED BUNTING

Emberiza melanocephala PM
BLACK-HEADED BUNTING

Miliaria calandra WV
CORN BUNTING

APPENDIX II

Passage Migrants in the Eastern Province of Saudi Arabia

The 127 species of migrants are listed below with some indication of their relative abundance during the two migration periods. SPRING is February through June and AUTUMN is from July through November.

'Abundant' means hundreds or more are regular in a given area.

'Common' means a maximum in tens.

'Scarce' means a maximum in single figures. There is a need here to qualify these terms and *'scarcer'* and *'less common'* are used where they are appropriate. Brackets are used to denote irregularity and a question mark where the status is uncertain.

'WV' means 'winter visitor'.

SPECIES		SPRING	AUTUMN	NOTES
Pelecanus onocrotalus	White Pelican	(scarce)	(scarce)	
Nycticorax nycticorax	Night Heron	(scarce)	common	also WV
Ardeola ralloides	Squacco Heron	common	common	also WV
Bubulcus ibis	Cattle Egret	scarce	scarce	
Egretta garzetta	Little Egret	common	common	also WV
Ardea cinerea	Grey Heron	?	scarce	WV?
Ardea purpurea	Purple Heron	scarce	common	
Ciconia ciconia	White Stork	(scarce)	scarce	
Plegadis falcinellus	Glossy Ibis	scarce	scarce	
Anas querquedula	Garganey	common	abundant	
Aythya nyroca	Ferruginous Duck	(scarce)	common?	also RB
Milvus migrans	Black Kite	scarce	(scarce)	(WV)
Circuetus gallicus	Short-toed Eagle	(scarce)	(scarce)	(WV)
Circus aeruginosus	Marsh Harrier	scarce	scarce	also WV
Circus cyaneus	Hen Harrier	(scarce)	(scarce)	
Circus macrourus	Pallid Harrier	scarce	common	also WV
Circus pygargus	Montagu's Harrier	scarce	scarce	
Buteo buteo	Buzzard	scarce	scarce	also WV
Aquila nipalensis	Steppe Eagle	scarce	scarce	also WV
Falco naumanni	Lesser Kestrel	common	(common)	
Falco tinnunculus	Kestrel	(scarce)	(scarce)	also WV
Falco subbuteo	Hobby	scarce	scarce	
Coturnix coturnix	Quail	(scarce)	scarce	

SPECIES		SPRING	AUTUMN	NOTES
Porzana porzana	Spotted Crake	scarce	scarce	(WV?)
Porzana parva	Little Crake	scarce	common	(WV)
Porzana pusilla	Baillon's Crake	(scarce)	scarce	
Crex crex	Corncrake	scarce	common	locally abundant in autumn
Dromas ardeola	Crab Plover	(scarce)	common	
Burhinus oedicnemus	Stone Curlew	(scarce)	(scarce)	
Glareola pratincola	Collared Pratincole	common	less common	
Charadrius dubius	Little Ringed Plover	(scarce)	(scarce)	
Charadrius mongolus	Lesser Sand Plover	common	common	also WV
Charadrius leschenaultii	Greater Sand Plover	common	common	also WV
Charadrius asiaticus	Caspian Plover	(common)	common	(WV)
Charadrius morinellus	Dotterel	(scarce)	(scarce)	also WV
Pluvialis squatarola	Grey Plover	common	common	also WV
Hoplopterus indicus	Red-wattled Plover	(scarce)	(scarce)	
Chettusia leucura	White-tailed Plover	scarce	scarce	(WV)
Calidris alba	Sanderling	abundant	common	also WV
Calidris minuta	Little Stint	common	common	also WV
Calidris temminckii	Temminck's Stint	scarce	scarce	also WV
Calidris ferruginea	Curlew Sandpiper	abundant	common	also WV
Limicola falcinellus	Broad-billed Sandpiper	scarce	scarce	(WV)
Philomachus pugnax	Ruff	common	common	also WV
Gallinago gallinago	Common Snipe	common	common	also WV
Numenius phaeopus	Whimbrel	scarce	scarce	
Tringa erythropus	Spotted Redshank	scarce	scarce	local WV
Tringa stagnatilis	Marsh Sandpiper	scarce	(common)	(WV)
Tringa nebularia	Greenshank	scarce	scarce	also WV
Tringa ochropus	Green Sandpiper	common	common	(WV)
Tringa glareola	Wood Sandpiper	common	common	scarce WV
Xenus cinereus	Terek Sandpiper	abundant	abundant	also WV
Actitis hypoleucos	Common Sandpiper	scarce	scarce	also WV
Arenaria interpres	Turnstone	abundant	common	also WV
Phalaropus lobatus	Red-necked Phalarope	(common)	(scarce)	
Stercorarius parasiticus	Arctic Skua	(scarce)	scarce	
Larus ichthyaetus	Great Black-headed Gull	(common)	?	also WV
Sterna hirundo	Common Tern	scarce	(scarce)	
Sterna saundersi	Saunders' Little Tern	?	abundant	
Chilidonias leucopterus	White-winged Black Tern	common	common	also WV
Streptopelia turtur	Turtle Dove	abundant	common	
Cuculus canorus	Cuckoo	(scarce)	scarce	
Otus scops	Scops Owl	scarce	scarce	
Caprimulgus europaeus	Nightjar	scarce	(scarce)	
Apus apus	Northern Swift	abundant	?	
Apus pallidus	Pallid Swift	common?	?	
Apus melba	Alpine Swift	(scarce)	(scarce)	
Merops superciliosus	Blue-cheeked Bee-eater	common	common	
Merops apiaster	Bee-eater	common	common	
Coracias garrulus	Roller	(common)	common	
Upupa epops	Hoopoe	common	common	(WV)
Jynx torquilla	Wryneck	(scarce)	scarce	

SPECIES		SPRING	AUTUMN	NOTES
Melanocorypha bimaculata	Bimaculated Lark	(common)	scarce	
Calandrella brachydactyla	Short-toed Lark	abundant	(abundant)	
Riparia riparia	Sand Martin	abundant	abundant	
Ptyonoprogne rupestris	Crag Martin	scarce	?	
Hirundo rustica	Swallow	abundant	abundant	
Hirundo daurica	Red-rumped Swallow	common	(scarce)	
Delichon urbica	House Martin	common	(scarce)	
Anthus campestris	Tawny Pipit	common	common	scarce WV
Anthus trivialis	Tree Pipit	scarce	scarce	(WV)
Anthus cervinus	Red-throated Pipit	common	(common)	(WV)
Motacilla flava	Yellow Wagtail	abundant	abundant	
Motacilla cinerea	Grey Wagtail	scarce	scarce	
Motacilla alba	White Wagtail	(common)	(common)	also WV
Luscinia luscinia	Thrush Nightingale	(scarce)	(scarce)	
Luscinia megarhynchos	Nightingale	scarce	(scarce)	
Irania gutturalis	White-throated Robin	scarce	(scarce)	
Phoenicurus phoenicurus	Redstart	common	(scarce)	
Saxicola rubetra	Whinchat	scarce	(scarce)	
Saxicola torquata	Stonechat	common	scarce	also WV
Oenanthe isabellina	Isabelline Wheatear	abundant	common	also WV
Oenanthe oenanthe	Northern Wheatear	common	common	
Oenanthe pleschanka	Pied Wheatear	abundant	common	
Oenanthe hispanica	Black-eared Wheatear	scarce	(scarce)	
Oenanthe deserti	Desert Wheatear	scarce	scarce	also WV
Monticola saxatilis	Rock Thrush	scarce	scarce	
Monticola solitarius	Blue Rock Thrush	scarce	scarce	(WV)
Locustella luscinioides	Savi's Warbler	scarce	scarce	
Acrocephalus schoenobaenus	Sedge Warbler	scarce	(scarce)	
Acrocephalus palustris	Marsh Warbler	common	?	
Acrocephalus scirpaceus	Reed Warbler	common	scarce	
Acrocephalus arundinaceus	Great Reed Warbler	(common)	scarce	
Hippolais languida	Upcher's Warbler	scarce	scarce	
Sylvia mystacea	Menetries' Warbler	(common)	scarce	(WV)
Sylvia hortensis	Orphean Warbler	scarce	scarce	
Sylvia nisoria	Barred Warbler	common	(common)	
Sylvia curruca	Lesser Whitethroat	common	less common	also WV
Sylvia communis	Whitethroat	common	less common	
Sylvia borin	Garden Warbler	scarce	scarce	
Sylvia atricapilla	Blackcap	scarce	scarce	
Phylloscopus collybita	Chiffchaff	abundant	?	also WV
Phylloscopus trochilus	Willow Warbler	abundant	(common)	
Muscicapa striata	Spotted Flycatcher	common	(common)	
Ficedula semitorquatus	Semi-collared Flycatcher	scarce	?	
Oriolus oriolus	Golden Oriole	scarce	scarce	
Lanius isabellinus	Isabelline Shrike	common	common	also WV
Lanius collurio	Red-backed Shrike	abundant	scarce	
Lanius minor	Lesser Grey Shrike	(common)	scarce	
Lanius excubitor	Great Grey Shrike	scarce	scarce	also WV
Lanius senator	Woodchat Shrike	common	common	
Lanius nubicus	Masked Shrike	scarce	scarce	(WV)
Sturnus roseus	Rose-coloured Starling	(scarce)	scarce	

SPECIES		SPRING	AUTUMN	NOTES
Petronia brachydactyla	Pale Rock Sparrow	(abundant)	(common)	(WV?)
Emberiza cineracea	Cinereous Bunting	(scarce)	(scarce)	
Emberiza hortulana	Ortolan Bunting	common	less common	
Emberiza melanocephala	Black-headed Bunting	(scarce)	scarce	

APPENDIX III

Geographic Co-ordinates

	LATITUDE (°N)	LONGITUDE (°E)
al-'Aba oasis	26°44′	49°45′
Abqaiq	25°56′	49°40′
Abu'Ali	27°20′	49°33′
Abu Hadriyah	27°20′	48°58′
'Ain Dar	25°59′	49°23′
'Anak	26°32′	50°01′
al-'Arabiyah island	27°46′	50°12′
al-'Aziziyah	26°11′	50°12′
Berri Oilfield	27°14′	49°40′
Dammam	26°26′	50°07′
Dhahran	26°18′	50°08′
al-Farisiyah island	27°59′	50°12′
Hanidh	26°35′	48°36′
Haradh	26°35′	50°08′
Harmaliyah	24°35′	49°30′
Harqus island	27°56′	49°41′
al-Hasa	25°20′	49°38′
Hofuf	25°20′	49°38′
al-Hunay	24°58′	48°45′
Jana island	27°22′	49°54′
Jabal 'Ain Dar	25°56′	49°23′
Jabal al-Arba'	25°17′	49°43′
Jabal Ghuraymil	25°48′	49°32′
Jabal Shadgam	26°04′	48°49′
Jafurah	25°00′	50°15′
Jawb	22°10′	49°51′
Jinnah island	27°22′	49°18′
Ju'aymah	26°51′	49°54′
Jubail	27°01′	49°40′
Judah	25°52′	48°50′
Jurayd island	27°11′	49°52′
Karan island	27°44′	49°50′
al-Kharj	24°10′	47°30′
al-Khobar	26°17′	50°12′
Khurais	25°06′	48°02′
Kurayn island	27°39′	49°50′

	LATITUDE (°N)	LONGITUDE (°E)
Manifa	27°40′	49°00′
Mulayjah	27°16′	48°25′
al-Musannah	29°02′	47°12′
Najd	25°00′	44°30′
Nariya	27°28′	48°27′
Nabak	24°24′	50°49′
Nata'	27°13′	48°25′
Qaisumah	28°20′	46°07′
al-Qarn	25°31′	49°36′
Qatif	26°36′	49°58′
Qurayyah	26°02′	50°09′
Ras Tanura	26°42′	50°06′
Ras az-Zawr	27°25′	49°04′
Safwa	26°39′	49°58′
Safaniya	27°58′	58°47′
Saihat	25°39′	50°03′
Salasil	26°42′	43°33′
Salwah	25°30′	50°40′
Samamik island	25°33′	50°19′
as-Sarrar	27°02′	48°17′
Shedgum plateau	25°40′	49°25′
Summan plateau	25°00′	47°00′
Summan escarpment	23°30′	48°50′
Tarut island	26°34′	50°40′
'Udhailiyah	25°08′	49°18′
'Unaybir island	24°55′	50°44′
al-'Uqayr	25°30′	50°10′
'Uray'irah	25°57′	48°53′
al-'Uyun	25°36′	49°34′
Wadi al-Batin	28°27′	45°58′
Wari'ah	27°42′	47°30′
Yabrin	23°15′	48°59′
az-Zakhnuniyah	25°33′	50°19′
Za'l	26°39′	50°06′
Zarnuqa	25°03′	49°41′

APPENDIX IV

AVERAGE MONTHLY RELATIVE HUMIDITY
1950–1976*

PERCENT RELATIVE HUMIDITY

80
70
60
50
40
30
20
10
0

JAN FEB MAR APR MAY JUN JUL AUG SEP OCT NOV DEC

AVERAGE MONTHLY RAINFALL
1939–1988*

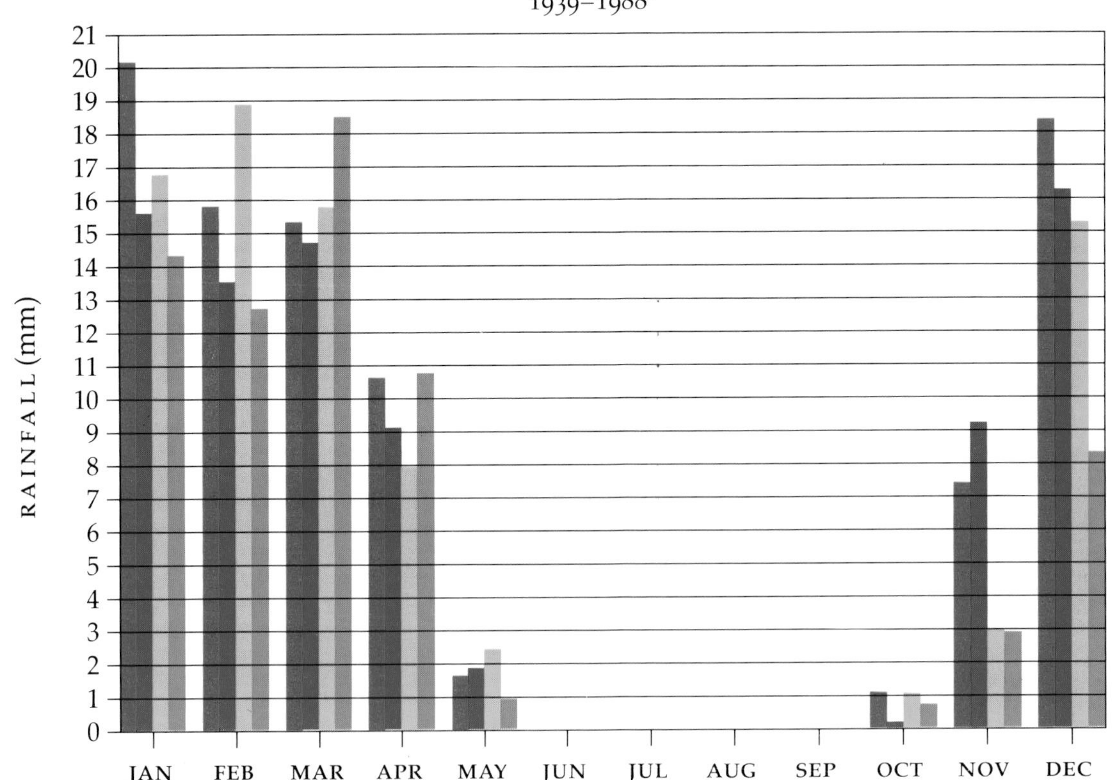

AVERAGE MONTHLY TEMPERATURE

1982–1988*

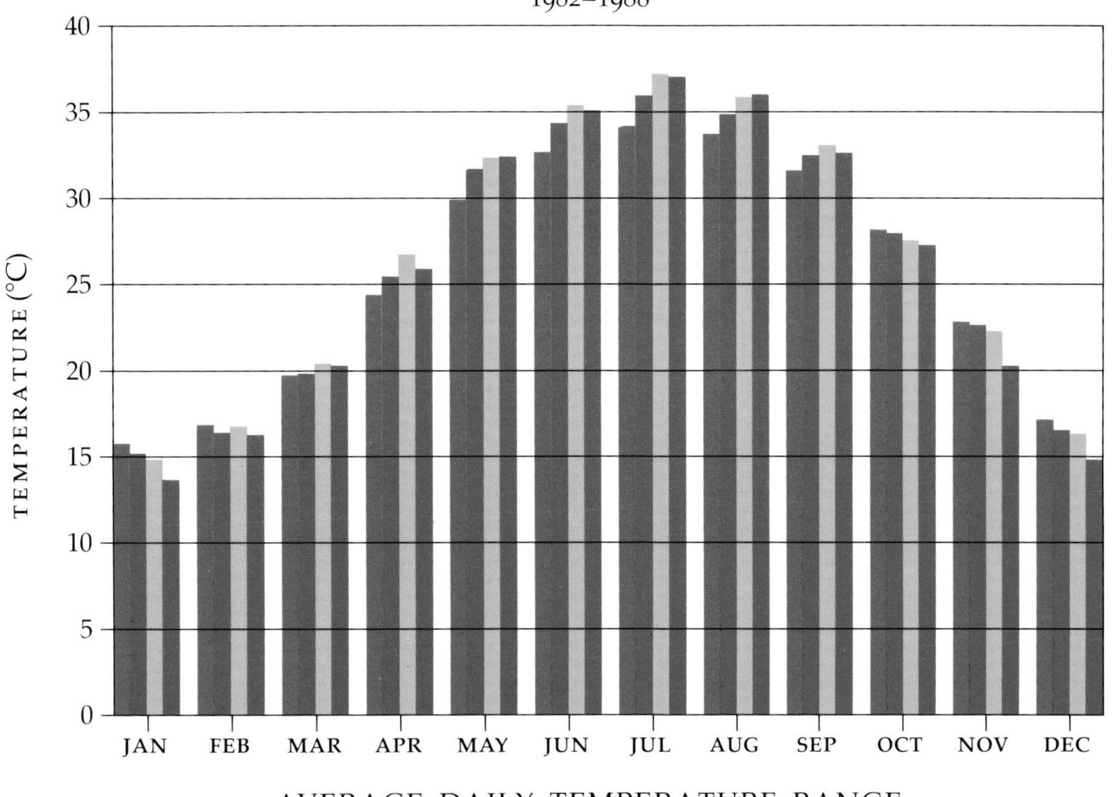

AVERAGE DAILY TEMPERATURE RANGE

1950–1976*

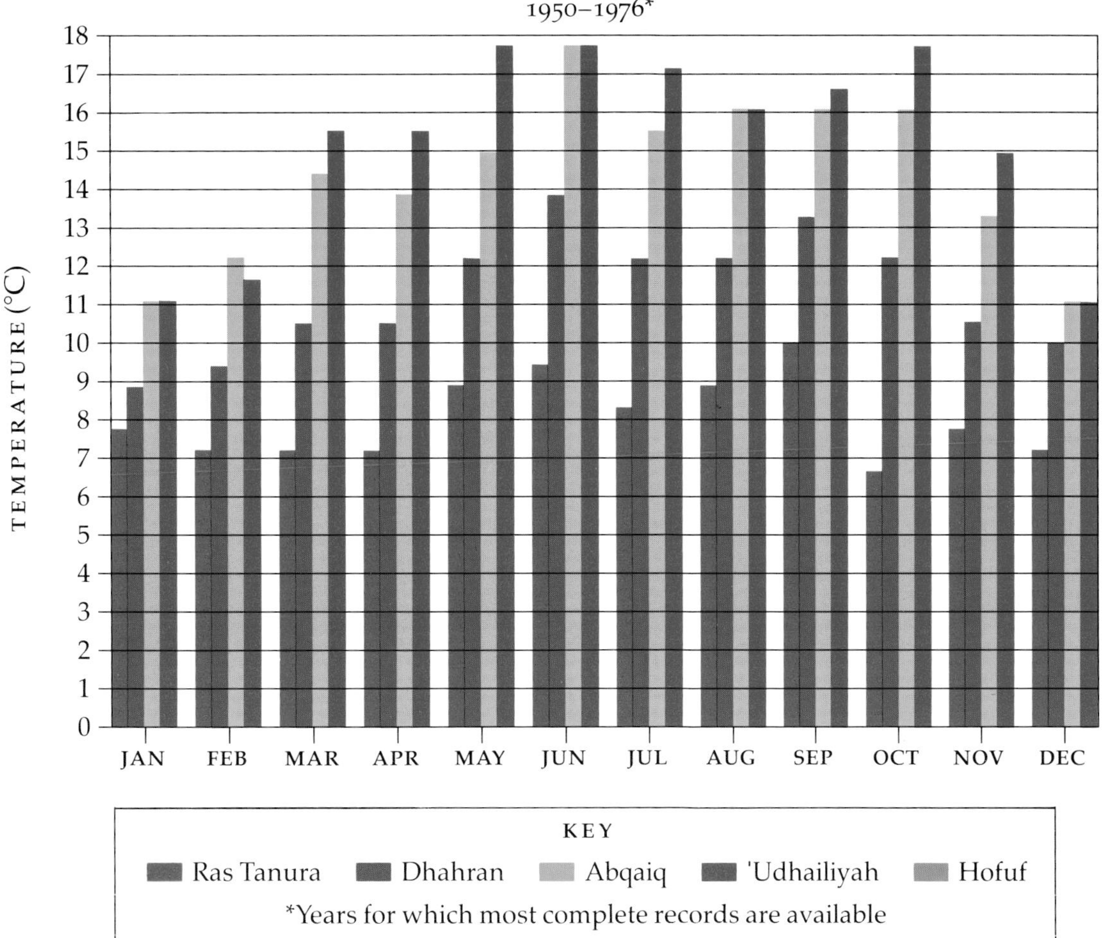

BIBLIOGRAPHY

MAJOR REFERENCE WORKS

BASSON, P. W., BURCHARD, J. E., HARDY, J. T. and PRICE, A. R. G., 1978 *Biotopes of the Western Arabian Gulf*. Aramco Department of Loss Prevention and Environmental Affairs, Dhahran.

CRAMP, S. and SIMMONS, K. E. C. (eds), 1977 *Handbook of the Birds of Europe, the Middle East and North Africa*. Birds of the Western Palaearctic. 7 volumes. Oxford University Press.

GENSBOL, B., 1986 *Guide to the Birds of Prey of Britain and Europe, North Africa and the Middle East*. Translated by Dr G. Vevers. Collins.

HEINZEL, H., FITTER, R. S. R. and PARSLOW, H., 1972 *The Birds of Britain and Europe with North Africa and the Middle East*. Collins.

HOLLOM, P. A. D., PORTER, R. F., CHRISTENSEN, S. and WILLIS, I., 1988 *Birds of the Middle East and North Africa*. T. & A. D. Poyser.

HUE, F. and ETCHECOPAR, R. D., 1971 *Les Oiseaux du Proche et du Moyen Orient de la Mediterranée aux contrafort de l'Himalaya*. (The birds of the Near and Middle East from the Mediterranean to the Himalayas.) Boubée. 948 pp, 429 distribution maps, 32 pls., 356 line drawings, 2 maps. (Covers the Levant, Syria, Iraq and Kuwait, but not the Arabian Peninsula.)

MEINERTZHAGEN, R., 1954 *Birds of Arabia*. Oliver & Boyd. Ch. 2 deals exclusively with desert coloration, Ch. 3 with distribution and migration; Ch. 4 is a general discussion of systematics and nomenclature. The rest of the book is devoted to a systematic list in the rather old Hartert order. Appendix A is a history of Arabian ornithology, Appendix B is a bibliography.

PORTER, R. F., WILLIS, I., CHRISTENSEN, S. and NIELSEN, B. P., 1981 *Flight identification of European Raptors*. 3rd edition, T. & A. D. Poyser.

VAURIE, C., 1959–1965 *The Birds of the Palaearctic Fauna*. Vol. 1–1959 Passeriformes, Vol. 2–1965 Non-passeriformes. Witherby.

CHECKLISTS

BUNDY, G. and WARR, F. E., 1980 A checklist of the birds of the Arabian Gulf States. *Sandgrouse* 1: pp. 4–49.

JENNINGS, M. C., 1981 *Birds of the Arabian Gulf*. Allen and Unwin.

EARLY EXPLORATION

BATES, G. L. and PHILBY, H. St. J. B., 1940 Birds of Arabia, unpub. ms, revised and checked by A. C. Trott in 1942, copied from duplicate ms of Philby's by Mrs Ousman at Jiddah. Includes species descriptions, specimens obtained and a history of early Arabian ornithology. Used by Meinertzhagen for his *Birds of Arabia*. Copies are held in the Aramco technical library, Dhahran; and at the British Museum (Nat. Hist.).

CHEESMAN, R. E., 1922 Zoological investigations in the Persian Gulf and Iraq. *J. Bombay Nat. Hist. Soc.* 28: pp. 1108–1110.

1923 From Oqair (Al Uqair) to the ruins of Salwa. *Geogrl. J.* 62(5): pp. 321–335.

1925 The deserts of Jafura and Jabrin. *Geogrl. J.* 65: pp. 112–141.

KINNEAR, N. B., 1931 On some birds from central South Arabia. *Ibis* (Series 13)1: pp. 698–701. (Details of 13 spp. collected by B. Thomas in 1930 on the edge of the Rub'al-Khali. Includes the finding of eggs of Golden/ Tawny Eagle.)

1933 'Birds of the Rub'al-Khali' pp. 395–397 of *The Empty Quarter* by H. St. J. B. Philby. Constable.

1934 On the birds seen or collected by Mr H. St. J. B. Philby during his expedition to cross the Rub'al-Khali. *J. Bombay Nat. Hist. Soc.* 37: 675–680. (19 spp.)

THOMAS, B., 1931 A journey into the Rub'al-Khali. *Geogrl. J.* 77(1): pp. 1–37. (Includes list of 15 collected spp.)
1932 *Arabia Felix: across the 'Empty Quarter' of Arabia*, Jonathan Cape. (Pp. 335–338 concern birds).
TICEHURST, C. B., 1923 Descriptions of new birds collected in the Persian Gulf by Sir Percy Cox and Major Cheesman. *Bull. Br. Orn. Club.* 43: pp. 71–73.
TICEHURST, C. B. and CHEESMAN, R. E., 1924 Descriptions of new species from central Arabia: *Prinia gracilis hufufae, Passer domesticus hufufae* and *Ammomanes deserti azizi*. *Bull. Br. Orn. Club.* 45: pp. 19–20 (Types 142.*, 195.*, 88.*).
1925 The birds of Jabrin, Jufura and Hasa in central and eastern Arabia, and of Bahrain Island, Persian Gulf. *Ibis* (Series 12)1: pp. 1–31, map & 4 photos. (90 spp. including Black Partridge, Night Heron, Eagle Owl and Merlin.)

REGIONAL NOTES, etc.

ANONYMOUS, 1971 Notes and Records, *Arabian Natural History Association*, Dhahran, Saudi Arabia. No. 1. Includes records of Terns from Juraid, and Jana Islands 16–19 August 1967; and three ringing recoveries of White Stork, Little Egret and Red-backed Shrike. (No further editions were published.)
ARNDT, R., 1986 Lake Lanhardt (Aramco Compound, Dhahran). *Aramco World Mag.*, Nov.–Dec. 1986: pp. 10–15.
BROWN, G. K., 1976 A Bird-watching Update. *J. Saudi Arabian Nat. Hist. Soc.* 18: p. 8. (Black-winged Stilt, Avocet and Ruddy Shelduck at Abqaiq Lagoons.)
EDDY, M. G., 1962 Birds observed in the Imhoff Gardens at Dhahran and at Ras Tanura, Saudi Arabia, 1959–62. *Postilla* 59: pp. 1–10.
FISHER, K. J., 1973 The breeding birds of Imhoff Gardens, Dhahran. *J. Saudi Arabian Nat. Hist. Soc.* 10: p. 17. (Little Grebe, Moorhen, Olivaceous Warbler, Rufous Bush Chat.)
GALLAGHER, M. D., 1969–1972 *Gulf Bird-Watchers' Newsletter*. 24 editions typewritten and duplicated. Edition 17 is devoted to seabirds of the Persian Gulf. Contains many new Arabian records.
GREEN, A. A., 1984 The avifauna of the Al Jawf region, north-west Saudi Arabia. *Sandgrouse* 6: pp. 48–58.
RABY, R., 1981 Notes from eastern Saudi Arabia. *OSME Bull.* 6: p. 9.
RIPLEY, S. D., 1951 Birds collected and noted round Dhahran, Saudi Arabia and Bahrain Island. *Postilla* 9: pp. 1–11. (Includes Type 90.* *Ammomanes deserti insularis*, Type 128.a. *Pycnonotus leucotis dactylus*, Type 142.a. *Prinia gracilis anguste*.)
WARR, F. E., 1972 Birds of Dhahran and Hasa Province (Saudi Arabia). (Unpub. typed checklist includes as Appendix 3 the birds of Farsi and Arabi islands, source FEW.)
1988 *A list of birds of the Eastern Province of Saudi Arabia*. (Privately printed.)
WARREN, J. A., 1977 Saudi Arabia (El Hasa province). *Army Bird Watching Soc. Bull.* 2/77: pp. 6–8 (para 33). (Includes a sight record of Dotterel; a supporting list of 200 spp. is held by the ABWS.)

NOTES ON SPECIFIC SPECIES

Reef Herons

BUNDY, G., 1985 Communal feeding by Western Reef Herons. *British Birds* 78: pp. 107–108.
IJZENDOORN, E. J. VAN, 1980 Eye colour of Western Reef Heron. *Dutch Birding* 2: p. 5.
NAIK, R. M. *et al*, 1981 The timing of breeding season and interbreeding between the colour phases in the Indian Reef Heron, *Egretta gularis*. *J. Bombay Nat. Hist. Soc.* 78: pp. 494–497.
NAIK, R. M. and PARASHARJA, B. M., 1983 The sequence of plumage change and polymorphism in the Indian Reef Heron. *Sandgrouse* 5: pp. 75–81.
STEINHAUX, G. H., 1980 On feeding action of Western Reef Heron. *Dutch Birding* 2: p. 49.

Raptors

BUNDY, G., 1985 Communal winter roosting by Imperial Eagles. *British Birds* 78: p. 108.
PLATT, J. B., 1985 Falcon breeding as a conservation tool in Arabia. *ICBP Tech. Publ.* 5: pp. 449–453.
VITTERY, A., 1980 The specific identity of the Buzzards of Central Anatolia. *OSME Bull.* 4: pp. 7–9.

Bustards

OSBORNE, P., COLLAR, N. and GORIUP, P., 1984 *Bustards: Intern. Symp. on Bustards*. Dubai, UAE 1984. Dubai Wildlife Research Centre & ICBP Bustard Specialist Group 32 pp.

Sand Plovers

BILJSMA, R. G., 1982 On leg colour of Greater Sand Plover. *Dutch Birding* 4: 27.

BRITTON, P. L., 1982 Identification of Sand Plovers. *British Birds* 75: 94–95.

FAIRBANK, R. J., 1982 Identification of Sand Plovers. *British Birds* 75: 95–96.

SINCLAIR, J. C. and NICHOLLS, G. H., 1980 Winter identification of Greater and Lesser Sand Plovers. *British Birds* 73: 206–213:586.

TAYLOR, P. B., 1983 Field identification of Sand Plovers in East Africa. *Dutch Birding* 5: pp. 37–66.

Dotterel

PALFERY, J., 1986 Dotterel wintering in Saudi Arabia. *Sandgrouse* 8: p. 112.

Seabirds

BAILEY, R. S., 1966 The sea-birds of the South-East coast of Arabia. *Ibis* 108(2): pp. 224–264. (Detailed paper on the distribution of pelagic species related to plankton density and sea temperature.)

BAKER, E. C. S., 1928 Type description of *Sterna albifrons praetermissa* from Buna Island, Persian Gulf. *Bull. Br. Orn. Club* 49: 39 (Type 45.a.)

BOURNE, W. R. P., 1965 The missing Petrels. *Bull. Br. Orn. Club* 85(6): 97–105. (Mentions Arabian Sea, Persian Gulf etc., on p. 102.)

BRITTON, P. L., 1982 The identification of White-cheeked Terns. *Dutch Birding* 4: pp. 55–57.

CLANCY, P. A., 1982 The Little Tern in South Africa. *Ostrich* 53: pp. 102–106. (Includes separation of Saunders' and Little Tern.)

CONNOR, R. J., 1980 About Terns *and* Terns of the Gulf. *Aramco World Mag.* 31(5): pp. 24–33.

GALLAGHER, M. D., SCOTT, D. A., ORMOND, R. F. G., CONNOR, R. J. and JENNINGS, M. C., 1984 The distribution and conservation of seabirds breeding on the coasts and islands of Iran and Arabia. *ICBP Tech. Pub.* 2: pp. 421–456.

GIBSON-HILL, C. A., 1948 The storm-petrels occurring in the Indian Ocean and adjacent seas. *J. Bombay Nat. Hist. Soc.* 47: pp. 443–448.

HARRISON, C. J. O., 1983 The occurrence of Saunders' Little Tern in the upper Arabian Gulf. *Sandgrouse* 5: pp. 100–101.

HARTERT, E., 1916 Description of *Sterna repressa* sp. nov. *Nov. Zool. Tring* 23: p. 288 (Type 42.*).

HOOGSTRAAL, H., OLIVER, R. M. and GUIRGIS, S. S., 1970 Larva, nymph and life cycle of *Ornithodorus* (*Alectorobius*) *muesebecki* (*Exodoidea; Argasidae*) a virus-infected parasite of birds and petroleum industry employees in the Arabian Gulf. *Annl. Entomol. Soc. Am.* 63(6): pp. 1762–1768. (Refers to breeding Socotra Cormorants and Ospreys on Kharg island.)

LOPPENTHIN, B., 1951 Seabirds of the Persian Gulf. *Proc. X. Intn. Orn. Congr.* pp. 603–610. (Notes made in winter 1937–38. Includes sight records from around Bushire of Great Black-backed Gull, Red-breasted Goose, Shelduck, Merganser and Arctic Skua.)

MORZER-BRUYNS, W. F. J. and VOOUS, K. H., 1965 Great Skuas *Stercorarius skua* in Northern Indian Ocean. *Ardea* 53: pp. 80–81. (This author has deposited notes of voyages in the Persian Gulf, Arabian and Red Seas from 1954 in Biological Section, Free University, Amsterdam.)

NAKAMURA, K., 1974 Observations on the seabirds in the Arabian Gulf. *Trans. Tokyo Univ. Fish* 1: pp. 13–16 and Appendix Table 2: pp. 108–112.

SALWEGTER, VAN 1965–1971 Unpub. notes of birds seen at sea in the Persian Gulf and Arabian Sea deposited in the Biological Section, Free University, Amsterdam, Holland.

TICEHURST, C. B., 1922 Remarks on *Phalacrocorax nigrogularis*, Forbes & Grant; the young in down, immature and adult. *Bull. Br. Orn. Club.* 42: pp. 120–121.

TUCK, G. S., 1972–1973 Seabirds of the Persian Gulf (The Gulf) and Gulf of Oman—A Survey. *Sea Swallow* 23.

Doves

JENNINGS, M. C., 1978 Namaqua Dove in the Middle East. *Orn. Soc. Middle East Bull.* 1: pp. 5–7.

Parakeets

ETCHECOPAR, R. D., 1969 Extension de *Psittacula krameri* (la Perruche à collier rose) au Moyen-orient. (Distribution of the Rose-ringed Parakeet in the Middle East.) *Oiseau Revue Fr. Orn.* 39: pp. 178–181.

Larks

BATES, G. L., 1935 Descriptions of forms of *Ammomanes cinctura* in Africa and Arabia. *Bull. Br. Orn. Club* 55: pp. 139–140.
1939 Races of *Ammomanes deserti* in Arabia. *Ibis* (Series 14)3: pp. 743–746.
BROWN, G. K. and PALFERY, J., 1986 The Small Skylark, a new species for Saudi Arabia. *Sandgrouse* 7: pp. 55–59.
DEAN, A. R., 1980 Field characters of the Desert and Bar-tailed Desert Larks. *British Birds* 73: pp. 476–477.
MORGAN, J. H. and PALFERY, J., 1986 Some notes on the Black-crowned Finch Lark. *Sandgrouse* 8: pp. 58–73.
OREEL, G. J., 1980 On field identification of Short-toed Larks. *Dutch Birding* 2: p. 115.
ROUND, P. D. and WALSH, T. A., 1981 The field identification and status of Dunn's Lark. *Sandgrouse* 3: pp. 78–83.
ROUND, P. D., 1985 Dunn's Lark. *British Birds* 78: p. 42.
TYE, A., 1988 Mystery photographs—Dunn's Lark (Saudi Arabia). *British Birds* 81(3): pp. 134–137.

Bulbuls

BATES, G. L., 1935 On the type-locality of *Pycnonotus x. xanthopygos* (Hemp. & Ehr.). *Bull. Br. Orn. Club* 55: pp. 118–119.

Wheatears

ALSTROM, P., 1985 Identification of Wheatear and Isabelline Wheatear. *British Birds* 78: pp. 304–305.
ARKELL, J., 1972 Wheatears: A Commentary. *J. Saudi Arabian Nat. Hist. Soc.* 4: pp. 7–8. (A guide to identification of white-crowned species.)
CLEMENT, P., 1987 Field identification of West Palaearctic Wheatears. *British Birds* 80: pp. 137–157, pp. 187–238.
MOUNTFORT, G., 1988 Crown colour of White-crowned Black Wheatear (Jordan). *British Birds* 81(2): pp. 78–79.
SHARROCK, J. T. R. and MULLARNEY, K., 1987 Apparent tail length of Isabelline Wheatear. *British Birds* 80: pp. 168–169.
TYE, A., 1987 Clinal variation and subspeciation in the White-crowned Black Wheatear *Oenanthe leucopyga. Bull. Brit. Orn. Club* 107: pp. 157–165.
WALLACE, D. I. M., 1984 Identification of Wheatear and Isabelline Wheatear. *British Birds* 77: pp. 363–365.

Crows

PILCHER, C. W. T., 1986 A breeding record of the House Crow in Kuwait with comments on the species' status in the Arabian Gulf. *Sandgrouse* 8: pp. 102–106.

Warblers

WILLIAMSON, K., 1960 *Identification for ringers*. The genera Locustella, Lusciniola, Acrocephalus and Hippolais. *Br. Trust Orn.* 1.
1962 The genus Phylloscopus. *Br. Trust Orn.* 2.
1964 The genus Sylvia. *Br. Trust Orn.* 3.

EXTINCT SPECIES

CARRUTHERS, A. D. M., 1922 The Arabian Ostrich. *Ibis* (Series 11)4: pp. 471–474.
CHEESMAN, R. E., 1923 Recent notes on the Arabian Ostrich. *Ibis* (Series 11)5(2): pp. 208–211, p. 359.
FORBES-WATSON, A. D., 1967 Eggs of the Arabian Ostrich. *E. African Wildlife J.* 5: p. 167.
GLEGG, W. E., 1948 Eggs of the Syrian Ostrich, *Struthio camelus syriacus. Bull. Br. Orn. Club* 69: pp. 6–8.
JENNINGS, M. C., 1986 The distribution of the extinct Arabian Ostrich *Struthio camelus syriacus* Rothschild, 1919. *Fauna of Saudi Arabia* 8: pp. 447–461.
LOWE, P. R., 1933 'Report on some struthious eggshell fragments collected by Mr Philby on his recent journey across Arabia' in Philby's *The Empty Quarter*. Constable, pp. 390–392.
PRATER, S. H., 1921 The Arabian Ostrich. *J. Bombay Nat. Hist. Soc.* 27: pp. 602–605.
1923 Survey of Iraq Fauna: pp. 43–46. Repeat of article on The Arabian Ostrich.
ROTHSCHILD, W., 1919 Description of a new sub-species of Ostrich from Syria. *Bull. Br. Orn. Club* 39: 81–83. (Type 1.* S. C. Syriacus.)
WEINSTEIN, J. M., 1984 Radio carbon dating in the Southern Levant (Ostrich eggshells). *Radiocarbon* 26(3): pp. 297–366.

FOSSIL REMAINS

THOMAS, H., SEN, S., KHAN, M., BATTAIL, B. and LIGABUE, G., 1981 The Lower Miocene Fauna of Al-Sarrar (Eastern Province, Saudi Arabia). *Atlal* 5: pp. 109–118.

ADAPTATIONS TO ARIDITY

DAWSON, W. R. and BARTHOLOMEW, G. A., 1968 Temperature regulation and water economy of desert birds. pp. 357–394 in *Desert Biology* (ed. G. W. Brown Jr.). Academic Press.
HARRISON, C. J. O., 1986 The Saharo–Sindian arid zone birds. *Sandgrouse* 7: pp. 64–69.
LEVGOREN, M. *et al*, 1986 Responses to saline drinking water in two desert phasianids, the Chukar and the Sand Partridge. *Physiol. Zool.* 59: pp. 123–129.
MACLEAN, G. L., 1983 Water transport by Sandgrouse. *Bio-Science* 33: pp. 365–369.
THOMAS, D. H., 1984 Sandgrouse as models of avian adaptations to deserts. *S. Afr. J. Zool.* 19(2): pp. 113–120.
1984 Adaptations of desert birds: Sandgrouse (*Pteroclididae*) as highly successful inhabitants of Afro-Asian arid lands. *J. Arid Environ.* 7: pp. 157–181.
THOMAS, D. H. (ed.), 1984 Adaptations of birds to desert conditions. Papers presented at a symposium during the 18th International Ornithological Congress. *J. Arid Environ.* 7(2): pp. 131–132.

MIGRATION

BROWN, J. N. B., 1980 The autumn bird migration and bird ringing records from the Gulf. *Bull. Emirates Nat. Hist. Group* (Abu Dhabi) 12: pp. 28–29.
CAMERON, R. A. D., CORNWALLIS, L., PERCIVAL, M. J. L. and SINCLAIR, A. R. E., 1967 The migration of Raptors and Storks through the Near East in Autumn. *Ibis* 109(4): pp. 489–501.
EMLEN, S. T., 1975 The Stellar-orientation System of a Migratory Bird. *Scientific American* August 1975. Offprint 1327.
GILBY, G. B., 1945 Migration of Swan to the Persian Gulf. *J. Bombay Nat. Hist. Soc.* 45: pp. 421–422.
MOREAU, R. E., 1972 The Palaearctic–African Bird Migration Systems. Academic Press. (A most important work with distribution maps and an excellent bibliography.)
PORTER, R. F. and BEAMAN, M. A. S., 1985 A résumé of raptor migration in Europe and the Middle East. *ICBP Tech. Publ.* 5: pp. 237–242.
SAUER, E. G. F., 1958 Celestial Navigation by Birds. *Scientific American* August 1958. Offprint 133.
SUPP, S., 1986 Bird migration in Saudi Arabia, in particular near Riyadh. *Vogelwarte* 33: pp. 317–330 (in German, English summary).
TUCKER, V. A., 1969 The Energetics Of Bird Flight. *Scientific American*, May 1969. Offprint 1141.

INDEX OF SPECIES BY LATIN NAME

Bold figures indicate the main entry for the species in the Systematic List. Figures in italics refer to pages on which illustrations appear.

INDEX OF SPECIES BY ENGLISH NAME

Bold figures indicate the main entry for the species in the Systematic List. Figures in italics refer to pages on which an illustration appears.